Preface

TO THE INSTRUCTOR

This study guide is designed to help your students master basic anatomy and physiology. It works in two ways.

First, the section of the preface titled "To the Student" contains detailed instructions on:

How to achieve good grades in anatomy and physiology

How to read the textbook

How to use the exercises in this study guide

How to use visual memory as a learning tool

How to use mnemonic devices as learning aids

How to prepare for an examination

How to take an examination

How to find out why questions were missed on an examination

Second, the study guide itself contains features that facilitate learning. These features include the following:

1. LEARNING OBJECTIVES, designed to break down the process of learning into small units. The questions in this study guide have been developed to help the student master the learning objectives identified at the beginning of each chapter in the text. The guide is also sequenced to correspond to key areas of each chapter. A variety of questions have been prepared to cover the material effectively and expose the student to multiple learning approaches.

2. CROSSWORD PUZZLES, to encourage the use of new vocabulary words and emphasize the proper spelling of these terms.

3. OPTIONAL APPLICATION QUESTIONS, particularly targeted for the health occupations student, but appropriate for any student of anatomy and physiology because they are based entirely on information contained within the chapter.

4. DIAGRAMS, with key features marked by numbers for identification. Students can easily check their work by comparing the diagram in the workbook with the equivalent figure in the text.

5. PAGE NUMBER REFERENCES, in the answer sections. Each answer is keyed to the appropriate text page. Additionally, questions are grouped into specific topics that correspond to the text. Each major topic of the study guide provides references to specific areas of the text so that students having difficulty with a particular grouping of questions have a specific reference area to assist them with remedial work. This is of great assistance to both instructor and student because remedial work is made easier and more effective when the area of weakness is identified accurately.

These features should make mastery of the material a rewarding experience for both instructor and student.

HOW TO ACHIEVE GOOD GRADES IN ANATOMY AND PHYSIOLOGY

This study guide is designed to help you be successful in learning anatomy and physiology. Before you begin using the study guide, read the following suggestions. Students who understand effective study techniques and who have good study habits are successful students.

HOW TO READ THE TEXTBOOK

Keep up with the reading assignments. Read the textbook assignment before the instructor covers the material in lecture. If you have failed to read the assignment beforehand, you will not grasp what the instructor is talking about in lecture. When you read, do the following:

1. As you finish reading a sentence, ask yourself if you understand it. If you do not, put a question mark in the margin by that sentence. If the instructor does not clear up the problem in lecture, ask him or her to explain it to you.
2. Do the learning objectives in the text. A learning objective is a specific task that you are expected to be able to do after you have read a chapter. It sets specific goals for the student and breaks down learning into small steps. It emphasizes the key points that the author is making in the chapter.
3. Underline and make notes in the margin to highlight key ideas, to mark something you need to reinforce at a later time, or to indicate things that you do not understand.
4. If you come to a word you do not understand, look it up in a dictionary. Write the word on one side of an index card and its definition on the other side. Carry these cards with you, and when you have a spare minute, use them like flash cards to learn multiplication tables. If you do not know how to spell or pronounce a word, you will have a hard time remembering it.
5. Carefully study each diagram and illustration as you read. Many students ignore these aids. The author included them to help students understand the material.
6. Summarize what you read. After finishing a paragraph, try to restate the main ideas. Do this again when you finish the chapter. Identify and review in your mind the main concepts of the chapter. Check to see if you are correct. In short, be an active reader. Do not just stare at a page or read it superficially.

Finally, attack each unit of learning with a positive mental attitude. Motivation and perseverance are prime factors in achieving successful grades. The combination of your instructor, the text, the study guide, and your dedicated work will lead to success for you in anatomy and physiology.

HOW TO USE THE EXERCISES IN THIS STUDY GUIDE

After you have read a chapter and learned all the new words, begin working with the study guide. Read the overview of the chapter, which summarizes the main points.

Familiarize yourself with the Topics for Review section, which emphasizes the learning objectives outlined in the text. Complete the questions and diagrams in the study guide. The questions are sequenced to follow the chapter outline and headings and are divided into small sections to facilitate learning. A variety of questions is offered throughout the study guide to help you cover the material effectively. The following examples are among the exercises that have been included to assist you.

Multiple Choice Questions

Multiple choice questions will have only one correct answer out of several possibilities for you to select. There are two types of multiple choice questions that you may not be acquainted with:

1. "None of the above is correct" questions. These questions test your ability to recall rather than recognize the correct answer. You

Study Guide to Accompany

THE HUMAN BODY
IN HEALTH AND DISEASE

SECOND EDITION

Prepared by
LINDA SWISHER, RN, EdD
Sarasota County Technical Institute
Sarasota, Florida

 Mosby

St. Louis Baltimore Boston Carlsbad Chicago Naples New York Philadelphia Portland
London Madrid Mexico City Singapore Sydney Tokyo Toronto Wiesbaden

A Times Mirror
Company

Vice President & Publisher: James M. Smith
Editor: Ronald E. Worthington, PhD
Developmental Editor: Jean Sims Fornango
Project Manager: Gayle May Morris
Production Editor: Karen M. Rehwinkel
Manufacturing Supervisor: Karen Lewis

Printed in the United States of America.

Mosby-Year Book, Inc.
11830 Westline Industrial Drive
St Louis, Missouri 63146

International Standard Book Number: 0-8151-8872-2
96 97 98 99 00 / 9 8 7 6 5 4 3 2 1

would select the "none of the above" choice only if all the other choices in that particular question were incorrect.

2. Sequence questions. These questions test your ability to arrange a list of structures in the correct order. In this type of question you are asked to determine the sequence of the structures given in the various choices, and then you are to select the structure listed that would be third in that sequence, as in this example.

Which one of the following structures would be the third through which food would pass?

a. Stomach   b. Mouth   c. Large intestine
d. Esophagus   e. Anus

The correct answer would be a.

Matching Questions

Matching questions ask the student to select the correct answer from a list of terms and to write the answer in the space provided.

True or False

True or false questions ask you to write T in the answer space, if you agree with that statement. If you disagree with the statement, you will circle the incorrect word(s) and write the correct word(s) in the answer space.

Identify the Incorrect Term

In questions that ask you to identify the incorrect term, three words are given that relate to each other in structure or function, and one more word is included that has no relationship, or has an opposing relationship to the other three terms. You are to circle the term that does not relate to the other terms. An example might be: iris, cornea, stapes, retina. You would circle the word stapes because all other terms refer to the eye.

Fill in the Blanks

Fill-in-the-blank questions ask you to recall a missing word or words and insert it or them into the answer blank(s). These questions may be sentences or paragraphs.

Application

Application questions ask you to make judgments about a situation based on the information in the chapter. These questions may ask you how you would respond to a situation or to suggest a possible diagnosis for a set of symptoms.

Charts

Several charts have been included that correspond to figures in the text. Areas have been omitted so that you can fill them in and test your recall of these important areas.

Identification

The study guide includes word find puzzles that allow you to identify key terms in the chapter in an interesting and challenging way.

Crossword Puzzles

Vocabulary words from the New Words section at the end of each chapter of the text have been developed into crossword puzzles. This not only encourages recall, but also proper spelling. Occasionally, an exercise uses scrambled words to encourage recall and spelling.

Labeling Exercises

Labeling exercises present diagrams with parts that are not identified. For each of these diagrams you are to print the name of each numbered part on the appropriately numbered line. You may choose to further distinguish the structures by coloring them with a variety of colors. After you have written down the names of all the structures to be identified, check your answers. When it comes time to review before an examination you can place a sheet of paper over the answers that you have already written on the lines. This procedure will allow you to test yourself without peeking at the answers.

After completing the exercises in the study guide, check your answers. If they are not correct, refer to the page listed with the answer, and review it for further clarification. If you still do not understand the question or the answer, ask your instructor for further explanation.

If you have difficulty with several questions from one section, refer to the pages given at the end of the section. After reviewing the section, try to answer the questions again. If you are still having difficulty, talk to your instructor.

HOW TO USE VISUAL MEMORY

Visual memory is another important tool in learning. If I asked you to picture in your mind an elephant, with all its external parts labeled, you could do that easily. Visual memory is a powerful key to learning. Whenever possible, try to build a memory picture. Remember, a picture is worth a thousand words.

Visual memory works especially well with the sequencing of items, such as circulatory pathways and the passage of air or food. Students who try to learn sequencing by memorizing a list of words do poorly on examinations. If they forget one word in the sequence, then they will forget all the words after the forgotten one as well. However, with a memory picture you can pick out the important features.

HOW TO USE MNEMONIC DEVICES

Mnemonic devices are little jingles that you memorize to help you remember things. If you make up your own, they will stick with you longer. Here are three examples of such devices:

"On Old Olympus' towering tops a Finn and German viewed some hops." This one is used to remember the cranial nerves. Each word begins with the same letter as does the name of one of the nerves.

"C. Hopkins CaFe where they serve Mg NaCl." This mnemonic device reminds you of the chemical symbols for the biologically important electrolytes.

"Roy G. Biv." This mnemonic device helps you remember the colors of the visible light spectrum.

HOW TO PREPARE FOR AN EXAMINATION

Prepare far in advance for an examination. Actually, your preparation for an examination should begin on the first day of class. Keeping up with your assignments daily makes the final preparation for an examination much easier. You should begin your final preparation at least three nights before the test. Last-minute studying usually means poor results and limited retention.

1. Make sure that you understand and can answer all of the learning objectives for the chapter on which you are being tested.
2. Review the appropriate questions in this study guide. Reviewing is something that you should do after every class and at the end of every study session. It is important to keep going over the material until you have a thorough understanding of the chapter and rapid recall of its contents. If review becomes a daily habit, studying for the actual examination will not be difficult. Go through each question and write down an answer. Do the same with the labeling of each structure on the appropriate diagrams. If you have already done this as part of your daily review, cover the answers with a piece of paper and quiz yourself again.
3. Check the answers that you have written down against the correct answers in the back of the study guide. Go back and study the areas in the text that refer to questions that you missed and then try to answer those questions again. If you still cannot answer a question or label a structure correctly, ask your instructor for help.
4. Ask yourself as you read a chapter what questions you would ask if you were writing a test on that unit. You will most likely ask yourself many of the questions that will show up on your examinations.
5. Get a good night's sleep before the test. Staying up late and upsetting your bio-rhythms will only make you less efficient during the test.

HOW TO TAKE AN EXAMINATION

The Day of the Test

1. Get up early enough to avoid rushing. Eat appropriately. Your body needs fuel, but a heavy meal just before a test is not a good idea.
2. Keep calm. Briefly look over your notes. If you have prepared for the test properly, there will be no need for last-minute cramming.
3. Make certain that you have everything you

need for the test: pens, pencils, test sheets, and so forth.

4. Allow enough time to get to the examination site. Missing your bus, getting stuck in traffic, or being unable to find a parking space will not put you in a good frame of mind to do well on the examination.

During the Examination

1. Pay careful attention to the instructions for the test.
2. Note any corrections.
3. Budget your time so that you will be able to finish the test.
4. Ask the instructor for clarification if you do not understand a question or an instruction.
5. Concentrate on your own test paper and do not allow yourself to be distracted by others in the room.

Hints for Taking a Multiple Choice Test

1. Read each question carefully. Pay attention to each word.
2. Cross out obviously wrong choices and think about those that are left.
3. Go through the test once, quickly answering the questions you are sure of. Then go back over the test and answer the rest of the questions.
4. Fill in the answer spaces completely and make your marks heavy. Erase completely if you make a mistake.
5. If you must guess, stick with your first hunch. Most often, students will change right answers to wrong ones.
6. If you will not be penalized for guessing, do not leave any blanks.

Hints for Taking an Essay Test

1. Budget time for each question.
2. Write legibly and try to spell words correctly.
3. Be concise, complete, and specific. Do not be repetitious or long-winded.
4. Organize your answer in an outline that helps not only the student but also the person who grades the test.
5. Answer each question as thoroughly as you can, but leave some room for possible additions.

Hints for Taking a Laboratory Practical Examination

Students have a hard time with this kind of test. Visual memory is very important here. To put it simply, you must be able to identify every structure you have studied. If you are unable to identify a structure, then you will be unable to answer any questions about that structure.

Possible questions that could appear on an examination of this type might include:

1. Identification of a structure, organ, feature.
2. Function of a structure, organ, feature.
3. Sequence questions for air flow, passage of food, urine, and so forth.
4. Disease questions (for example, if an organ fails, what disease will result?).

HOW TO FIND OUT WHY QUESTIONS WERE MISSED ON AN EXAMINATION

After the Examination

Go over your test after it has been scored to see what you missed and why you missed it. You can pick up important clues that will help you on future examinations. Ask yourself these questions:

1. Did I miss questions because I did not read them carefully?
2. Did I miss questions because I had gaps in my knowledge?
3. Did I miss questions because I could not determine scientific words?
4. Did I miss questions because I did not have good visual memory of things?

Be sure to go back and learn the things you did not know. Chances are these topics will come up on the final examination.

Your grades in other classes will improve as well when you apply these study methods. Learning should be fun. With these helpful hints and this study guide you should be able to achieve the grades you desire. Good luck!

Acknowledgements

I wish to express my appreciation to the staff of Mosby-Year Book, especially Ron Worthington and Jean Fornango for opening this door. My continued admiration and thanks to Gary Thibodeau and Kevin Patton for an outstanding text. Your time and dedication to science education will, hopefully, create a better quality of health care for the future.

Special thanks to Randy Fagan for her perseverance and enthusiasm while transposing the written word to typed script.

A. Christine Payne and her computer combined efforts to produce crossword puzzles and word finds for the units. Her creativity added the variety necessary to stimulate the learning process.

To my daughter Amanda, Bill, my students, colleagues, and friends, my thanks for your assistance and support.

Finally, it is to the designer of the human body that this book is dedicated. What a miraculous creation!

LINDA SWISHER, RN, EdD

Contents

CHAPTER 1

An Introduction to the Structure and Function of the Body

A command of terminology is necessary for a student to be successful in any area of science. This chapter defines the terminology and concepts that are basic to the field of anatomy and physiology. Building a firm foundation in these language skills will assist you with all future chapters.

The study of anatomy and physiology involves the structure and function of an organism and the relationship of its parts. It begins with a basic organization of the body into different structural levels. Beginning with the smallest level (the cell) and progressing to the largest, most complex level (the system), this chapter familiarizes you with the terminology and the levels of organization needed to facilitate the study of the body as a part or as a whole.

It is also important to be able to identify and to describe specific body areas or regions as we progress in this field. The anatomical position is used as a reference position when dissecting the body into planes, regions, or cavities. The terminology defined in this chapter allows you to describe the areas efficiently and accurately.

Finally, the process of homeostasis is reviewed. This state of relative constancy in the chemical composition of body fluids is necessary for good health. In fact, the very survival of the body depends on the successful maintenance of homeostasis.

TOPICS FOR REVIEW

Before progressing to Chapter 2, you should have an understanding of the structural levels of organization; the planes, regions, and cavities of the body; the terminology used to describe these areas; and the concept of homeostasis as it relates to the survival of the species.

STRUCTURAL LEVELS OF ORGANIZATION

Match the term on the left with the proper selection on the right.

_____ 1. Organism
_____ 2. Cells
_____ 3. Tissue
_____ 4. Organ
_____ 5. Systems

A. Many similar cells that act together to perform a common function
B. The most complex units that make up the body
C. A group of several different kinds of tissues arranged to perform a special function
D. Denotes a living thing
E. The smallest "living" units of structure and function in the body

ANATOMICAL POSITION

Match the term on the left with the proper selection on the right.

_____ 6. Body
_____ 7. Arms
_____ 8. Feet
_____ 9. Prone
_____ 10. Supine

A. At the sides
B. Face upward
C. Erect
D. Face downward
E. Forward

▷ *If you have had difficulty with this section, review pages 1-3.*

ANATOMICAL DIRECTIONS, PLANES, OR BODY SECTIONS

Fill in the crossword puzzle.

11. Upper or above
12. Lower or below
13. Horizontal plane
14. Front (abdominal side)
15. Toward the side of the body
16. Toward the midline of the body
17. Farthest from the point of origin of a body point

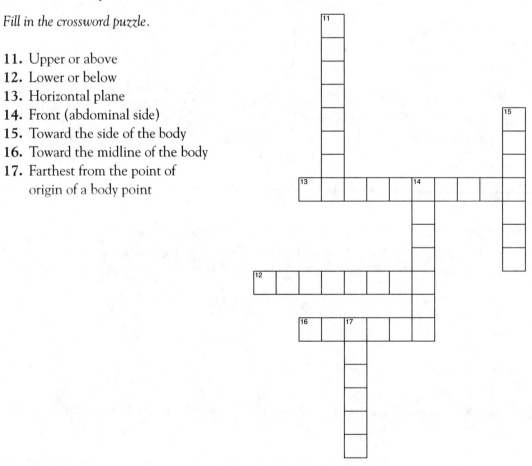

Circle the correct answer.

18. The stomach is (superior or inferior) to the diaphragm.
19. The nose is located on the (anterior or posterior) surface of the body.
20. The lungs lie (medial or lateral) to the heart.
21. The elbow lies (proximal or distal) to the forearm.
22. The skin is (superficial or deep) to the muscles below it.
23. A midsagittal plane divides the body into (equal or unequal) parts.
24. A frontal plane divides the body into (anterior and posterior or superior and inferior) sections.
25. A transverse plane divides the body into (right and left or upper and lower) sections.
26. A coronal plane may also be referred to as a (sagittal or frontal) plane.

▷ *If you have had difficulty with this section, review pages 3-5.*

BODY CAVITIES

Select the correct term from the choices given and insert the letter in the answer blank.

      (a) Ventral cavity   (b) Dorsal cavity

_____ 27. Thoracic
_____ 28. Cranial
_____ 29. Abdominal
_____ 30. Pelvic
_____ 31. Mediastinum
_____ 32. Spinal
_____ 33. Pleural

▷ *If you have had difficulty with this section, review pages 5-6.*

BODY REGIONS

Circle the one that does not belong.

34. Axial   Head   Trunk   Extremities
35. Axillary   Cephalic   Brachial   Antecubital
36. Frontal   Orbital   Plantar   Nasal
37. Carpal   Crural   Plantar   Pedal
38. Cranial   Occipital Tarsal   Temporal

▷ *If you have had difficulty with this section, review pages 6-11.*

If the following statement is true, insert "T" in the answer blank. If the statement is false, circle the incorrect word(s) and insert the correct word(s) in the answer blank.

_____ 39. The term *autopsy* comes from the Greek words *auto* (self) and *opsis* (view).

_____ 40. Autopsies are usually performed in four stages.

_____ 41. In the first stage of an autopsy, the exterior of the body is examined for abnormalities such as wounds or scars.

_____ 42. The face, arms, and legs are usually dissected during the second stage of an autopsy.

_____ 43. Microscopic examination of tissues occurs during all stages of an autopsy.

_____ 44. Tests to analyze the chemical content of body fluids or to determine the presence of infectious organisms may also be performed during an autopsy.

▷ *If you have had difficulty with this section, review page 8.*

THE BALANCE OF BODY FUNCTIONS

Fill in the blanks.

45. _____ depends on the body's ability to maintain or restore homeostasis.

46. *Homeostasis* is the term used to describe the relative constancy of the body's

_____ _____.

47. During exercise, homeostasis is disrupted and body CO_2 levels _____.

48. Changes and functions that occur during the early years are called _____.

49. Changes and functions that occur after young adulthood are called

_____.

50. Homeostatic control mechanisms are categorized as either _____ or

_____ feedback loops.

51. Negative feedback loops are _____ mechanisms.

52. Positive feedback control loops are _____.

▷ *If you have had difficulty with this section, review pages 11-13.*

APPLYING WHAT YOU KNOW

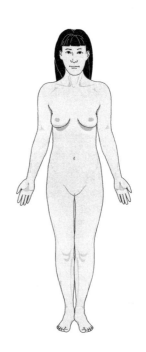

53. Mrs. Fagan has had an appendectomy. The nurse is preparing to change the dressing. She knows that the appendix is located in the right iliac inguinal region, the distal portion extending at an angle into the hypogastric region. Place an X on the diagram where the nurse will place the dressing.

54. Mrs. Suchman noticed a lump in her breast. Dr. Reeder noted on her chart that a small mass was located in the left breast medial to the nipple. Place an X where Mrs. Suchman's lump would be located.

55. Heather was injured in a bicycle accident. X-ray films revealed that she had a fracture of the right patella. A cast was applied beginning at the distal femoral region and extending to the pedal region. Place an X where Heather's cast begins and ends.

56. WORD FIND

Can you find 18 terms from this chapter in the box of letters? Words may be spelled top to bottom, bottom to top, right to left, left to right or diagonally.

```
N H L T E B W N G N M M Y X A
O O H A V U U C L W E P N G L
I M U N I T S A I D E M W A L
T E R T V C T S I C J S R T K
A O N O P T I A I W A T Y R H
Z S Q S I R L F A T N R G O W
I T W G P R O I R E T S O P F
N A A Z J E E X V E E H L H Z
A S N L M C T P I C P D O Y T
G I C A Y U O X U M N U I V P
R S M R T N U K B S A Y S V M
O R C U R O I R B S Q L Y U G
L H X E M P M E T S Y S H V S
U W L L Q D U Y Y N E E P J B
Q N Z P K D B O D C G I N J A
```

Anatomy	Organization	Superficial
Atrophy	Physiology	Superior
Homeostasis	Pleural	System
Medial	Posterior	Thoracic
Mediastinum	Proximal	Tissue
Organ	Sagittal	Ventral

DORSAL AND VENTRAL BODY CAVITIES

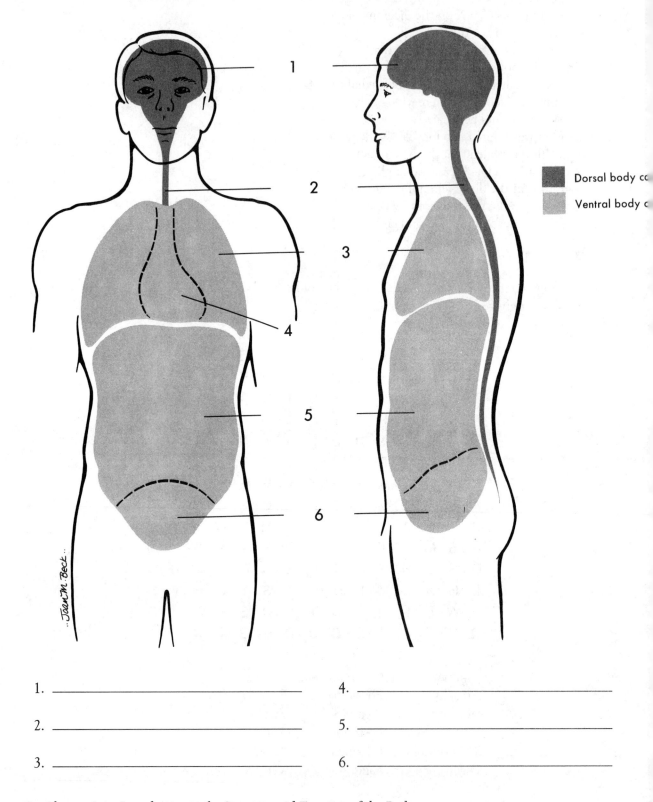

Dorsal body c

Ventral body c

1. _____	4. _____
2. _____	5. _____
3. _____	6. _____

DIRECTIONS AND PLANES OF THE BODY

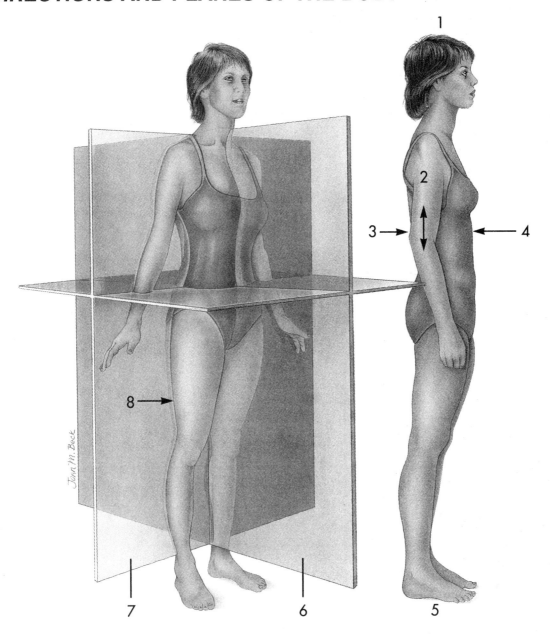

1. _____   5. _____

2. _____   6. _____

3. _____   7. _____

4. _____   8. _____

REGIONS OF THE ABDOMEN

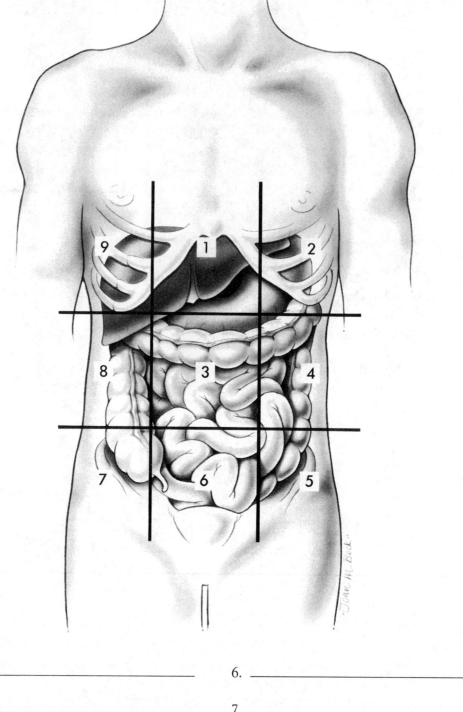

1. _____

2. _____

3. _____

4. _____

5. _____

6. _____

7. _____

8. _____

9. _____

CHAPTER 2

Cells and Tissues

Cells are the smallest structural units of living things. Therefore, because we are living, we are made up of a mass of cells. Human cells can be viewed only microscopically. They vary in shape and size. The three main parts of a cell are the cytoplasmic membrane, the cytoplasm, and the nucleus. As you review the chapter on cells, you will be amazed at the cells' resemblance to the body as a whole. You will identify miniature circulatory systems, reproductive systems, digestive systems, power plants much like the muscular system, and many other systems that will aid in your understanding of these systems in future chapters.

Cells, just like humans, depend on water, food, gases, elimination of wastes, and numerous other substances to survive. The movement of these substances in and out of the cells is accomplished by two primary methods: passive transport processes and active transport processes. In passive transport processes no cellular energy is required to effect movement through the cell membrane. However, in active transport, cellular energy is required to provide movement through the cell membrane.

Cell reproduction completes the study of cells. A basic explanation of DNA, "the hereditary molecule," gives us a proper respect for the capability of the cell to transmit physical and mental traits from generation to generation. Reproduction of the cell, mitosis, is a complex process requiring several stages. These stages are outlined and diagrammed in the text to facilitate learning.

This chapter concludes with the discussion of tissues. The four main types of tissues (epithelial, connective, muscle, and nervous) are reviewed. Knowledge of the characteristics, location, and function of these tissues is necessary to complete your understanding of the next structural level of organization.

TOPICS FOR REVIEW

Before progressing to Chapter 3, you should have an understanding of the structure and function of the smallest living unit in the body—the cell. Your review should also include the methods by which substances are moved through the cell membrane and the stages necessary for the cell to reproduce. The study of this chapter is completed with an understanding of tonicity and body tissues and the function they perform in the body.

CELLS

Match the term on the left with the proper selection on the right.

Group A

———— 1. Cytoplasm
———— 2. Plasma membrane
———— 3. Cholesterol
———— 4. Nucleus
———— 5. Centrioles

A. Component of plasma membrane
B. Controls reproduction of the cell
C. "Living matter"
D. Paired organelles
E. Surrounds cells

Group B

———— 6. Ribosomes
———— 7. Endoplasmic reticulum
———— 8. Mitochondria
———— 9. Lysosomes
———— 10. Golgi apparatus

A. "Power plants"
B. "Digestive bags"
C. "Chemical processing and packaging center"
D. "Protein factories"
E. "Smooth and rough"

Fill in the blanks.

11. The fat molecule ————————————— helps stabilize the phospholipid molecules to

 prevent breakage of the plasma membrane.

12. A procedure performed before transplanting an organ from one individual to another is

 ——————————— ———————————.

13. Fine, hairlike extensions found on the exposed or free surfaces of some cells are called

 ———————————.

14. This organelle is distinguished by the fact that it has two types. It may be either smooth or rough

 ——————————— ———————————.

15. ————————————— are usually attached to rough endoplasmic reticulum and pro-

 duce enzymes and other protein compounds.

16. The ————————————— provide energy-releasing chemical reactions that go on con-

 tinuously.

17. The organelles that can digest and destroy microbes that invade the cell are called

 ———————————.

18. Mucus is an example of a product manufactured by the —————————————

 ———————————.

19. These rod-shaped structures, _____, play an important role during cell division.

20. _____ _____ are threadlike structures made up of proteins and DNA.

21. When the immune system mounts a significant attack against the donated tissue, a _____ _____ occurs.

22. The procedure used to test for the presence of antibodies produced in response to the HIV virus is known as _____.

▷ *If you have had difficulty with this section, review pages 19-25.*

MOVEMENT OF SUBSTANCES THROUGH CELL MEMBRANES

Circle the correct choice.

23. The energy required for active transport processes is obtained from:
   A. ATP   C. Diffusion
   B. DNA   D. Osmosis

24. An example of a passive transport process is:
   A. Permease system   C. Pinocytosis
   B. Phagocytosis   D. Diffusion

25. Movement of substances from a region of high concentration to a region of low concentration is known as:
   A. Active transport   C. Cellular energy
   B. Passive transport   D. Concentration gradient

26. Osmosis is the _____ of water across a selectively permeable membrane.
   A. Filtration   C. Active transport
   B. Equilibrium   D. Diffusion

27. _____ involves the movement of solutes across a selectively permeable membrane by the process of diffusion.
   A. Osmosis   C. Dialysis
   B. Filtration   D. Phagocytosis

28. A specialized example of diffusion is:
    A. Osmosis
    B. Permease system
    C. Filtration
    D. All of the above

29. This movement always occurs down a hydrostatic pressure gradient.
    A. Osmosis
    B. Filtration
    C. Dialysis
    D. Facilitated diffusion

30. The uphill movement of a substance through a living cell membrane is:
    A. Osmosis
    B. Diffusion
    C. Active transport process
    D. Passive transport process

31. The ion pump is an example of this type of movement.
    A. Gravity
    B. Hydrostatic pressure
    C. Active transport process
    D. Passive transport process

32. An example of a cell that uses phagocytosis is the:
    A. White blood cell
    B. Red blood cell
    C. Muscle cell
    D. Bone cell

33. A saline solution that contains a higher concentration of salt than living red blood cells would be:
    A. Hypotonic
    B. Hypertonic
    C. Isotonic
    D. Homeostatic

34. A red blood cell becomes engorged with water and will eventually lyse, releasing hemoglobin into the solution. This solution is _____ to the red blood cell.
    A. Hypotonic
    B. Hypertonic
    C. Isotonic
    D. Homeostatic

▷ *If you have had difficulty with this section, review pages 25-29.*

CELL REPRODUCTION AND HEREDITY

Circle the one that does not belong.

35. DNA	Adenine	Uracil	Thymine
36. Complementary base pairing	Guanine	RNA	Cytosine
37. Anaphase	Specific sequence	Gene	Base pairs
38. RNA	Ribose	Thymine	Uracil
39. Translation	Protein synthesis	mRNA	Interphase
40. Cleavage furrow	Anaphase	Prophase	2 daughter cells
41. "Resting"	Prophase	Interphase	DNA replication
42. Identical	2 nuclei	Telophase	Metaphase
43. Metaphase	Prophase	Telophase	Gene

▷ *If you have had difficulty with this section, review pages 30-36.*

TISSUES

44. Fill in the missing area.

TISSUE	LOCATION	FUNCTION
Epithelial		
1. Simple squamous	1a. Alveoli of lungs	1a. _____
	1b. Lining of blood and lymphatic vessels	1b. _____
2. Stratified squamous	2a. _____	2a. Protection
	2b. _____	2b. Protection
3. Simple columnar	3. _____	3. Protection, secretion, absorption
4. _____	4. Urinary bladder	4. Protection
5. Pseudostratified	5. _____	5. Protection
6. Simple cuboidal	6. Glands; kidney tubules	6. _____
Connective		
1. Areolar	1. _____	1. Connection
2. _____	2. Under skin	2. Protection; insulation
3. Dense fibrous	3. Tendons; ligaments; fascia; scar tissue	3. _____
4. Bone	4. _____	4. Support, protection
5. Cartilage	5. _____	5. Firm but flexible support
6. Blood	6. Blood vessels	6. _____
7. _____	7. Red bone marrow	7. Blood cell formation
Muscle		
1. Skeletal (striated voluntary)	1. _____	1. Movement of bones
2. _____	2. Wall of heart	2. Contraction of heart
3. Smooth	3. _____	3. Movement of substances along ducts; change in diameter of pupils and shape of lens; "gooseflesh"
Nervous		
1. _____	1. _____	1. Irritability, conduction

▶ *If you have had difficulty with this section, review Table 2-6 and pages 36-47.*

APPLYING WHAT YOU KNOW

45. Mr. Fee's boat capsized, and he was stranded on a deserted shoreline for 2 days without food or water. When found, he had swallowed a great deal of seawater. He was taken to the emergency room in a state of dehydration. In the space to the right, draw the appearance of the red blood cells as they would appear to the laboratory technician.

46. The nurse was instructed to dissolve a pill in a small amount of liquid medication. As she dropped the capsule into the liquid, she was interrupted by the telephone. On her return to the medication cart, she found the medication completely dissolved and apparently scattered evenly throughout the liquid. This phenomenon did not surprise her since she was aware from her knowledge of cell transport that _____ had created this distribution.

47. Ms. Bence has emphysema and has been admitted to the hospital unit with oxygen per nasal cannula. Emphysema destroys the tiny air sacs in the lungs. These tiny air sacs, alveoli, provide what function for Ms. Bence?

48. Merrily was 5'4" and weighed 115 lbs. She appeared very healthy and fit, yet her doctor advised her that she was "overfat." What might be the explanation for this assessment?

49. WORD FIND

Can you find the 16 terms from this chapter in the box of letters? Words may be spelled top to bottom, bottom to top, right to left, left to right, or diagonally.

```
A P D I E V E W N P F E H Y X
I G I Z N S R L X S T W F Z S
R J V N N T A I L M R P H M F
D W U E O O E H B E A D U G F
N W I U I C I R P O N N F B W
O P U R S H Y T P O S A W X K
H X F O U R Y T A H L O G A W
C L Z N F O Y P O R A E M R M
O U I X F M L F O S T S T E O
T T B Y I A B C O T I L E S D
I V S O D T T M I T O S I S U
M N A A I L E N L N N N F R
E O K K I D C Q H B I V I T H
E K T X B Z A E A L S A E C K
S B Z R P M V L X W Z A Z C V
```

Chromatid	Diffusion	Mitochondria	Pinocytosis
Cilia	Filtration	Mitosis	Ribosome
Cuboidal	Hypotonic	Neuron	Telophase
DNA	Interphase	Organelle	Translation

DID YOU KNOW?

The largest single cell in the human body is the female sex cell, the ovum. The smallest single cell in the human body is the male sex cell, the sperm.

CELLS AND TISSUES

ACROSS

2. Last stage of mitosis
5. Shriveling of cell due to water withdrawal
7. Fat
8. Cartilage cell
10. Ribonucleic acid (abbreviation)
12. Specialized example of diffusion
13. First stage of mitosis

DOWN

1. Having an osmotic pressure greater than that of the solution of which it is compared
3. Cell organ
4. Energy source for active transport
6. Nerve cell
9. Occurs when substances scatter themselves evenly throughout an available space
11. Reproduction process of most cells
12. Chemical "blueprint" of the body (abbreviation)

CELL STRUCTURE

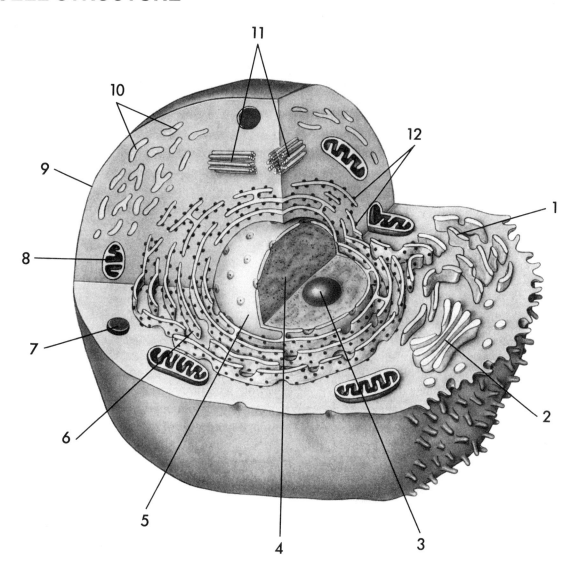

1. _____

2. _____

3. _____

4. _____

5. _____

6. _____

7. _____

8. _____

9. _____

10. _____

11. _____

12. _____

MITOSIS

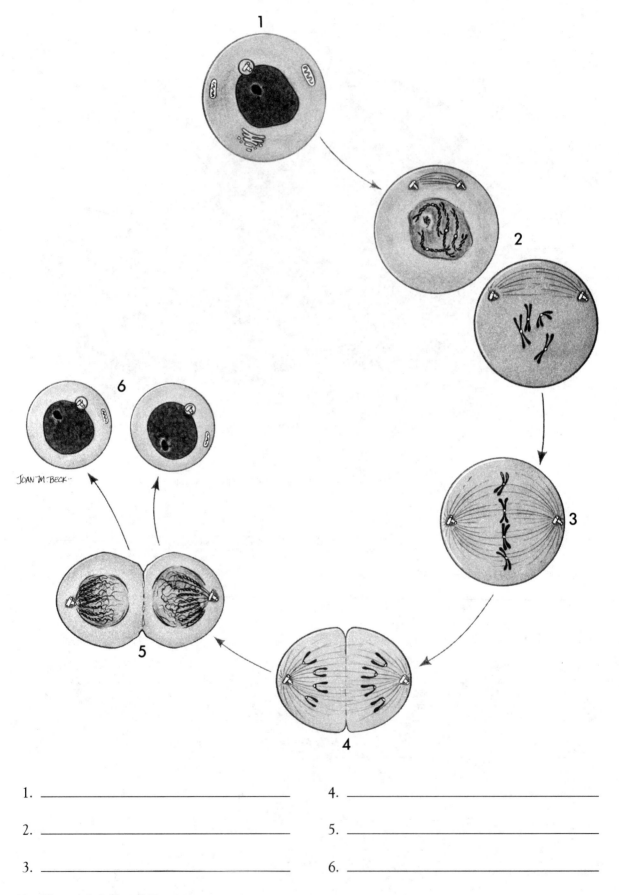

JOAN M BECK

1. _____

2. _____

3. _____

4. _____

5. _____

6. _____

TISSUES

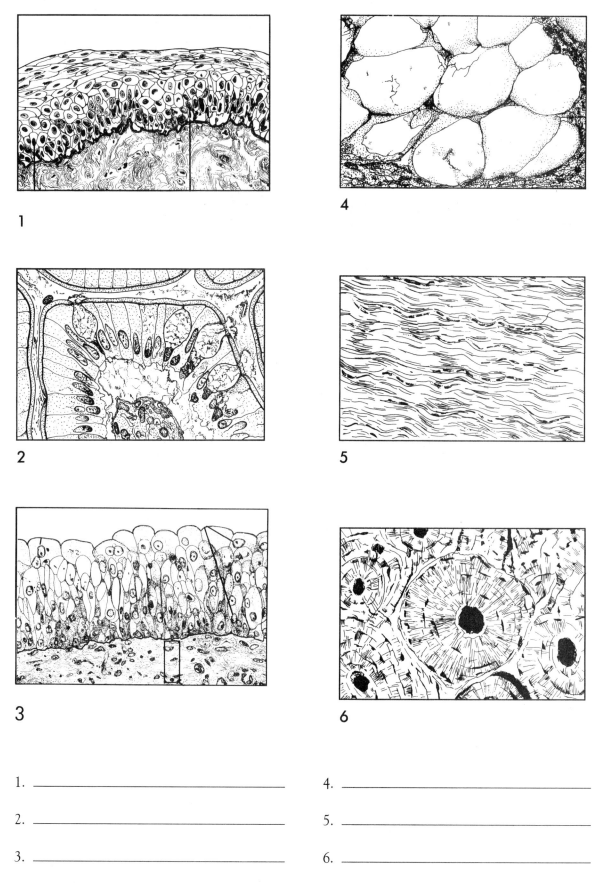

1

2

3

4

5

6

1. _____

2. _____

3. _____

4. _____

5. _____

6. _____

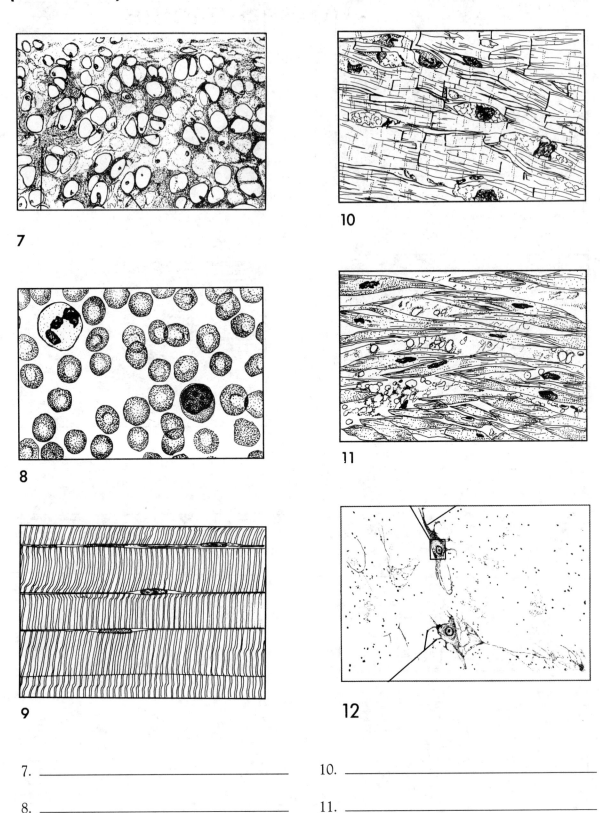

7

8

9

10

11

12

7. _____

8. _____

9. _____

10. _____

11. _____

12. _____

Organ Systems of the Body

A smooth-running automobile is the result of many systems working together harmoniously. The engine, the fuel system, the exhaust system, the brake system, and the cooling system are but a few of the many complex structural units that the automobile as a whole relies on to keep it functioning smoothly. So it is with the human body. We, too, depend on the successful performance of many individual systems working together to create and maintain a healthy human being.

When you have completed your review of the 11 major organ systems and the organs that make up these systems, you will find your understanding of the performance of the body as a whole much more meaningful.

TOPICS FOR REVIEW

Before progressing to Chapter 4, you should have an understanding of the 11 major organ systems and be able to identify the organs that are included in each system. Your review should also include current approaches to organ replacement.

ORGAN SYSTEMS OF THE BODY

Match the term on the left with the proper selection on the right.

Group A

————	1. Integumentary	A. Hair
————	2. Skeletal	B. Spinal cord
————	3. Muscular	C. Hormones
————	4. Nervous	D. Tendons
————	5. Endocrine	E. Joints

Group B

————	6. Circulatory	A. Esophagus
————	7. Lymphatic	B. Ureters
————	8. Urinary	C. Larynx
————	9. Digestive	D. Genitalia
————	10. Respiratory	E. Spleen
————	11. Reproductive	F. Capillaries

Circle the one that does not belong.

12.	Pharynx	Trachea	Mouth	Alveoli
13.	Uterus	Rectum	Gonads	Prostate
14.	Veins	Arteries	Heart	Pancreas
15.	Pineal	Bladder	Ureters	Urethra
16.	Tendon	Smooth	Joints	Voluntary
17.	Pituitary	Brain	Spinal cord	Nerves
18.	Cartilage	Joints	Ligaments	Tendons
19.	Hormones	Pituitary	Pancreas	Appendix
20.	Thymus	Nails	Hair	Oil glands
21.	Esophagus	Pharynx	Mouth	Trachea
22.	Thymus	Spleen	Tonsils	Liver

Fill in the missing area.

SYSTEM	ORGANS	FUNCTIONS
23. Integumentary	Skin, nails, hair, sense receptors, sweat glands, oil glands	_____ _____
24. Skeletal	_____	Support, movement, storage of minerals, blood formation
25. Muscular	Muscles	_____
26. _____	Brain, spinal cord, nerves	Communication, integration, control, recognition of sensory stimuli
27. Endocrine	_____	Secretion of hormones; communication, integration, control
28. Circulatory	Heart, blood vessels	_____
29. Lymphatic	_____	Transportation, immune system
30. _____	Kidneys, ureters, bladder, urethra	Elimination of wastes, electrolyte balance, acid-base balance, water balance
31. Digestive	_____	Digestion of food, absorption of nutrients
32. _____	Nose, pharynx, larynx, trachea, bronchi, lungs	Exchange of gases in the lungs
33. Reproductive	_____	Survival of species; production of sex cells, fertilization, development, birth; nourishment of offspring; production of hormones

▷ *If you have had difficulty with this section, review pages 55-66 and the chapter summary on pages 70 and 71.*

ORGAN REPLACEMENT

Fill in the blanks.

34. An organ not required for life to continue is a _____

    _____.

35. Many people suffering from deafness have had their hearing partially restored by "artificial ears"

    called _____ _____.

36. One of the earliest devices to augment vital functions was the "artificial kidney" or

    _____ _____.

37. An example of an artificial heart is the _____.

38. One approach that offers the hope of a permanent solution to loss of vital organ function is

    _____ _____.

39. After cancerous breasts are removed, "new" breasts can be formed from skin and muscle tissue

    using a method known as _____ _____.

40. The advantage to using a patient's own tissues in organ replacement is that the possibility of

    _____ is eliminated.

▷ *If you have had difficulty with this section, review pages 66-69.*

APPLYING WHAT YOU KNOW

46. Myrna was 15 years old and had not yet started menstruating. Her family physician decided to consult two other physicians, each of whom specialized in a different system. Specialists in the areas of _____ and _____ were consulted.

47. Brian was admitted to the hospital with second-degree and third-degree burns over 50% of his body. He was placed in isolation, so when Jenny went to visit him, she was required to wear a hospital gown and mask. Why was Brian placed in isolation? Why was Jenny required to wear special attire?

48. Sheila had a mastectomy to remove a cancerous lesion in her breast. Her body rejected the breast implant used to reconstruct her breast. Is there another breast reconstruction option to offer Sheila? If so, explain this option.

49. WORD FIND

Can you find 11 organ systems? Words may be spelled top to bottom, bottom to top, right to left, left to right, or diagonally.

```
Y  R  A  T  N  E  M  U  G  E  T  N  I  R  F
H  N  E  R  V  O  U  S  K  I  R  J  M  G  T
L  Y  M  P  H  A  T  I  C  I  S  Y  Y  U  I
B  N  X  Y  R  O  T  A  L  U  C  R  I  C  W
P  E  L  R  E  O  M  J  M  S  O  M  M  P  S
C  C  W  M  A  N  D  L  A  T  E  L  E  K  S
R  R  K  E  M  L  I  U  A  A  V  V  U  K  N
D  K  X  P  D  J  U  R  C  J  I  R  Q  E  M
C  D  B  V  C  V  I  C  C  T  K  W  C  X
X  R  Q  Q  D  P  H  C  S  O  I  X  P  A  Z
M  F  M  U  S  Y  D  E  V  U  D  V  Y  K  E
U  E  S  E  C  Z  G  T  Q  D  M  N  E  K  O
P  Y  R  A  N  I  R  U  C  T  C  N  E  W  H
N  H  T  N  D  E  P  S  I  X  A  Q  O  I  E
```

Circulatory	Lymphatic	Respiratory
Digestive	Muscular	Skeletal
Endocrine	Nervous	Urinary
Integumentary	Reproductive	

DID YOU KNOW?

Muscles comprise 40% of your body weight. Your skeleton, however, only accounts for 18% of your body weight.

ORGAN SYSTEMS

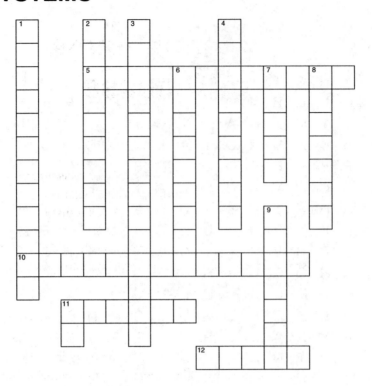

ACROSS

5. Specialized signal of nervous system (two words)
10. Skin
11. Testes and ovaries
12. Undigested residue of digestion

DOWN

1. Inflammation of the appendix
2. Vulva, penis, and scrotum
3. Heart and blood vessels
4. Subdivision of circulatory system
6. System of hormones
7. Waste product of kidneys
8. Agent that causes change in the activity of a structure
9. Chemical secretion of endocrine system
11. Gastrointestinal tract (abbreviation)

CHAPTER **4**

Mechanisms of Disease

One of our foremost concerns is health. We are fascinated and constantly confronted with information regarding what is necessary to be in good health, what is required for proper maintenance of the body, and what behaviors are responsible for disease.

Organisms play an important role in health. They are microscopic structures that are present everywhere. We need some organisms in the preparation of foods, in industry and agriculture, in connection with the problems of shelter or clothing, and in combating disease.

However, many organisms are responsible for disease. They attack and disturb the normal homeostasis of the body and adversely affect our health. Many varieties of organisms exist. They are often classified by shape, size, function, or staining properties. To prevent disease we must prevent pathogenic or disease-producing organisms from entering the body. This is not an easy task because we are surrounded by pathogenic organisms. Thus it is important that we understand the transmission and control of these organisms to fully comprehend the mechanisms of disease.

TOPICS FOR REVIEW

Before progressing to Chapter 5, you should familiarize yourself with disease terminology and patterns of disease. You should continue your review by studying pathophysiology and pathogenic organisms. Finally, an understanding of tumors, cancer, and inflammation is necessary to conclude your knowledge of this chapter.

STUDYING DISEASE

Match the term on the left with the proper selection on the right.

Group A

_____ 1. Pathology

_____ 2. Signs

_____ 3. Symptoms

_____ 4. Syndrome

_____ 5. Etiology

A. Subjective abnormalities

B. Study of disease

C. Collection of different signs and symptoms that present a clear picture of a pathological condition

D. Study of factors involved in causing a disease

E. Objective abnormalities

Group B

_____ 6. Latent

_____ 7. Convalescence

_____ 8. Pandemics

_____ 9. Endemic

_____ 10. Pathogenesis

A. Recovery

B. Disease native to a local region

C. "Hidden" stage

D. Affects large geographic regions

E. Actual pattern of a disease's development

▷ *If you have had difficulty with this section, review page 75.*

PATHOPHYSIOLOGY

Fill in the blanks.

11. _____ is the organized study of the underlying physiological processes associated with disease.

12. Many diseases are best understood as disturbances of _____.

13. Altered or _____ genes can cause abnormal proteins to be made.

14. An organism that lives in or on another organism to obtain its nutrients is called a

_____.

15. Abnormal tissue growths may also be referred to as _____.

16. Autoimmunity literally means _____ _____.

17. Genetic factors, age, lifestyle, stress, environmental factors, and preexisting conditions are

_____ _____ that may be responsible for pre-disposing a person to disease.

18. Scientists at the _____ _____

_____ _____ continuously track the inci-

dence and spread of disease in this country and worldwide.

19. Conditions caused by psychological factors are sometimes called _____

disorders.

20. A primary condition can put a person at risk for developing a _____

condition.

▷ *If you have difficulty with this section, review pages 76-78.*

PATHOGENIC ORGANISMS

Circle the best answer.

21. The smallest of all pathogens, microscopic nonliving particles, are called:
    A. Bacteria
    B. Fungi
    C. Viruses
    D. Protozoa

22. A tiny, primitive cell without a nucleus is called a:
    A. Bacterium
    B. Fungus
    C. Virus
    D. Protozoa

23. An example of a viral disease is:
    A. Diarrhea
    B. Mononucleosis
    C. Syphilis
    D. Toxic shock syndrome

24. Bacteria that require oxygen for metabolism are classified as:
    A. Gram positive
    B. Gram negative
    C. Aerobic
    D. Anaerobic

25. Bacilli are shaped like:
    A. Spheres
    B. Curves
    C. Squares
    D. Rods

26. Without chlorophyll, _____ cannot produce their own food, so they must consume or para-
    sitize other organisms.
    A. Bacteria
    B. Fungi
    C. Viruses
    D. Protozoa

27. Protozoa include:
    A. Amoebas
    B. Flagellates
    C. Ciliates
    D. All of the above

28. Pathogenic animals include the following:
    A. Nematodes
    B. Platyhelminths
    C. Arthropods
    D. All of the above

29. The key to preventing diseases caused by pathogenic organisms is to:
    A. Have an annual physical
    B. Stop them from entering the body
    C. Isolate yourself from all disease-carrying individuals
    D. None of the above

30. The destruction of all living organisms is known as:
    A. Disinfection
    B. Antisepsis
    C. Sterilization
    D. Isolation

31. Ways in which pathogens can spread include:
    A. Person-to-person contact
    B. Environmental contact
    C. Opportunistic invasion
    D. Transmission by vector
    E. All of the above

32. Compounds produced by certain living organisms that kill or inhibit pathogens are:
    A. Antiseptics
    B. Antibiotics
    C. Disinfectants
    D. Sterilizers

▷ *If you have had difficulty with this section, review pages 79-87.*

TUMORS AND CANCER

Circle the correct answer.

33. Benign tumors usually grow (slowly or quickly).

34. Malignant tumors (are or are not) encapsulated.

35. An example of a benign tumor that arises from epithelial tissue is (papilloma or lipoma).

36. A general term for malignant tumors that arise from connective tissues is (melanoma or sarcoma).

37. Abnormal, undifferentiated tumor cells are often produced by a process called (hyperplasia or anaplasia).

38. A cancer specialist is an (osteologist or oncologist).

39. The Papanicolaou test is a (biopsy or MRI).

40. (Staging or Grading) involves classifying a tumor based on its size and the extent of its spread.

41. Cachexia involves a loss of (appetite or hair).

▷ *If you have had difficulty with this section, review pages 88-92.*

WARNING SIGNS OF CANCER

List the seven warning signs of cancer.

42. _____

43. _____

44. _____

45. _____

46. _____

47. _____

48. _____

▷ *If you have had difficulty with this section, review page 90.*

INFLAMMATION

If the statement is true, write "T" in the answer blank. If the statement is false, correct the statement by circling the incorrect term and inserting the correct term in the answer blank.

_____ 49. As tissue cells are damaged, they release inflammation mediators such as histamines, prostaglandins, and kinins.

_____ 50. Inflammatory exudate is quickly removed by lymphatic vessels and is carried to lymph nodes, which act as filters.

_____ 51. Inflammation mediators can also act as signals that attract red blood cells to the injury site.

_____ 52. The movement of white blood cells in response to chemical attractants is called *chemotaxis*.

_____ 53. When new cells are similar to those that they replace, the process is known as *replacement*.

_____ 54. Fevers usually subside after the irritant has been eliminated.

_____ 55. The fever response in children and in the elderly often differs from that in the normal adult.

APPLYING WHAT YOU KNOW

56. Trent was examined by his doctor and was diagnosed as having a rhinovirus. Does he have need for concern? Why or why not?

57. Julius was 2 years old and was experiencing rectal itching and insomnia. The pediatrician told Julius' mother that he suspected a nematode. What is the common term for the specific nematode that might cause these symptoms?

58. Shirley was cleaning her house and wanted to use the most appropriate and effective aseptic method to prevent the spread of germs. What would you suggest?

59. Mr. and Mrs. Tolsma adopted a child of Chinese descent. Mrs. Tolsma researched the "gene pool" of the child to alert her to any special concerns. What is a "gene pool" and how will this information assist Mr. and Mrs. Tolsma in the rearing of their child?

60. Shane decided to become a paramedic. His application for school suggested that he receive the series of vaccinations for hepatitis B. Why?

61. WORD FIND

Can you find 18 terms from this chapter in the box of letters? Words may be spelled top to bottom, bottom to top, right to left, left to right, or diagonally.

```
N  P  E  S  D  B  S  L  A  A  C  E  R
W  O  L  S  I  C  I  M  E  D  I  P  E
X  V  I  O  F  S  X  V  R  E  N  A  T
O  D  P  T  U  E  A  D  O  N  C  R  U
H  S  O  V  A  S  T  T  P  O  U  A  C
Y  S  M  P  U  M  O  A  S  M  B  S  A
Y  P  A  R  O  I  M  B  I  A  A  I  I
N  L  I  O  S  R  E  A  F  L  T  T  D
W  V  J  T  C  Z  H  C  L  L  I  E  Y
W  Q  K  O  W  G  C  T  Q  F  O  C  M
V  Q  F  Z  I  F  G  E  R  P  N  F  A
K  E  N  O  Q  E  J  R  B  A  F  I  L
B  B  J  A  F  E  N  I  C  C  A  V  H
W  Z  F  H  R  B  S  U  D  M  Q  D  C
M  X  E  C  K  M  B  M  K  U  O  Z  P
```

Acute	Chlamydia	Metastasis
Adenoma	Ciliate	Parasite
Arthropod	Epidemic	Protozoa
Bacterium	Incubation	Spore
Biopsy	Inflammation	Vaccine
Chemotaxis	Lipoma	Virus

DID YOU KNOW?

As many as 500,000 Americans die from cancer each year, making it the second leading cause of death in the United States after cardiovascular disease. Half of all cancers are diagnosed in people under age 67.

The hepatitis B virus (HBV) has infected more than 200 million people worldwide.

MECHANISMS OF DISEASE

ACROSS

1. Roundworm
3. "Cancer gene"
5. Rod-shaped cells
6. Round cells
7. Spreads disease to other organisms
9. Lack chlorophyll
10. Possess pseudopodia
11. Tissue swelling

DOWN

2. Glandular cancer
4. Microscopic organism
8. Thick inflammatory exudate

MAJOR GROUPS OF PATHOGENIC PROTOZOA

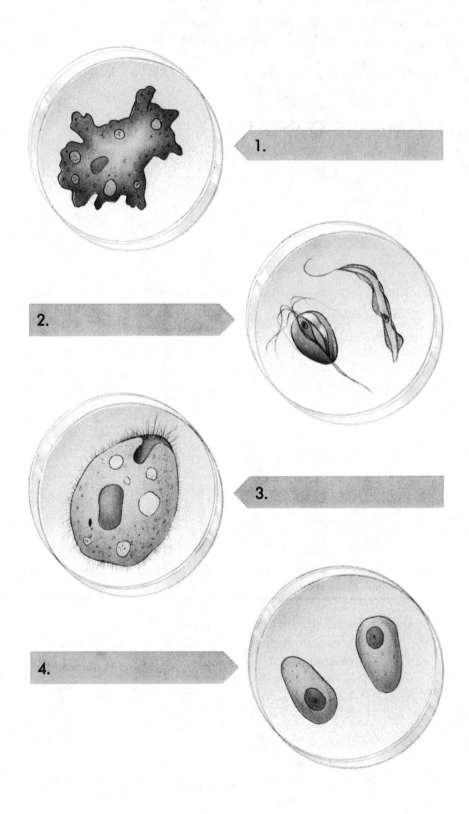

1.

2.

3.

4.

EXAMPLES OF PATHOGENIC ANIMALS

1.

2.

3.

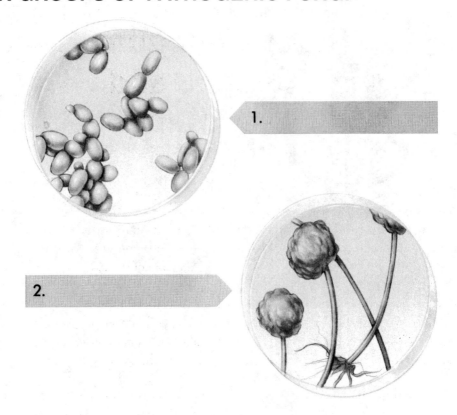

1.

2.

CHAPTER 5

The Integumentary System and Body Membranes

More of our time, attention, and money are spent on this system than any other one. Every time we look into a mirror we become aware of the integumentary system, as we observe our skin, hair, nails, and the appendages that give luster and comfort to this system. The discussion of the skin begins with the structure and function of the two primary layers called the *epidermis* and *dermis*. It continues with an examination of the appendages of the skin, which include the hair, receptors, nails, sebaceous glands, and sudoriferous glands. Your study of skin concludes with a review of one of the most serious and frequent threats to the skin—burns. An understanding of the integumentary system provides you with an appreciation of the danger that severe burns could pose to this system.

Membranes are thin, sheetlike structures that cover, protect, anchor, or lubricate body surfaces, cavities, or organs. The two major categories are *epithelial* and *connective*. Each type is located in specific areas of the body and is vulnerable to specific disease conditions. Knowledge of the location and function of these membranes prepares you for the study of their relationship to other systems and the body as a whole.

TOPICS FOR REVIEW

Before progressing to Chapter 6, you should have an understanding of the skin, its appendages, major skin disorders, and infections. Your review should include the classification of burns and the method used to estimate the percentage of body surface area affected by burns. A knowledge of the types of body membranes, their location, and their function is necessary to complete your study of this chapter.

CLASSIFICATION OF BODY MEMBRANES

Select the best answer.

        (a) Cutaneous   (b) Serous   (c) Mucous   (d) Synovial

_____ 1. Pleura

_____ 2. Lines joint spaces

_____ 3. Respiratory tract

_____ 4. Skin

_____ 5. Peritoneum

_____ 6. Contains no epithelium

_____ 7. Urinary tract

_____ 8. Lines body surfaces that open directly to the exterior

▷ *If you have had difficulty with this section, review pages 105-107.*

THE SKIN

Match the term on the left with the proper selection on the right.

<u>Group A</u>

_____ 9. Integumentary system   A. Outermost layer of skin

_____ 10. Epidermis   B. Deeper of the two layers of skin

_____ 11. Dermis   C. Allows for rapid absorption of injected

_____ 12. Subcutaneous   material

_____ 13. Cutaneous membrane   D. The skin is the primary organ

                                     E. Composed of dermis and epidermis

<u>Group B</u>

_____ 14. Keratin   A. Protective protein

_____ 15. Melanin   B. Blue-gray color of skin resulting from a

_____ 16. Stratum corneum   decrease in oxygen

_____ 17. Dermal papillae   C. Rows of peglike projections

_____ 18. Cyanosis   D. Brown pigment

                                     E. Outer layer of epidermis

Select the best answer.

        (a) Epidermis   (b) Dermis

_____ 19. Tightly packed epithelial cells

_____ 20. Nerves

_____ 21. Fingerprints

_____ 22. Blisters

_____ 23. Keratin

_____ 24. Connective tissue

_____ 25. Follicle

_____ 26. Sebaceous gland

_____ 27. Sweat gland

_____ 28. More cellular than other layer

▷ *If you have had difficulty with this section, review pages 107-110, 115.*

Fill in the blanks.

29. The three most important functions of the skin are _____,

    _____, and _____.

30. _____ prevents the sun's ultraviolet rays from penetrating the interior

    of the body.

31. The hair of a newborn infant is called _____.

32. Hair growth begins from a small cap-shaped cluster of cells called the

    _____ _____.

33. Hair loss of any kind is called _____.

34. The _____ _____ muscle produces "goose

    pimples."

35. Meissner's corpuscle is generally located rather close to the skin surface and is capable of detect-

    ing sensations of _____ _____.

36. The most numerous, important, and widespread sweat glands in the body are the

    _____ sweat glands.

37. The _____ sweat glands are found primarily in the axilla and in the

    pigmented skin areas around the genitals.

38. _____ has been described as "nature's skin cream."

Circle the correct answer.

39. A first-degree burn (will or will not) blister.

40. A second-degree burn (will or will not) scar.

41. A third-degree burn (will or will not) have pain immediately.

42. According to the "rule of nines," the body is divided into (9 or 11) areas of 9%.

43. Destruction of the subcutaneous layer occurs in (second- or third-) degree burns.

▷ *If you have had difficulty with this section, review pages 108-117.*

DISORDERS OF THE SKIN

Circle the correct choice.

44. Any disorders of the skin may be called:
    A. Dermatitis
    B. Dermatosis
    C. Dermatotomy
    D. None of the above

45. Any measurable variation from the normal structure of a tissue is known as a/an:
    A. Lesion
    B. Burn
    C. Blister
    D. Erythema

46. An example of a papule is a:
    A. Scratch
    B. Bedsore
    C. Freckle
    D. Wart

47. An example of a skin disorder that may produce fissures is:
    A. Acne
    B. A bedsore
    C. Psoriasis
    D. Athlete's foot

48. The skin is the _____ line of defense against microbes that invade the body's internal environment.
    A. First
    B. Second
    C. Third
    D. Fourth

49. Tinea is a fungal infection and may appear as:
    A. Ringworm
    B. Jock itch
    C. Athlete's foot
    D. All of the above

50. Furuncles are local staphylococci infections and are also known as:
    A. Scabies
    B. Warts
    C. Boils
    D. Impetigo

51. The most common type of skin cancer is:
    A. Squamous cell
    B. Basal cell
    C. Melanoma
    D. Kaposi's sarcoma

▷ *If you had difficulty with this section, review pages 115-123.*

Unscramble the words.

52. PIDEEMIRS ◻︎◻︎◻︎⦿⦿⦿◻︎◻︎◻︎

53. REKTAIN ◻︎⦿◻︎⦿◻︎◻︎◻︎

54. AHIR ⦿◻︎⦿⦿

55. UGONAL ◻︎◻︎◻︎◻︎⦿◻︎

56. DRTONIDEHYA ⦿⦿◻︎◻︎◻︎◻︎◻︎◻︎◻︎◻︎◻︎

Take the circled letters, unscramble them, and
fill in the statement.
What Amanda's mother gave her after every date.

57. ◻︎◻︎◻︎◻︎◻︎◻︎ ◻︎◻︎◻︎◻︎◻︎◻︎◻︎

APPLYING WHAT YOU KNOW

58. Mr. Ziven was admitted to the hospital with second-degree and third-degree burns. Both arms, the anterior trunk, the right anterior leg, and the genital region were affected by the burns. The doctor quickly estimated that _____% of Mr. Ziven's body had been burned.

59. Mrs. James complained to her doctor that she had severe pain in her chest and feared that she was having a heart attack. An ECG revealed nothing unusual, but Mrs. James insisted that every time she took a breath she experienced pain. What might be the cause of Mrs. James' pain?

60. Mrs. Collins was born with a rare condition known as *xeroderma pigmentosum*. What activity should she avoid?

61. After investigating the scene of the crime, Officer Gorski announced that dermal papillae were found that could help solve the case. What did he mean?

Can you find the 15 terms from this chapter in the box of letters? Words may be spelled top to bottom, bottom to top, right to left, left to right, or diagonally.

```
S  U  D  O  R  I  F  E  R  O  U  S  V  K  R
E  J  U  Q  U  E  S  T  E  C  N  O  H  Y  U
I  S  J  L  M  E  L  A  N  O  C  Y  T  E  H
R  I  M  U  E  N  O  T  I  R  E  P  H  S  B
O  M  K  N  V  A  S  T  R  L  A  N  U  G  O
T  R  G  U  F  G  A  U  C  E  G  O  V  W  D
A  E  A  L  P  R  D  I  O  N  T  F  D  R  N
L  D  V  A  D  M  L  C  P  D  H  S  L  Z  F
I  I  N  Y  N  L  R  L  A  M  E  N  I  R  E
P  P  H  Q  O  N  E  U  X  R  R  F  E  L  G
E  E  Z  F  J  U  M  Y  O  U  U  O  C  C  B
D  Z  P  E  R  J  Y  U  V  F  C  I  I  E  O
G  J  S  I  W  J  S  K  C  D  T  N  O  Z  C
C  O  S  M  Z  M  F  I  B  U  G  U  X  O  J
X  Y  P  M  E  I  W  E  C  V  S  U  G  B  I
```

Apocrine	Epidermis	Mucus
Blister	Follicle	Peritoneum
Cuticle	Lanugo	Pleurisy
Dehydration	Lunula	Serous
Depilatories	Melanocyte	Sudoriferous

DID YOU KNOW?

Because the dead cells of the epidermis are constantly being worn and washed away, we get a new outer skin layer every 27 days.

SKIN/BODY MEMBRANES

ACROSS

1. Inflammation of the serous membrane that lines the chest and covers the lungs
4. Cutaneous
9. Membrane that lines joint spaces
10. "Goose pimples" (two words)
11. Cushionlike sacs found between moving body parts
12. Deeper of the two primary skin layers

DOWN

1. Forms the lining of serous body cavities
2. Oil gland
3. Bluish-gray color of skin due to decreased oxygen
5. Tough waterproof substance that protects body from excess fluid loss
6. Sweat gland
7. Brown pigment
8. Covers the surface of organs found in serous body cavities

LONGITUDINAL SECTION OF THE SKIN

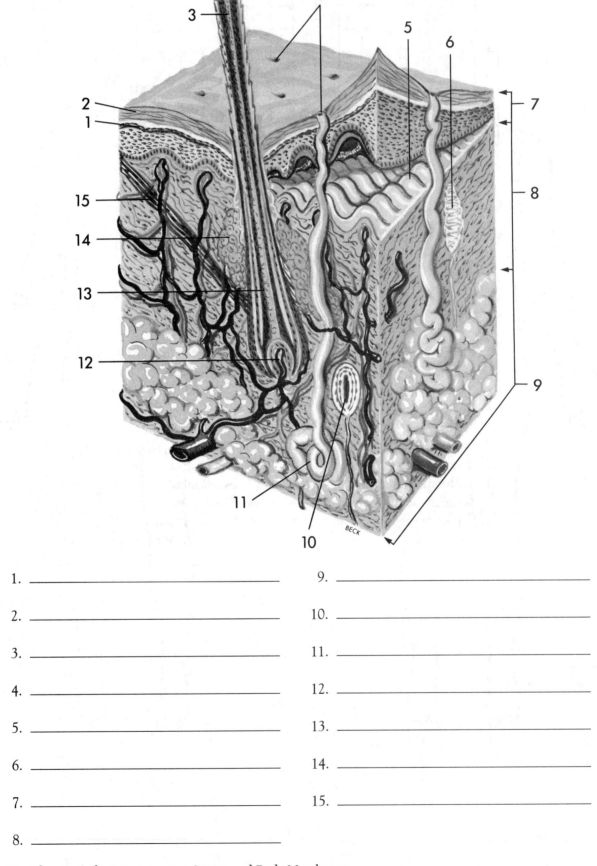

1. _____
2. _____
3. _____
4. _____
5. _____
6. _____
7. _____
8. _____

9. _____
10. _____
11. _____
12. _____
13. _____
14. _____
15. _____

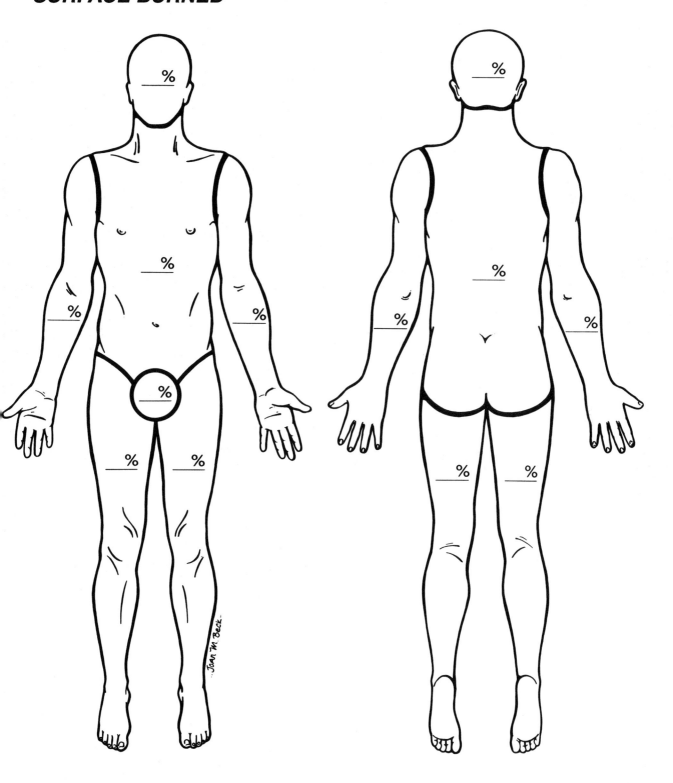

The Skeletal System

How strange we would look without our skeleton! It is the skeleton that provides us with the rigid, supportive framework that gives shape to our bodies. But this is just the beginning, because the skeleton also protects the organs beneath it, maintains homeostasis of blood calcium, produces blood cells, and assists the muscular system in providing movement for us.

After reviewing the microscopic structure of bone and cartilage, you will understand how skeletal tissues are formed, their differences, and their importance in the human body. Your microscopic investigation will make the study of this system easier as you logically progress from this view to macroscopic bone formation and growth and visualize the structure of long bones.

The skeleton is divided into two main divisions: the axial skeleton and the appendicular skeleton. All of the 206 bones of the human body may be classified into one of these two areas. And, although we can divide them neatly by this system, we are still aware that subtle differences exist between a man's and a woman's skeleton. These structural differences provide us with insight into the differences in function between men and women.

Finally, three types of joints exist in the body. They are synarthrosis, amphiarthrosis, and diarthrosis. It is important to have a knowledge of these joints to understand how movement is facilitated by articulations.

TOPICS FOR REVIEW

Before progressing to Chapter 7, you should familiarize yourself with the functions of the skeletal system, the structure and function of bone and cartilage, bone formation and growth, and the types of joints found in the body. Additionally, your understanding of the skeletal system should include identification of the two major subdivisions of the skeleton, the bones found in each area, and any differences that exist between a man's and a woman's skeleton. Your study should conclude with a review of the major skeletal disorders.

FUNCTIONS OF THE SKELETAL SYSTEM
TYPES OF BONES
STRUCTURE OF LONG BONES

Fill in the blanks.

1. There are ＿＿＿＿＿＿＿＿＿＿＿＿ types of bones.

2. The ＿＿＿＿＿＿＿＿＿＿ ＿＿＿＿＿＿＿＿＿＿ is the hollow area inside

   the diaphysis of a bone.

3. A thin layer of cartilage covering each epiphysis is the ＿＿＿＿＿＿＿＿＿＿

   ＿＿＿＿＿＿＿＿＿＿.

4. The ＿＿＿＿＿＿＿＿＿＿ lines the medullary cavity of long bones.

5. ＿＿＿＿＿＿＿＿＿＿ is used to describe the process of blood cell formation.

6. Blood cell formation is a vital process carried on in ＿＿＿＿＿＿＿＿＿＿

   ＿＿＿＿＿＿＿＿＿＿ ＿＿＿＿＿＿＿＿＿＿.

7. The ＿＿＿＿＿＿＿＿＿＿ is a strong fibrous membrane covering a long bone except at

   joint surfaces.

8. Bones may be classified by shape. Those shapes include ＿＿＿＿＿＿＿＿＿＿,

   ＿＿＿＿＿＿＿＿＿＿, ＿＿＿＿＿＿＿＿＿＿, and

   ＿＿＿＿＿＿＿＿＿＿.

9. Bones serve as a safety-deposit box for ＿＿＿＿＿＿＿＿＿＿, a vital substance required

   for normal nerve and muscle function.

10. As muscles contract and shorten, they pull on bones and thereby ＿＿＿＿＿＿＿＿＿＿

    them.

▶ *If you have had difficulty with this section, review pages 131-132.*

MICROSCOPIC STRUCTURE OF BONE AND CARTILAGE

Match the term on the left with the proper selection on the right.

Group A

_____ 11. Trabeculae
_____ 12. Compact
_____ 13. Spongy
_____ 14. Periosteum
_____ 15. Cartilage

A. Outer covering of bone
B. Dense bone tissue
C. Fibers embedded in a firm gel
D. Needlelike threads of spongy bone
E. Ends of long bones

Group B

_____ 16. Osteocytes
_____ 17. Canaliculi
_____ 18. Lamellae
_____ 19. Chondrocytes
_____ 20. Haversian system

A. Connect lacunae
B. Cartilage cells
C. Structural unit of compact bone
D. Bone cells
E. Ring of bone

▷ *If you have had difficulty with this section, review pages 132-134.*

BONE FORMATION AND GROWTH

If the statement is true, write T in the answer blank. If the statement is false, correct the statement by circling the incorrect term and inserting the correct term in the answer blank.

_____ 21. When the skeleton forms in a baby before birth, it consists of cartilage and fibrous structures.

_____ 22. The diaphyses are the ends of the bone.

_____ 23. Bone-forming cells are known as *osteoclasts*.

_____ 24. It is the combined action of osteoblasts and osteoclasts that sculpts bones into their adult shapes.

_____ 25. The point of articulation between the epiphysis and diaphysis of a growing long bone is susceptible to injury if over-stressed.

_____ 26. The epiphyseal plate can be seen in both external and cutaway views of an adult long bone.

_____ 27. The shaft of a long bone is known as the articulation.

_____ 28. Cartilage in the newborn becomes bone when it is replaced with calcified bone matrix deposited by osteoblasts.

_____ 29. When epiphyseal cartilage becomes bone, growth begins.

_____ 30. The epiphyseal cartilage is visible, if present, on x-ray films.

▷ *If you have had difficulty with this section, review pages 134-140.*

DIVISIONS OF SKELETON

Circle the correct choice.

31. Which one of the following is <u>not</u> a part of the axial skeleton?
    A. Scapula
    B. Cranial bones
    C. Vertebra
    D. Ribs
    E. Sternum

32. Which one of the following is <u>not</u> a cranial bone?
    A. Frontal
    B. Parietal
    C. Occipital
    D. Lacrimal
    E. Sphenoid

33. Which of the following is <u>not</u> correct?
    A. A baby is born with a straight spine.
    B. In the adult the sacral and thoracic curves are convex.
    C. The normal curves of the adult spine provide greater strength than a straight spine.
    D. A curved structure has more strength than a straight one of the same size and materials.

34. True ribs:
    A. Attach to the cartilage of other ribs
    B. Do not attach to the sternum
    C. Attach directly to the sternum without cartilage
    D. Attach directly to the sternum by means of cartilage

35. The bone that runs along the lateral side of your forearm is the:
    A. Humerus
    B. Ulna
    C. Radius
    D. Tibia

36. The shinbone is also known as the:
    A. Fibula
    B. Femur
    C. Tibia
    D. Ulna

37. The bones in the palm of the hand are called:
    A. Metatarsals
    B. Tarsals
    C. Carpals
    D. Metacarpals

38. Which one of the following is <u>not</u> a bone of the upper extremity?
    A. Radius
    B. Clavicle
    C. Humerus
    D. Ilium

39. The heel bone is known as the:
    A. Calcaneus
    B. Talus
    C. Metatarsal
    D. Phalanges

40. The mastoid process is part of which bone?
    A. Parietal
    B. Temporal
    C. Occipital
    D. Frontal

41. When a baby learns to walk, which area of the spine becomes concave?
    A. Lumbar   C. Cervical
    B. Thoracic   D. Coccyx

42. Which bone is the "funny" bone?
    A. Radius   C. Humerus
    B. Ulna   D. Carpal

43. There are how many pair of true ribs?
    A. 14   C. 5
    B. 7   D. 3

44. The 27 bones in the wrist and the hand allow for more:
    A. Strength   C. Protection
    B. Dexterity   D. Red blood cell products

45. The longest bone in the body is the:
    A. Tibia   C. Femur
    B. Fibula   D. Humerus

46. Distally, the _____ articulates with the patella.
    A. Femur   C. Tibia
    B. Fibula   D. Humerus

47. These bones form the cheek bones:
    A. Mandible   C. Maxillary
    B. Palatine   D. Zygomatic

48. In a child, there are five of these bones. In an adult, they are fused into one:
    A. Pelvic   C. Sacrum
    B. Lumbar vertebrae   D. Carpals

49. The spinal cord enters the cranium through a large hole (foramen magnum) in this bone:
    A. Temporal   C. Occipital
    B. Parietal   D. Sphenoid

Circle the one that does not belong.

50. Cervical	Thoracic	Coxal bone	Coccyx
51. Pelvic girdle	Ankle	Wrist	Axial
52. Frontal	Occipital	Maxilla	Sphenoid
53. Scapula	Pectoral girdle	Ribs	Clavicle
54. Malleus	Vomer	Incus	Stapes
55. Ulna	Ilium	Ischium	Pubis
56. Carpal	Phalanges	Metacarpal	Ethmoid
57. Ethmoid	Parietal	Occipital	Nasal
58. Anvil	Atlas	Axis	Cervical

▷ *If you have had difficulty with this section, review pages 136-149.*

DIFFERENCES BETWEEN A MAN'S AND A WOMAN'S SKELETON

Choose the right answer.

(a) Male   (b) Female

_____ 59. Funnel-shaped pelvis

_____ 60. Broader-shaped pelvis

_____ 61. Wider pubic angle

_____ 62. Larger

_____ 63. Wider pelvic inlet

▷ *If you have had difficulty with this section, review pages 151-152.*

BONE MARKINGS

From the choices given, match the bone with its identification marking. Bones may be used more than once.

A. Mastoid	K. Acetabulum
B. Pterygoid process	L. Symphysis pubis
C. Foramen magnum	M. Ilium
D. Sella turcica	N. Greater trochanter
E. Mental foramen	O. Medial malleolus
F. Conchae	P. Calcaneus
G. Xiphoid process	Q. Acromion process
H. Glenoid cavity	R. Frontal sinuses
I. Olecranon process	S. Condyloid process
J. Ischium	T. Tibial tuberosity

_____ 64. Occipital   _____ 71. Sphenoid

_____ 65. Sternum   _____ 72. Ethmoid

_____ 66. Coxal bone   _____ 73. Scapula

_____ 67. Femur   _____ 74. Tibia

_____ 68. Ulna   _____ 75. Frontal

_____ 69. Temporal   _____ 76. Mandible

_____ 70. Tarsals

▷ *If you have had difficulty with this section, review pages 137-149, 153.*

JOINTS (ARTICULATIONS)

Circle the correct answer.

77. Freely movable joints are (amphiarthroses or diarthroses).

78. The sutures in the skull are (synarthrotic or amphiarthrotic) joints.

79. All (diarthrotic or amphiarthrotic) joints have a joint capsule, a joint cavity, and a layer of cartilage over the ends of the two joining bones.

80. (Ligaments or tendons) grow out of periosteum and attach two bones together.

81. The (articular cartilage or epiphyseal cartilage) absorbs jolts.

82. Gliding joints are the (least movable or most movable) of the diarthrotic joints.

83. The knee is the (largest or smallest) joint.

84. Hinge joints allow motion in (2 or 4) directions.

85. The saddle joint at the base of each of our thumbs allows for greater (strength or mobility).

86. When you rotate your head, you are using a (gliding or pivot) joint.

▷ *If you have had difficulty with this section, review pages 154-158.*

Fill in the blanks.

87. _____ is an imaging technique that allows a physician to examine the

    internal structure of a joint without the use of extensive surgery.

88. One of the most common skeletal tumors and one of the most rapidly fatal is

    _____.

89. A common bone disease characterized by excessive loss of calcified matrix and collagenous fiber is

    _____.

90. A metabolic disorder involving mineral loss in bones is _____.

91. A metabolic disorder that is often asymptomatic and affects older adults is

    _____.

92. The general name for bacterial infections of bone and marrow tissue is _____.

93. Closed fractures, also known as _____ _____,

do not pierce the skin.

94. _____ _____ are breaks that produce many

fragments.

95. The most common noninflammatory joint disease is _____ or

_____ _____

_____.

96. Three major types of arthritis are _____,

_____, and _____.

97. One form of infectious arthritis, _____ _____,

was identified in 1975 in Connecticut and has since spread across the continent.

▷ *If you have had difficulty with this section, review pages 158-163.*

UNSCRAMBLE THE BONES

98. ETVERRBAE

99. BPSUI

100. SCALUPA

101. IMDBALNE

102. APNHGAELS

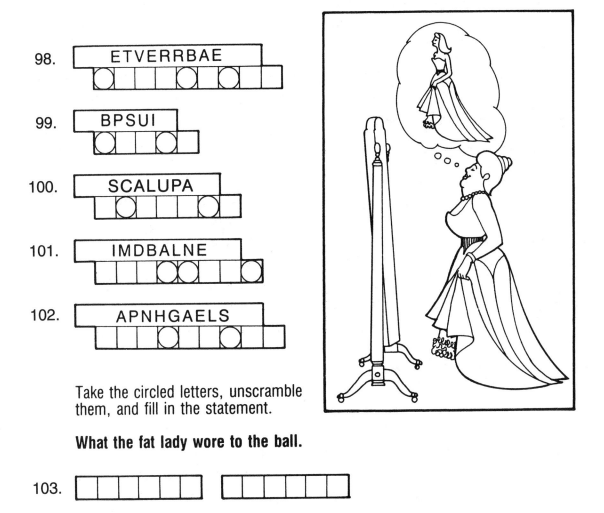

Take the circled letters, unscramble them, and fill in the statement.

What the fat lady wore to the ball.

103.

APPLYING WHAT YOU KNOW

104. Mrs. Perine has advanced cancer of the bone. As the disease progresses, Mrs. Perine requires several blood transfusions throughout her therapy. She asks the doctor one day to explain the necessity for the transfusions. What explanation might the doctor give to Mrs. Perine?

105. Dr. Kennedy, an orthopedic surgeon, called the admissions office of the hospital and advised that he would be admitting a patient in the next hour with an epiphyseal fracture. Without any other information, the patient is assigned to the pediatric ward. What prompted this assignment?

106. Mrs. Van Skiver, age 60, noticed when she went in for her physical examination that she was one-half inch shorter than she was on her last visit. Dr. Veazey suggested she begin a regimen of dietary supplements of calcium, vitamin D, and a prescription for sex hormone therapy. What bone disease did Dr. Veazey suspect?

107. Mrs. LaGasse was moving and experienced severe, sharp pain in her lower back while lifting some boxes. The pain was not relieved by traditional home remedies or pain medication. She finally sought the advice of a physician after being unable to relieve the pain for 48 hours. What might be a possible diagnosis?

108. WORD FIND

Can you find 14 terms from this chapter in the box of letters? Words may be spelled top to bottom, bottom to top, right to left, left to right, or diagonally.

```
A R T I C U L A T I O N N U T
M M L T N I N G U I H J N C G
P R P E R I O S T E U M A N B
H V P G U A T B M E O P R F G
I N V R N O B O F S M H X E R
A G J O A J P E T O E O H T Q
R U R B X O E E C A S G I S B
T S S Y I M O Q N U O O L X Q
H J I E A B P U N Q L E Q K S
R I S I L U C I L A N A C X R
O I N A M A S Q M A Q K E C T
S T S A L C O E T S O U I D G
E T S Y F W L N M P U F N U F
S B H Q H L O U S A R X I T V
R P M P A F M G X K D S L G A
```

Amphiarthroses	Fontanels	Osteoclasts
Articulation	Hemopoiesis	Periosteum
Axial	Lacunae	Sinus
Canaliculi	Lamella	Trabeculae
Compact	Osteoblasts	

DID YOU KNOW?

The bones of the hands and feet make up more than half of the total 206 bones of the body.

Approximately 25 million Americans have osteoporosis. Four out of five are women.

The bones of the middle ear are mature at birth.

SKELETAL SYSTEM

ACROSS

4. Cartilage cells
6. Spaces in bones where osteocytes are found
8. Chest
9. Freely movable joints
11. Process of blood cell formation
13. Space inside cranial bone

DOWN

1. Joint
2. Suture joints
3. Bone absorbing cells
4. Type of bone
5. Ends of long bones
7. Covers long bone except at its joint surfaces
10. Division of skeleton
12. Bone cell

LONGITUDINAL SECTION OF LONG BONE

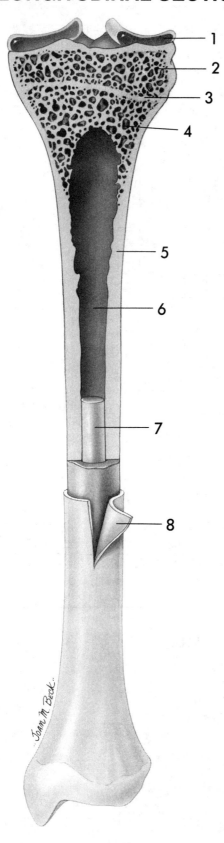

1. _____

2. _____

3. _____

4. _____

5. _____

6. _____

7. _____

8. _____

ANTERIOR VIEW OF SKELETON

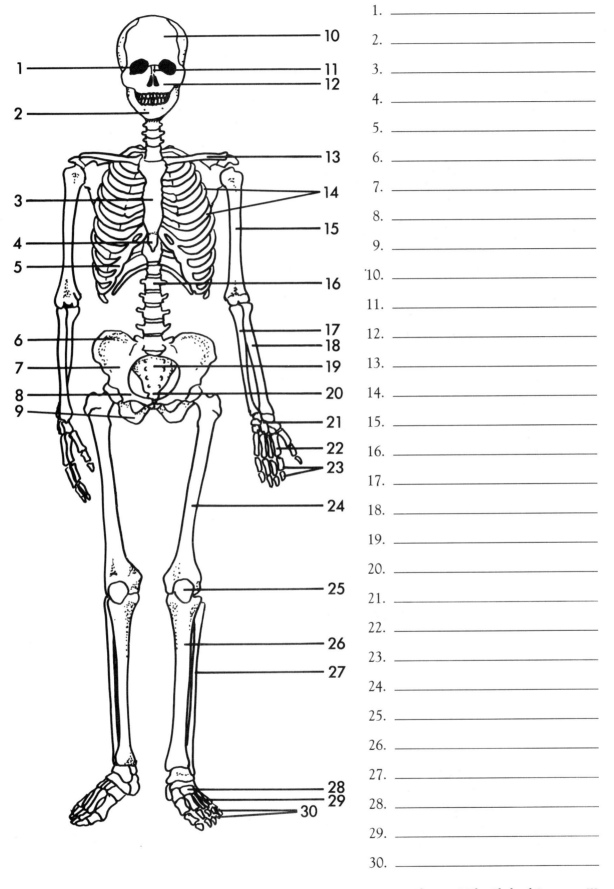

1. _____
2. _____
3. _____
4. _____
5. _____
6. _____
7. _____
8. _____
9. _____
10. _____
11. _____
12. _____
13. _____
14. _____
15. _____
16. _____
17. _____
18. _____
19. _____
20. _____
21. _____
22. _____
23. _____
24. _____
25. _____
26. _____
27. _____
28. _____
29. _____
30. _____

POSTERIOR VIEW OF SKELETON

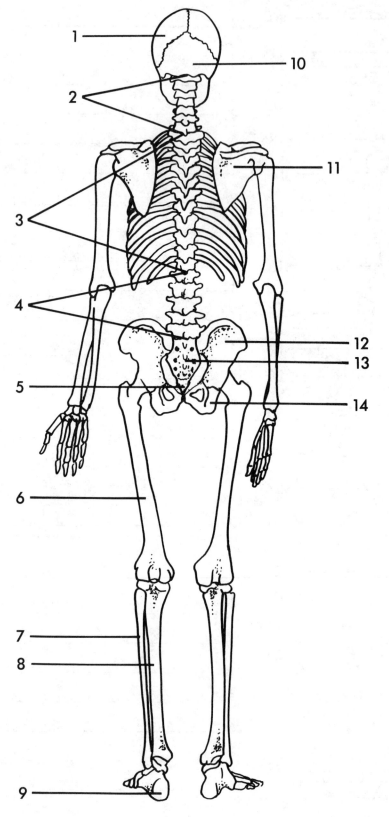

1. _____

2. _____

3. _____

4. _____

5. _____

6. _____

7. _____

8. _____

9. _____

10. _____

11. _____

12. _____

13. _____

14. _____

SKULL VIEWED FROM THE RIGHT SIDE

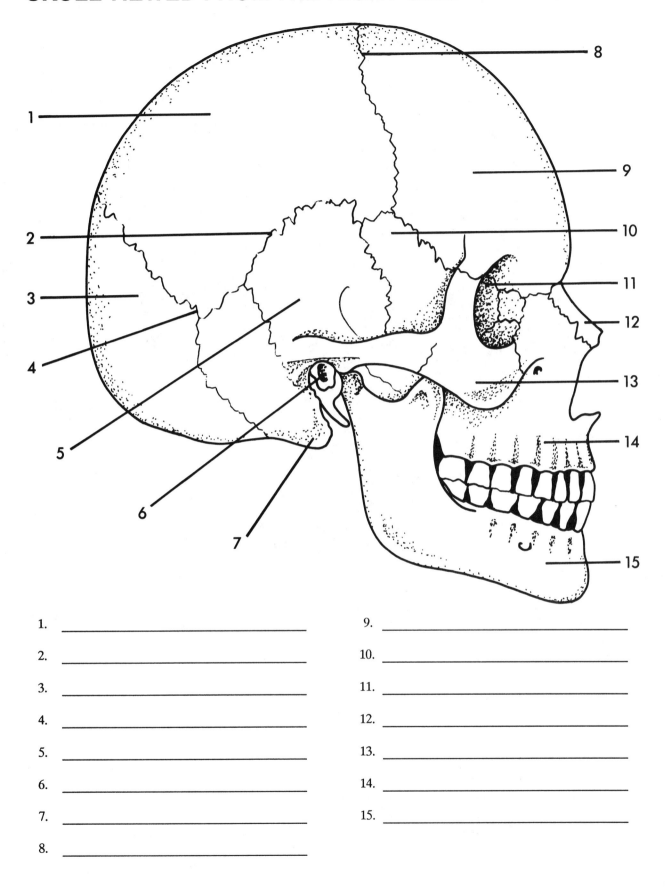

1. _____

2. _____

3. _____

4. _____

5. _____

6. _____

7. _____

8. _____

9. _____

10. _____

11. _____

12. _____

13. _____

14. _____

15. _____

SKULL VIEWED FROM THE FRONT

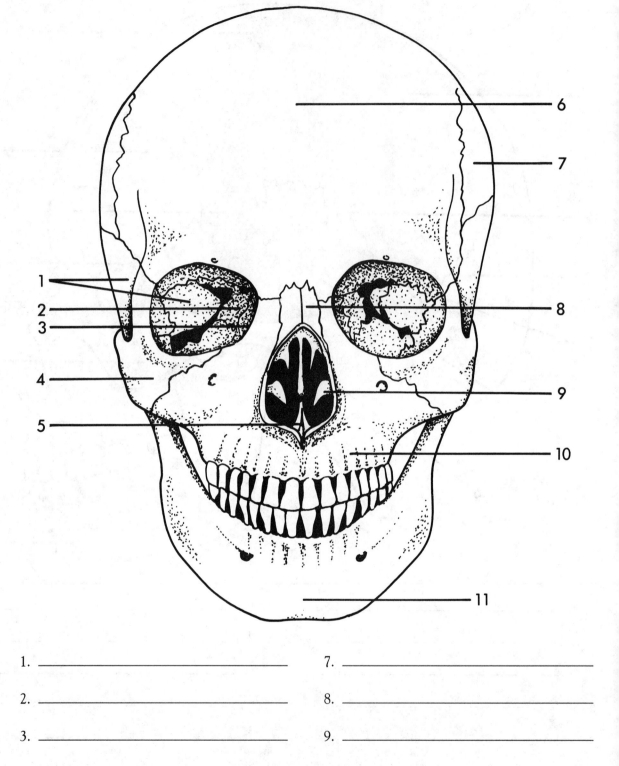

1. _____

2. _____

3. _____

4. _____

5. _____

6. _____

7. _____

8. _____

9. _____

10. _____

11. _____

STRUCTURE OF A DIARTHROTIC JOINT

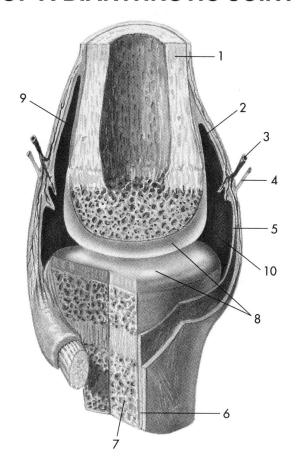

1. _____   6. _____

2. _____   7. _____

3. _____   8. _____

4. _____   9. _____

5. _____   10. _____

CHAPTER **7**   # The Muscular System

The muscular system is often referred to as the "power system," and rightfully so, because it is this system that provides the motion necessary to move the body and perform organic functions. Just as an automobile relies on the engine to provide motion, the body depends on the muscular system to perform both voluntary and involuntary types of movement. Walking, breathing, and the digestion of food are but a few examples of body functions that require the healthy performance of the muscular system.

Although this system has several functions, the primary purpose is to provide movement or power. Muscles produce power by contracting. The ability of a large muscle or muscle group to contract depends on the ability of microscopic muscle fibers that contract within the larger muscle. An understanding of these microscopic muscle fibers will assist you as you progress in your study to the larger muscles and muscle groups.

Muscle contractions may be one of several types: isotonic, isometric, twitch, or tetanic. When skeletal or voluntary muscles contract, they provide us with a variety of motions. Flexion, extension, abduction, adduction, and rotation are examples of these movements that provide us with both strength and agility.

Muscles must be used to keep the body healthy and in good condition. Scientific evidence keeps pointing to the fact that the proper use and exercise of muscles may improve longevity. An understanding of the structure and function of the muscular system may therefore add quality and quantity to our lives.

TOPICS FOR REVIEW

Before progressing to Chapter 8, you should familiarize yourself with the structure and function of the three major types of muscle tissue. Your review should include the microscopic structure of skeletal muscle tissue, how a muscle is stimulated, the major types of skeletal muscle contractions, and the skeletal muscle groups. Your study should conclude with an understanding of the types of movements produced by skeletal muscle contractions and the major muscular disorders.

MUSCLE TISSUE

Select the correct term from the choices given and insert the letter(s) in the answer blank.

      (a) Skeletal muscle   (b) Cardiac muscle   (c) Smooth muscle

_____ 1. Striated

_____ 2. Cells branch frequently

_____ 3. Moves food into stomach

_____ 4. Nonstriated

_____ 5. Voluntary

_____ 6. Keeps blood circulating through its vessels

_____ 7. Involuntary

_____ 8. Attaches to bone

_____ 9. Hollow internal organs

_____ 10. Maintenance of normal blood pressure

▷ *If you have had difficulty with this section, review page 169.*

STRUCTURE OF SKELETAL MUSCLES

Match the term on the left with the proper selection on the right.

Group A

_____ 11. Origin	A.	The muscle unit excluding the ends
_____ 12. Insertion	B.	Attachment to the more movable bone
_____ 13. Body	C.	Fluid-filled sacs
_____ 14. Tendons	D.	Attachment to more stationary bone
_____ 15. Bursae	E.	Anchor muscles to bones

MICROSCOPIC STRUCTURE

Match the term on the left with the proper selection on the right.

Group B

_____ 16. Muscle fibers
_____ 17. Actin
_____ 18. Sarcomere
_____ 19. Myosin
_____ 20. Myofilaments

A. Protein that forms thick myofilaments
B. Basic functional unit of skeletal muscle
C. Protein that forms thin myofilaments
D. Microscopic threadlike structures found in skeletal muscle fibers
E. Specialized contractile cells of muscle tissue

▷ *If you have had difficulty with this section, review pages 169-171.*

FUNCTIONS OF SKELETAL MUSCLE

Fill in the blanks.

21. Muscles move bones by _____ on them.

22. As a rule, only the _____ bone moves.

23. The _____ bone moves toward the _____

    bone.

24. Of all the muscles contracting simultaneously, the one mainly responsible for producing a particu-

    lar movement is called the _____ _____ for

    that movement.

25. As prime movers contract, other muscles called _____ relax.

26. The biceps brachii is the prime mover during flexing, and the brachialis is its helper or

    _____ muscle.

27. We are able to maintain our body position because of a specialized type of skeletal muscle con-

    traction called _____ _____ .

28. _____ _____ maintains body posture by

    counteracting the pull of gravity.

29. A decrease in temperature, a condition known as _____, will drastically affect cellular activity and normal body function.

30. Energy required to produce a muscle contraction is obtained from

_____.

▶ *If you have had difficulty with this section, review pages 171-173.*

FATIGUE
ROLE OF OTHER BODY SYSTEMS
MOTOR UNIT
MUSCLE STIMULUS

If the statement is true, write T on the answer blank. If the statement is false, correct the statement by circling the incorrect term and inserting the correct term in the answer blank.

_____ 31. The point of contact between the nerve ending and the muscle fiber is called a *motor neuron*.

_____ 32. A motor neuron together with the cells it innervates is called a *motor unit*.

_____ 33. If muscle cells are stimulated repeatedly without adequate periods of rest, the strength of the muscle contraction will decrease, resulting in fatigue.

_____ 34. The depletion of oxygen in muscle cells during vigorous and prolonged exercise is known as *fatigue*.

_____ 35. An adequate stimulus will contract a muscle cell completely because of the "must" theory.

_____ 36. When oxygen supplies run low, muscle cells produce ATP and other waste products during contraction.

_____ 37. In a laboratory setting a single muscle fiber can be isolated and subjected to stimuli of varying intensities so that it can be studied.

_____ 38. The minimal level of stimulation required to cause a fiber to contract is called the *threshold stimulus*.

_____ 39. Smooth muscles bring about movements by pulling on bones across movable joints.

_____ 40. A nervous system disorder that shuts off impulses to certain skeletal muscles may result in paralysis.

TYPES OF SKELETAL MUSCLE CONTRACTION

Circle the correct choice.

41. When a muscle does not shorten and no movement results, the contraction is:
    A. Isometric
    B. Isotonic
    C. Twitch
    D. Tetanic

42. Walking is an example of which type of contraction?
    A. Isometric
    B. Isotonic
    C. Twitch
    D. Tetanic

43. Pushing against a wall is an example of which type of contraction?
    A. Isotonic
    B. Isometric
    C. Twitch
    D. Tetanic

44. Endurance training is also known as:
    A. Isometrics
    B. Hypertrophy
    C. Aerobic training
    D. Strength training

45. Benefits of regular exercise include all of the following except:
    A. Improved lung functioning
    B. More efficient heart
    C. Less fatigue
    D. Atrophy

46. Twitch contractions can be easily seen in:
    A. Isolated muscles prepared for research
    B. A great deal of normal muscle activity
    C. During resting periods
    D. None of the above

47. Individual contractions "melt" together to produce a sustained contraction or:
    A. Twitch
    B. Tetanus
    C. Isotonic response
    D. Isometric response

48. In most cases, isotonic contraction of muscle produces movement at a/an:
    A. Insertion
    B. Origin
    C. Joint
    D. Bursa

49. Prolonged inactivity causes muscles to shrink in mass, a condition called:
    A. Hypertrophy
    B. Disuse atrophy
    C. Paralysis
    D. Muscle fatigue

50. Muscle hypertrophy can be best enhanced by a program of:
    A. Isotonic exercise
    B. Better posture
    C. High-protein diet
    D. Strength training

▷ *If you have had difficulty with this section, review pages 173-176.*

SKELETAL MUSCLE GROUPS

Choose the proper function(s) for the muscles listed below and place the letter(s) in the answer blank.

(a) Flexor	(d) Adductor
(b) Extensor	(e) Rotator
(c) Abductor	(f) Dorsiflexor or plantar flexor

_____ 51. Deltoid

_____ 52. Tibialis anterior

_____ 53. Gastrocnemius

_____ 54. Biceps brachii

_____ 55. Gluteus medius

_____ 56. Soleus

_____ 57. Iliopsoas

_____ 58. Pectoralis major

_____ 59. Gluteus maximus

_____ 60. Triceps brachii

_____ 61. Sternocleidomastoid

_____ 62. Trapezius

_____ 63. Gracilis

▷ *If you have had difficulty with this section, review pages 180-188.*

TYPES OF MOVEMENTS PRODUCED BY SKELETAL MUSCLE CONTRACTIONS

Circle the correct choice.

64. A movement that makes the angle between two bones smaller is:
    A. Flexion   C. Abduction
    B. Extension   D. Adduction

65. Moving a part toward the midline is:
    A. Flexion   C. Abduction
    B. Extension   D. Adduction

66. Moving a part away from the midline is:
    A. Flexion
    B. Extension
    C. Abduction
    D. Adduction

67. When you move your head from side to side as in shaking your head "no" you are _____ a muscle group.
    A. Rotating
    B. Pronating
    C. Supinating
    D. Abducting

68. _____ occurs when you turn the palm of your hand from an anterior to posterior position.
    A. Dorsiflexion
    B. Plantar flexion
    C. Supination
    D. Pronation

69. Dorsiflexion refers to:
    A. Hand movements
    B. Eye movements
    C. Foot movements
    D. Head movements

▷ *If you have had difficulty with this section, review pages 186-188.*

MAJOR MUSCULAR DISORDERS

Circle the correct answer.

70. Muscle strains are characterized by (myalgia or fibromyositis).

71. Crush injuries can cause (hemoglobin or myoglobin) to accumulate in the blood and result in kidney failure.

72. A viral infection of the nerves that controls skeletal muscle movement is known as (poliomyelitis or muscular dystrophy).

73. (Muscular dystrophy or Myasthenia gravis) is a group of genetic diseases characterized by atrophy of skeletal muscle tissues.

74. (Muscular dystrophy or Myasthenia gravis) is an autoimmune disease in which the immune system attacks muscle cells at the neuromuscular junction.

▷ *If you have difficulty with this section, review pages 189-190.*

APPLYING WHAT YOU KNOW

75. Casey noticed pain whenever she reached for anything in her cupboards. Her doctor told her that the small fluid-filled sacs in her shoulder were inflamed. What condition did Casey have?

76. The nurse was preparing an injection for Mrs. Tatakis. The amount to be given was 2 ml. What area of the body will the nurse most likely select for this injection?

77. Chris was playing football and pulled a band of fibrous connective tissue that attached a muscle to a bone. What is the common term for this tissue?

78. WORD FIND

Can you find the 25 muscle terms in the box of letters? Words may be spelled top to bottom, bottom to top, right to left, left to right, or diagonally.

```
G  A  S  T  R  O  C  N  E  M  I  U  S  D  U
M  S  G  I  O  N  O  I  S  N  E  T  X  E  U
U  R  N  N  T  O  M  S  R  B  S  F  D  T  T
S  U  I  S  C  I  B  O  N  T  P  N  E  A  R
C  B  R  E  U  X  V  T  O  O  E  C  L  I  A
L  Q  T  R  D  E  C  O  D  A  C  M  T  R  P
E  T  S  T  B  L  M  N  N  V  I  E  O  T  E
X  F  M  I  A  F  Y  I  E  Y  B  N  I  S  Z
S  I  A  O  V  I  E  C  T  L  S  S  D  I  I
S  Y  H  N  S  S  R  O  T  A  T  O  R  G  U
U  A  M  G  A  R  H  P  A  I  D  J  N  R  S
E  H  A  T  R  O  P  H  Y  L  N  J  T  E  B
L  N  O  H  T  D  E  U  G  I  T  A  F  N  T
O  R  I  G  I  N  O  S  N  V  S  B  Z  Y  L
S  B  V  T  O  J  C  T  R  I  C  E  P  S  S
```

Abductor   Flexion   Soleus
Atrophy   Gastrocnemius   Striated
Biceps   Hamstrings   Synergist
Bursa   Insertion   Tendon
Deltoid   Isometric   Tenosynovitis
Diaphragm   Isotonic   Trapezius
Dorsiflexion   Muscle   Triceps
Extension   Origin
Fatigue   Rotator

DID YOU KNOW?

If all of your muscles pulled in one direction, you would have the power to move 25 tons.

THE MUSCULAR SYSTEM

ACROSS

2. Shaking your head "no"
6. Muscle shrinkage
7. Toward the body's midline
9. Produces movement opposite to prime movers
12. Movement that makes joint angles larger
13. Small fluid-filled sac between tendons and bones

DOWN

1. Increase in size
3. Away from the body's midline
4. Turning your palm from an anterior to posterior position
5. Attachment to the more movable bone
7. Protein which composes myofilaments
8. Attachment to the more stationary bone
10. Assists prime movers with movement
11. Anchors muscles to bones

1. _____

2. _____

3. _____

4. _____

5. _____

6. _____

7. _____

8. _____

9. _____

10. _____

11. _____

12. _____

13. _____

14. _____

15. _____

16. _____

17. _____

18. _____

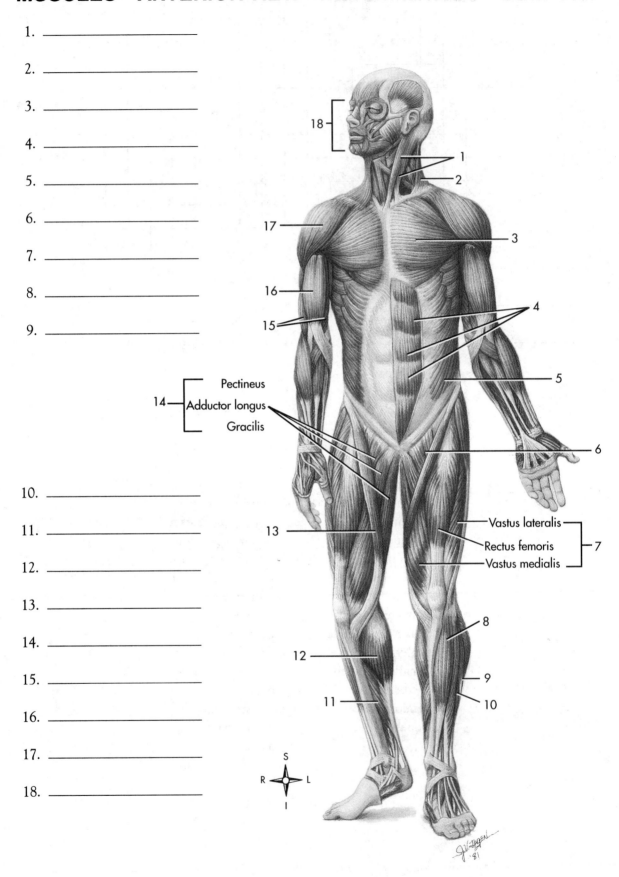

Pectineus
Adductor longus
Gracilis

Vastus lateralis
Rectus femoris
Vastus medialis

MUSCLES—POSTERIOR VIEW

1. _____

2. _____

3. _____

4. _____

5. _____

6. _____

7. _____

8. _____

9. _____

10. _____

11. _____

12. _____

13. _____

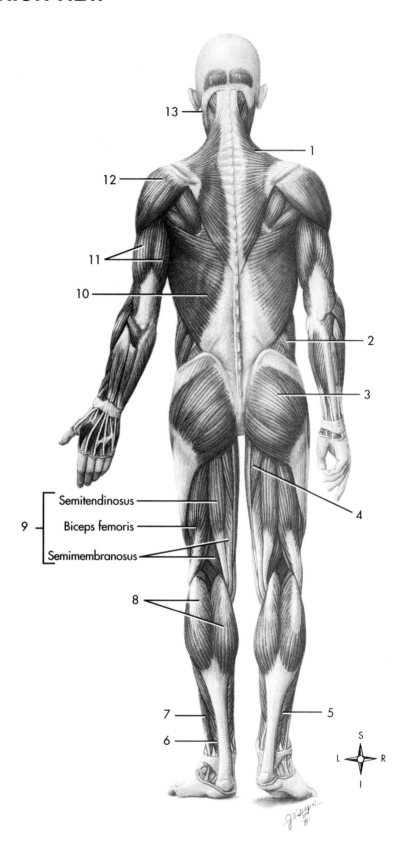

Semitendinosus

Biceps femoris

Semimembranosus

CHAPTER **8**   The Nervous System

The nervous system organizes and coordinates the millions of impulses received each day to make communication with and enjoyment of our environment possible. The functioning unit of the nervous system is the neuron. Three types of neurons—sensory, motor, and interneurons—exist and are classified according to the direction in which they transmit impulses. Nerve impulses travel over routes made up of neurons and provide the rapid communication that is necessary for maintaining life. The central nervous system is made up of the spinal cord and brain. The spinal cord provides access to and from the brain by means of ascending and descending tracts. In addition, the spinal cord functions as the primary reflex center of the body. The brain can be subdivided for easier learning into the brain stem, cerebellum, diencephalon, and cerebrum. These areas provide the extraordinary network necessary to receive, interpret, and respond to the simplest or most complex impulses.

While you concentrate on this chapter, your body is performing a multitude of functions. Fortunately for us, the beating of the heart, the digestion of food, breathing, and most of our other day-to-day processes do not require our supervision or thought. They function automatically, and the division of the nervous system that regulates these functions is known as the *autonomic nervous system*.

The autonomic nervous system consists of two divisions called the *sympathetic system* and the *parasympathetic system*. The sympathetic system functions as an emergency system and prepares us for "fight" or "flight." The parasympathetic system dominates control of many visceral effectors under normal everyday conditions. Together, these two divisions regulate the body's automatic functions in an effort to assist with the maintenance of homeostasis. Your understanding of this chapter will alert you to the complexity and functions of the nervous system and the "automatic pilot" of your body—the autonomic system.

TOPICS FOR REVIEW

Before progressing to Chapter 9, you should review the organs and divisions of the nervous system, the structure and function of the major types of cells in this system, the structure and function of a reflex arc, and the transmission of nerve impulses. Your study should include the anatomy and physiology of the brain and spinal cord and the nerves that extend from these two areas.

Finally, an understanding of the autonomic nervous system, the specific functions of the subdivisions of this system, and the major disorders of the nervous system are necessary to complete the review of this chapter.

ORGANS AND DIVISIONS OF THE NERVOUS SYSTEM

Match the term on the left with the proper selection on the right.

Group A

_____ 1. Sense organ
_____ 2. Central nervous system
_____ 3. Peripheral nervous system
_____ 4. Autonomic nervous system

A. Subdivision of peripheral nervous system
B. Ear
C. Brain and spinal cord
D. Nerves that extend to the outlying parts of the body

Group B

_____ 5. Dendrite
_____ 6. Schwann cell
_____ 7. Motor neuron
_____ 8. Nodes of Ranvier
_____ 9. Fascicles
_____ 10. Epineurium

A. Indentations between adjacent Schwann cells
B. Branching projection of neuron
C. Also known as *efferent*
D. Forms myelin outside the CNS
E. Tough sheath that covers the whole nerve
F. Groups of wrapped axons

CELLS OF NERVOUS SYSTEM NERVES

Select the best choice for the following words and insert the correct letter in the answer blank.

    (a) Neurons   (b) Neuroglia

_____ 11. Axon

_____ 12. Connective tissue

_____ 13. Astrocytes

_____ 14. Sensory

_____ 15. Conduct impulses

_____ 16. Forms the myelin sheath around central nerve fibers

_____ 17. Phagocytosis

_____ 18. Efferent

_____ 19. Multiple sclerosis

_____ 20. Neurilemma

▶ *If you have had difficulty with this section, review pages 199-202.*

REFLEX ARCS

Fill in the blanks.

21. The simplest kind of reflex arc is a _____

    _____ _____.

22. Three-neuron arcs consist of all three kinds of neurons, _____,

    _____, and _____.

23. Impulse conduction in a reflex arc normally starts in _____.

24. A _____ is the microscopic space that separates the axon of one neu-

    ron from the dendrites of another neuron.

25. A _____ is the response to impulse conduction over reflex arcs.

26. Contraction of a muscle that causes it to pull away from an irritating stimulus is known as the

    _____ _____.

27. A _____ is a group of nerve-cell bodies located in the peripheral ner-

    vous system.

28. All _____ lie entirely within the gray matter of the central nervous sys-

    tem.

29. In a patellar reflex, the nerve impulses that reach the quadriceps muscle (the effector) result in

    the classic _____ _____ response.

30. _____ _____ forms the **H**-shaped inner core

    of the spinal cord.

▷ *If you have had difficulty with this section, review pages 204-206.*

NERVE IMPULSES
THE SYNAPSE

Circle the correct answer.

31. Nerve impulses (do or do not) continually race along every nerve cell's surface.

32. When a stimulus acts on a neuron, it (increases or decreases) the permeability of the stimulated point of its membrane to sodium ions.

33. An inward movement of positive ions leaves a/an (lack or excess) of negative ions outside.

34. The plasma membrane of the (presynaptic neuron or postsynaptic neuron) makes up a portion of the synapse.

35. A synaptic knob is a tiny bulge at the end of the (presynaptic or postsynaptic) neuron's axon.

36. Acetylcholine is an example of a (neurotransmitter or protein molecule receptor).

37. Neurotransmitters are chemicals that allow neurons to (communicate or reproduce) with one another.

38. Neurotransmitters are distributed (randomly or specifically) into groups of neurons.

39. Catecholamines may play a role in (sleep or reproduction).

40. Endorphins and enkephalins are neurotransmitters that inhibit conduction of (fear or pain) impulses.

▶ *If you have had difficulty with this section, review pages 206-209.*

CENTRAL NERVOUS SYSTEM
DIVISIONS OF THE BRAIN

Circle the correct choice.

41. The portion of the brain stem that joins the spinal cord to the brain is the:
    A. Pons
    B. Cerebellum
    C. Diencephalon
    D. Hypothalamus
    E. Medulla

42. Which one of the following is <u>not</u> a function of the brain stem?
    A. Conducts sensory impulses from the spinal cord to the higher centers of the brain
    B. Conducts motor impulses from the cerebrum to the spinal cord
    C. Controls heartbeat, respiration, and blood vessel diameter
    D. Contains centers for speech and memory

43. Which one of the following is not part of the diencephalon?
    A. Cerebrum
    B. Thalamus
    C. Pituitary gland
    D. Third ventricle gray matter

44. ADH is produced by the:
    A. Pituitary gland
    B. Medulla
    C. Mammillary bodies
    D. Third ventricle
    E. Hypothalamus

45. Which one of the following is not a function of the hypothalamus?
    A. It helps control the rate of heartbeat.
    B. It helps control the constriction and dilation of blood vessels.
    C. It helps control the contraction of the stomach and intestines.
    D. It produces releasing hormones that control the release of certain anterior pituitary hormones.
    E. All of the above are functions of the hypothalamus.

46. Which one of the following parts of the brain helps in the association of sensations with emotions, as well as aiding in the arousal or alerting mechanism?
    A. Pons
    B. Hypothalamus
    C. Cerebellum
    D. Thalamus
    E. None of the above is correct

47. Which of the following is not true of the cerebrum?
    A. Its lobes correspond to the bones that lie over them.
    B. Its grooves are called gyri.
    C. Most of its gray matter lies on the surface of the cerebrum.
    D. Its outer region is called the cerebral cortex.
    E. Its two hemispheres are connected by a structure called the corpus callosum.

48. Which one of the following is not a function of the cerebrum?
    A. Willed movement
    B. Consciousness
    C. Memory
    D. Conscious awareness of sensations
    E. All of the above are functions of the cerebrum

49. The area of the cerebrum responsible for the perception of sound lies in the _____ lobe.
    A. Frontal
    B. Temporal
    C. Occipital
    D. Parietal

50. Visual perception is located in the _____ lobe.
    A. Frontal
    B. Temporal
    C. Parietal
    D. Occipital
    E. None of the above is correct

51. Which one of the following is not a function of the cerebellum?
    A. Maintains equilibrium
    B. Helps produce smooth, coordinated movements
    C. Helps maintain normal posture
    D. Associates sensations with emotions

52. Within the interior of the cerebrum are a few islands of gray matter known as:
    A. Fissures   C. Gyri
    B. Basal ganglia   D. Myelin

53. A cerebrovascular accident is commonly referred to as (a):
    A. Stroke   C. Tumor
    B. Parkinson's disease   D. Multiple sclerosis

54. Parkinson's disease is a disease of the:
    A. Myelin   C. Neuroglia
    B. Axons   D. Cerebral nuclei

55. The largest section of the brain is the:
    A. Cerebellum   C. Cerebrum
    B. Pons   D. Midbrain

▷ *If you have had difficulty with this section, review pages 210-215.*

BRAIN STUDIES
BRAIN DISORDERS

Select the best choice and insert the correct letter in the answer blank.

A.	SPECT	E.	Cerebral palsy	I.	Dementia
B.	MRI	F.	EEG	J.	PET
C.	CT	G.	Huntington's disease		
D.	Hemiplegia	H.	CVA		

_____ 56. Stroke

_____ 57. Paralysis of one side of the body

_____ 58. Crippling disease that involves permanent, nonprogressive damage to motor control areas of the brain

_____ 59. Imaging technique for brain that involves scanning the head with a revolving x-ray generator

_____ 60. Scanning method that determines the functional characteristics of the brain by introducing a radioactive substance into the blood supply of the brain

_____ 61. Used to visualize blood flow in brain

_____ 62. Scanning method that uses a magnetic field to induce brain tissues to emit radio waves

_____ 63. Measurement of electrical activity of the brain

_____ 64. Characteristic of Alzheimer's disease

_____ 65. Inherited disease characterized by chorea

▷ *If you have had difficulty with this section, review pages 215-217.*

SPINAL CORD

If the statement is true, write T on the answer blank. If the statement is false, correct the statement by circling the incorrect term and inserting the correct term in the answer blank.

_____ 66. The spinal cord is approximately 24 to 25 inches long.

_____ 67. The spinal cord ends at the bottom of the sacrum.

_____ 68. The extension of the meninges beyond the cord is convenient for performing CAT scans without danger of injuring the spinal cord.

_____ 69. Bundles of myelinated nerve fibers—dendrites—make up the white
outer columns of the spinal cord.

_____ 70. Ascending tracts conduct impulses up the cord to the brain and
descending tracts conduct impulses down the cord from the brain.

_____ 71. Tracts are functional organizations in that all the axons that compose
a tract serve several functions.

_____ 72. A loss of sensation caused by a spinal cord injury is called *paralysis*.

▷ *If you have had difficulty with this section, review pages 218-221.*

COVERINGS AND FLUID SPACES OF THE BRAIN AND SPINAL CORD

Circle the one that does not belong.

73. Meninges   Pia mater   Ventricles   Dura mater

74. Arachnoid   Middle layer   CSF   Cobweblike

75. CSF   Ventricles   Subarachnoid space   Pia mater

76. Tough   Outer layer   Dura mater   Choroid plexus

77. Brain tumor   Subarachnoid space   CSF   Fourth lumbar vertebra

CRANIAL NERVES

78. Fill in the missing areas on the chart below.

NERVE	CONDUCTS IMPULSES	FUNCTION
I _____	From nose to brain	Sense of smell
II Optic	From eye to brain	_____
III Oculomotor	_____	Eye movements
IV _____	From brain to external eye muscles	Eye movements
V Trigeminal	From skin and mucous membrane of head and from teeth to brain; also from brain to chewing muscles	_____
VI Abducens	_____	Turning eyes outward
VII Facial	From taste buds of tongue to brain; from brain to face muscles	_____
VIII _____	From ear to brain	Hearing; sense of balance
IX Glossopharyngeal	_____	Sensations of throat, taste, swallowing movements, secretion of saliva
X _____	From throat, larynx, and organs in thoracic and abdominal cavities to brain; also from brain to muscles of throat and to organs in thoracic and abdominal cavities	Sensations of throat, larynx, and of thoracic and abdominal organs; swallowing, voice production, slowing of heartbeat, acceleration of peristalsis (gut movements)
XI Accessory	From brain to certain shoulder and neck muscles	_____
XII _____	From brain to muscles of tongue	Tongue movements

▷ *If you have had difficulty with this section, review page 226, Table 8-2.*

CRANIAL NERVES
SPINAL NERVES

Select the best choice for the following words and insert the correct letter in the answer blank.

      (a) Cranial nerves   (b) Spinal nerves

_____ 79. 12 pairs

_____ 80. Dermatome

_____ 81. Vagus

_____ 82. Shingles

_____ 83. 31 pairs

_____ 84. Optic

_____ 85. C-1

_____ 86. Plexus

▷ *If you have had difficulty with this section, review pages 225-227.*

AUTONOMIC NEVOUS SYSTEM

Match the term on the left with the proper selection on the right.

_____ 87. Autonomic nervous system
_____ 88. Autonomic neurons
_____ 89. Preganglionic neurons
_____ 90. Visceral effectors
_____ 91. Sympathetic system
_____ 92. Somatic nervous system

A. Divisions of ANS
B. Tissues to which autonomic neurons conduct impulses
C. Voluntary actions
D. Regulates body's involuntary functions
E. Motor neurons that make up the ANS
F. Conduct impulses between the spinal cord and a ganglion

SYMPATHETIC NERVOUS SYSTEM
PARASYMPATHETIC NERVOUS SYSTEM

Circle the correct choice.

93. Dendrites and cell bodies of sympathetic preganglionic neurons are located in the:
    A. Brain stem and sacral portion of the spinal cord
    B. Sympathetic ganglia
    C. Gray matter of the thoracic and upper lumbar segments of the spinal cord
    D. Ganglia close to effectors

94. Which of the following is not correct?
    A. Sympathetic preganglionic neurons have their cell bodies located in the lateral gray column of certain parts of the spinal cord
    B. Sympathetic preganglionic axons pass along the dorsal root of certain spinal nerves
    C. There are synapses within sympathetic ganglia
    D. Sympathetic responses are usually widespread, involving many organs

95. Another name for the parasympathetic nervous system is:
    A. Thoracolumbar
    B. Craniosacral
    C. Visceral
    D. ANS
    E. Cholinergic

96. Which statement is not correct?
    A. Sympathetic postganglionic neurons have their dendrites and cell bodies in sympathetic ganglia or collateral ganglia.
    B. Sympathetic ganglions are located in front of and at each side of the spinal column.
    C. Separate autonomic nerves distribute many sympathetic postganglionic axons to various internal organs.
    D. Very few sympathetic preganglionic axons synapse with postganglionic neurons.

97. Sympathetic stimulation usually results in a/an:
    A. Response by numerous organs
    B. Response by only one organ
    C. Increase in peristalsis
    D. Constriction of pupils

98. Parasympathetic stimulation frequently results in a/an:
    A. Response by only one organ
    B. Response by numerous organs
    C. Fight or flight syndrome
    D. Increase in heartbeat

Choose the correct response and insert the letter in answer blanks.

        (a) Sympathetic control   (b) Parasympathetic control

_____   99. Constricts pupils

_____   100. "Goose pimples"

_____   101. Increases sweat secretion

_____   102. Increases secretion of digestive juices

_____   103. Constricts blood vessels

_____   104. Slows heartbeat

_____   105. Relaxes bladder

_____   106. Increases epinephrine secretion

_____   107. Increases peristalsis

_____   108. Stimulates lens for near vision

▷ *If you have had difficulty with this section, review pages 229-231.*

AUTONOMIC NEUROTRANSMITTERS
AUTONOMIC NERVOUS SYSTEM AS A WHOLE

Fill in the blanks.

109. Sympathetic preganglionic axons release the neurotransmitter _____.

110. Axons that release norepinephrine are classified as _____.

111. Axons that release acetylcholine are classified as _____.

112. The function of the autonomic nervous system is to regulate the body's involuntary functions in

      ways that maintain or restore _____.

113. Your _____ _____ is determined by the

      combined forces of the sympathetic and parasympathetic nervous system.

114. According to some physiologists, meditation leads to _____ sympathetic activity and changes opposite to those of the fight or flight syndrome.

115. _____ is a malignant tumor of the sympathetic nervous system.

▷ *If you have had difficulty with this section, review pages 232-234.*

Unscramble the words.

116. RONNESU
⬜⬜⬜⬜⬜⬜⭕

117. APSYENS
⬜⭕⬜⭕⭕⬜⬜

118. CIATUNOMO
⬜⭕⬜⬜⬜⭕⭕⬜

119. SHTOMO ULMSEC
⬜⬜⬜⬜⭕⭕ ⬜⬜⬜⬜⭕⬜

Take the circled letters, unscramble them, and fill in the statement.

What the man hoped the IRS agent would be during his audit.

120. ⬜⬜⬜⬜⬜⬜⬜⬜⬜⬜⬜⬜⬜

APPLYING WHAT YOU KNOW

121. Mr. Hemstreet suffered a cerebrovascular accident and it was determined that the damage affected the left side of his cerebrum. On which side of his body will he most likely notice any paralysis?

122. Baby Dania was born with an excessive accumulation of cerebrospinal fluid in the ventricles. A catheter was placed in the ventricle and the fluid was drained by means of a shunt into the circulatory bloodstream. What condition does this medical history describe?

123. Mrs. Muhlenkamp looked out her window to see a man trapped under the wheel of a car. Although slightly built, Mrs. Muhlenkamp rushed to the car, lifted it, and saved the man underneath the wheel. What division of the autonomic nervous system made this seemingly impossible task possible?

124. Lynn's heart raced and her palms became clammy as she watched the monster at the local theater. When the movie was over, however, she told her friends that she was not afraid at all. She appeared to be as calm as before the movie. What division of the autonomic nervous system made this possible?

125. Bill is going to his boss for his annual evaluation. He is planning to ask for a raise and hopes the evaluation will be good. Which subdivision of the autonomic nervous system will be active during this conference? Should he have a large meal before his appointment? Support your answer with facts from the chapter.

126. WORD FIND

Can you find the 14 terms from the chapter in the box of letters? Words may be spelled top to bottom, bottom to top, right to left, left to right, or diagonally.

```
M  C  C  D  Q  S  Y  N  A  P  S  E  Q  G  O
E  N  A  Q  D  W  H  N  W  E  J  N  A  L  W
S  R  O  T  P  E  C  E  R  Y  Z  N  I  S  M
I  D  S  X  E  K  N  O  K  X  G  G  C  Y  Y
J  O  T  R  A  C  T  D  F  L  O  N  E  N  A
R  P  W  E  K  O  H  X  I  D  A  L  H  A  M
F  A  L  O  N  A  Y  O  E  I  I  I  X  P  C
C  M  Z  I  F  D  N  N  L  N  G  Z  U  T  Z
S  I  N  V  C  G  D  G  Z  A  N  A  K  I  P
G  N  A  T  Z  R  O  W  V  A  M  Y  T  C  O
K  E  N  D  O  R  P  H  I  N  S  I  L  C  X
C  P  Q  G  C  J  X  F  J  D  Q  S  N  L  F
X  U  L  I  H  I  G  Q  A  N  S  W  O  E  U
A  I  M  H  Q  E  X  K  D  B  W  Y  T  F  S
A  A  D  A  X  O  C  K  G  B  F  H  B  T  K
```

Axon	Glia	Serotonin
Catecholamines	Microglia	Synapse
Dopamine	Myelin	Synaptic cleft
Endorphins	Oligodendroglia	Tract
Ganglion	Receptors	

DID YOU KNOW?

Although all pain is felt and interpreted in the brain, it has no pain sensation itself—even when cut!

THE NERVOUS SYSTEM

ACROSS

4. Bundle of axons located within the CNS
8. Transmits impulses toward the cell body
9. Neurons that conduct impulses from a ganglion
10. Astrocytes
11. Pia mater
13. Nerve cells
14. Transmits impulses away from the cell body
15. Peripheral nervous system (abbreviation)

DOWN

1. Neuroglia
2. Peripheral beginning of a sensory neuron's dendrite
3. Two neuron arc (two words)
5. Neurotransmitter
6. Cluster of nerve cell bodies outside the central nervous system
7. Area of brain stem

11. Fatty substance found around some nerve fibers
12. Where impulses are transmitted from one neuron to another

NEURON

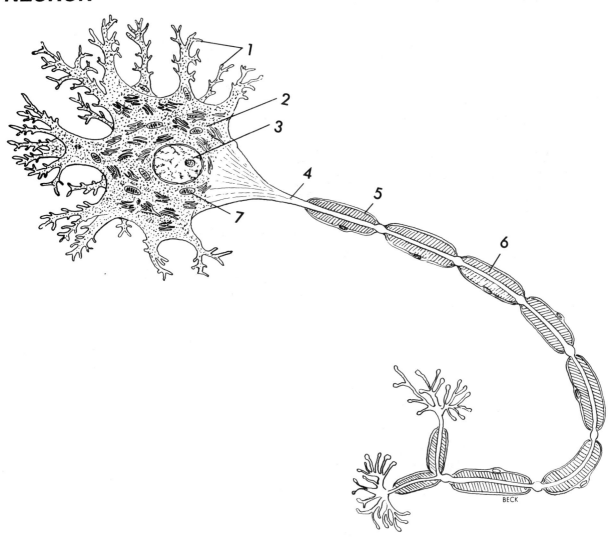

1. _____ 5. _____

2. _____ 6. _____

3. _____ 7. _____

4. _____

CRANIAL NERVES

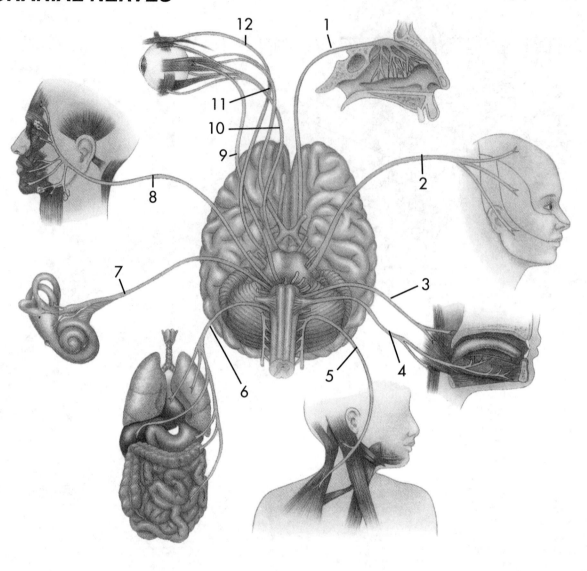

1. _____

2. _____

3. _____

4. _____

5. _____

6. _____

7. _____

8. _____

9. _____

10. _____

11. _____

12. _____

NEURAL PATHWAY INVOLVED IN THE PATELLAR REFLEX

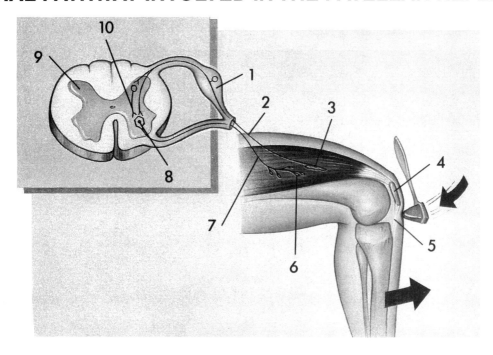

1. _____

2. _____

3. _____

4. _____

5. _____

6. _____

7. _____

8. _____

9. _____

10. _____

THE CEREBRUM

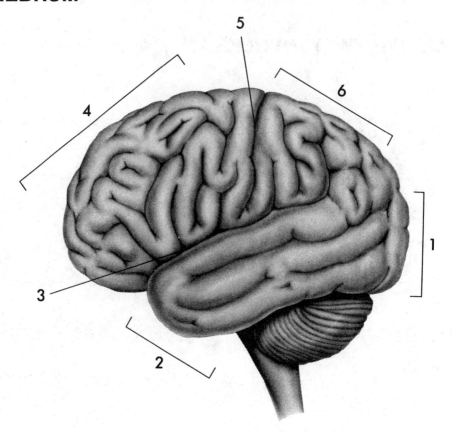

1. _____   4. _____

2. _____   5. _____

3. _____   6. _____

SAGITTAL SECTION OF THE CENTRAL NERVOUS SYSTEM

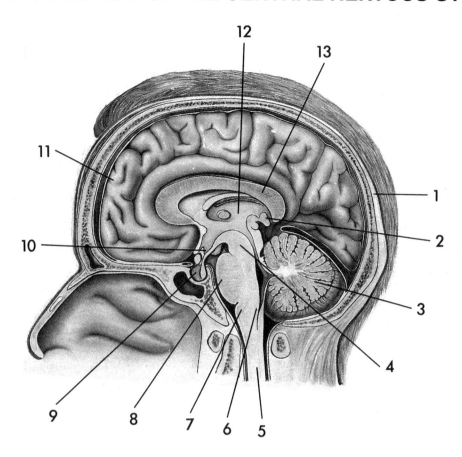

1. _____   8. _____

2. _____   9. _____

3. _____   10. _____

4. _____   11. _____

5. _____   12. _____

6. _____   13. _____

7. _____

NEURON PATHWAYS

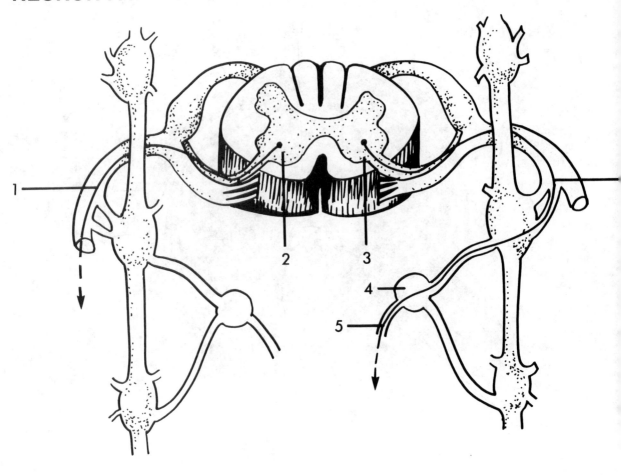

1. _____ 4. _____

2. _____ 5. _____

3. _____ 6. _____

CHAPTER **9**   # The Senses

Consider this scene for a moment. You are walking along a beautiful beach, watching the sunset. You notice the various hues and are amazed at the multitude of shades that cover the sky. The waves are indeed melodious as they splash along the shore, and you wiggle your feet with delight as you sense the warm, soft sand trickling between your toes. You sip on a soda and then inhale the fresh salt air as you continue your stroll along the shore. It is a memorable scene, but one that would not be possible without the assistance of your sense organs. The sense organs pick up messages that are sent over nerve pathways to specialized areas in the brain for interpretation. They make communication with and enjoyment of the environment possible. The visual, auditory, tactile, olfactory, and gustatory sense organs not only protect us from danger but also add an important dimension to our daily pleasures of life.

Your study of this chapter will give you an understanding of another one of the systems necessary for homeostasis and survival.

TOPICS FOR REVIEW

Before progressing to Chapter 10, you should review the classification of sense organs and the process for converting a stimulus into a sensation. Your study should also include an understanding of the special sense organs and the general sense organs.

CLASSIFICATION OF SENSE ORGANS
CONVERTING A STIMULUS INTO A SENSATION
GENERAL SENSE ORGANS

Match the term on the left with the proper selection on the right.

———— 1. Special sense organ

———— 2. General sense organ

———— 3. Free nerve endings

———— 4. Krause's end-bulbs

———— 5. Taste

A. Chemoreceptors

B. Meissner's corpuscles

C. Pain, crude touch, and temperature

D. Eye

E. Touch

▷ *If you have had difficulty with this section, review pages 241-242 and Table 9-1.*

SPECIAL SENSE ORGANS
THE EYE

Circle the correct choice.

6. The "white" of the eye is more commonly called the:
   A. Choroid
   B. Cornea
   C. Sclera
   D. Retina
   E. None of the above is correct

7. The "colored" part of the eye is known as the:
   A. Retina
   B. Cornea
   C. Pupil
   D. Sclera
   E. Iris

8. The transparent portion of the sclera, referred to as the "window" of the eye, is the:
   A. Retina
   B. Cornea
   C. Pupil
   D. Iris

9. The mucous membrane that covers the front of the eye is called the:
   A. Cornea
   B. Coroid
   C. Conjunctiva
   D. Ciliary body
   E. None of the above is correct

10. The structure that can contract or dilate to allow more or less light to enter the eye is the:
    A. Lens
    B. Choroid
    C. Retina
    D. Cornea
    E. Iris

11. When the eye is looking at objects far in the distance, the lens is _____ and the ciliary muscle is _____.
    A. Rounded, contracted
    B. Rounded, relaxed
    C. Slightly rounded, contracted
    D. Slightly curved, relaxed
    E. None of the above is correct

12. The lens of the eye is held in place by the:
    A. Ciliary muscle
    B. Aqueous humor
    C. Vitreous humor
    D. Cornea

13. When the lens loses its elasticity and can no longer bring near objects into focus, the condition is known as:
    A. Glaucoma
    B. Presbyopia
    C. Astigmatism
    D. Strabismus

14. The fluid in front of the lens that is constantly being formed, drained, and replaced in the anterior cavity is the:
    A. Vitreous humor
    B. Protoplasm
    C. Aqueous humor
    D. Conjunctiva

15. If drainage of the aqueous humor is blocked, the internal pressure within the eye will increase and a condition known as _____ could occur.
    A. Presbyopia
    B. Glaucoma
    C. Color blindness
    D. Cataracts

16. The rods and cones are the visual receptors and are located on the:
    A. Sclera
    B. Cornea
    C. Choroid
    D. Retina

17. Photoreception is the sense of:
    A. Vision
    B. Smell
    C. Taste
    D. Balance

18. The "blind spot" may also be referred to as the:
    A. Fovea centralis
    B. Macula lutea
    C. Retinal artery
    D. Optic disc

▷ *If you have had difficulty with this section, review pages 244-247 and Table 9-2.*

VISUAL DISORDERS

Select the best answer from the choices given and insert the letter in the answer blank.

   A. Strabismus   F. Conjunctivitis
   B. Retinopathy   G. Nyctalopia
   C. Myopia   H. Hyperopia
   D. Glaucoma   I. Scotoma
   E. Astigmatism   J. Cataracts

_____ 19. Nearsightedness

_____ 20. An irregularity in the cornea

_____ 21. "Pink-eye"

_____ 22. "Cross-eyes"

_____ 23. Cloudy spots in the eye's lens

_____ 24. Often caused by diabetes mellitus

_____ 25. Farsightedness

_____ 26. "Night blindness"

_____ 27. Loss of only the center of the visual field

_____ 28. Excessive intraocular pressure caused by abnormal accumulation of aqueous humor

▶ *If you have had difficulty with this section, review pages 248-251*

THE EAR

Select the best answer from the choices given and insert the letter in the answer blank.

   (a) External ear   (b) Middle ear   (c) Inner ear

_____ 29. Malleus   _____ 34. Auditory canal

_____ 30. Perilymph   _____ 35. Semicircular canals

_____ 31. Incus   _____ 36. Stapes

_____ 32. Ceruminous glands   _____ 37. Tympanic membrane

_____ 33. Cochlea   _____ 38. Organ of Corti

Fill in the blanks.

39. The external ear has two parts: the _____ and the _____

_____ _____.

40. Another name for the tympanic membrane is the _____.

41. The bones of the middle ear are referred to, collectively, as _____.

42. The stapes presses against a membrane that covers a small opening, the

   _____ _____.

43. A middle ear infection is called _____ _____.

44. The _____ is located adjacent to the oval window between the semicir-

   cular canals and the cochlea.

45. Located within the semicircular canals and the vestibule are _____ for

   balance and equilibrium.

46. The sensory cells in the _____ _____ are

   stimulated when movement of the head causes the endolymph to move.

▷ *If you have had difficulty with this section, review pages 252-253.*

HEARING DISORDERS

Select the best answer from the choices given and insert the letter in the answer blank.

A.	Tinnitus	D.	Otitis media
B.	Presbycusis	E.	Mastoiditis
C.	Otosclerosis	F.	Meniere's disease

_____ 47. Inherited bone disorder that impairs conduction by causing structural irregularities in
the stapes

_____ 48. "Ringing in the ear"

_____ 49. Middle ear infection

_____ 50. Untreated otitis media can lead to this condition

_____ 51. Progressive hearing loss associated with aging

_____ 52. Chronic inner ear disease characterized by progressive nerve deafness and vertigo

▷ *If you had difficulty with this section, review pages 253-256.*

TASTE RECEPTORS
SMELL RECEPTORS
GENERAL SENSE ORGANS

Circle the correct answer.

53. Structures known as (papillae or olfactory cells) are found on the tongue.

54. Nerve impulses generated by stimulation of taste buds travel primarily through two (cranial or spinal) nerves.

55. To be detected by olfactory receptors, chemicals must be dissolved in the watery (mucus or plasma) that lines the nasal cavity.

56. The pathways taken by olfactory nerve impulses and the areas where these impulses are interpreted are closely associated with areas of the brain important in (hearing or memory).

57. Receptors responsible for the sense of smell are known as (chemoreceptors or mechanoreceptors).

▷ *If you have had difficulty with this section, review pages 256-257.*

APPLYING WHAT YOU KNOW

58. Mr. Nay was an avid swimmer and competed regularly in his age group. He had to withdraw from the last competition because of an infection of his ear. Antibiotics and analgesics were prescribed by the doctor. What is the medical term for his condition?

59. Mrs. Metheny loved the out-of-doors and spent a great deal of her spare time basking in the sun on the beach. Her physician suggested that she begin wearing sunglasses regularly when he noticed milky spots beginning to appear on Mrs. Metheny's lenses. What condition was Mrs. Metheny's physician trying to prevent from occurring?

60. Amanda repeatedly became ill with throat infections during her first few years of school. Lately, however, she has noticed that whenever she has a throat infection, her ears become very sore also. What might be the cause of this additional problem?

61. Keith was hit in the nose with a baseball during practice. His sense of smell was temporarily gone. What nerve receptors were damaged during the injury?

62. WORD FIND

Can you find 19 terms from this chapter in the box of letters? Words may be spelled top to bottom, bottom to top, right to left, left to right, or diagonally.

```
M  E  C  H  A  N  O  R  E  C  E  P  T  O  R
H  R  A  T  B  Q  I  R  T  B  N  H  M  A  E
P  F  T  Y  R  O  T  C  A  F  L  O  X  R  C
G  U  A  Y  I  N  A  I  H  C  A  T  S  U  E
G  P  R  A  C  E  R  U  M  E  N  O  P  X  P
I  E  A  I  P  O  Y  B  S  E  R  P  K  D  T
W  L  C  P  L  Y  N  E  Y  K  E  I  T  O  O
C  Q  T  O  I  B  R  J  B  S  F  G  L  M  R
Z  U  S  R  C  L  E  O  U  J  R  M  N  N  S
F  D  M  E  O  H  L  Q  T  N  A  E  Y  I  S
H  I  D  P  N  D  L  A  M  A  C  N  X  S  Z
A  M  L  Y  E  S  S  E  E  D  T  T  M  Z  H
D  D  M  H  S  F  E  X  A  Y  I  S  I  I  A
J  C  G  N  J  T  I  S  L  P  O  G  U  V  J
P  H  G  Y  A  K  H  S  U  C  N  I  G  G  A
```

Cataracts	Gustatory	Presbyopia
Cerumen	Hyperopia	Receptors
Cochlea	Incus	Refraction
Cones	Mechanoreceptor	Rods
Conjunctiva	Olfactory	Senses
Eustachian	Papillae	
Eye	Photopigment	

DID YOU KNOW?

Glaucoma is the leading cause of blindness among African Americans.

THE SENSES

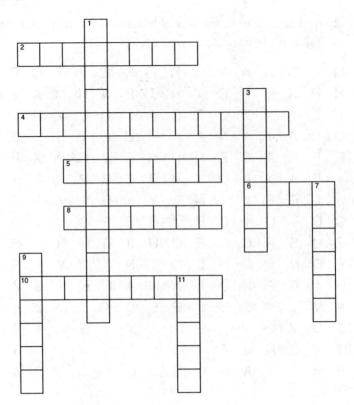

ACROSS

2. Bones of the middle ear
4. Located in anterior cavity in front of lens (two words)
5. External ear
6. Transparent body behind pupil
8. Front part of this coat is the ciliary muscle and iris
10. Membranous labyrinth filled with this fluid

DOWN

1. Located in posterior cavity (two words)
3. Organ of Corti located here
7. White of the eye
9. Innermost layer of the eye
11. Hole in center of iris

EYE

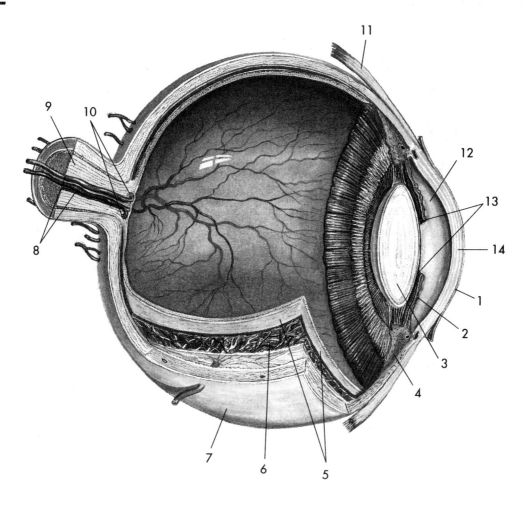

1. _____

2. _____

3. _____

4. _____

5. _____

6. _____

7. _____

8. _____

9. _____

10. _____

11. _____

12. _____

13. _____

14. _____

EAR

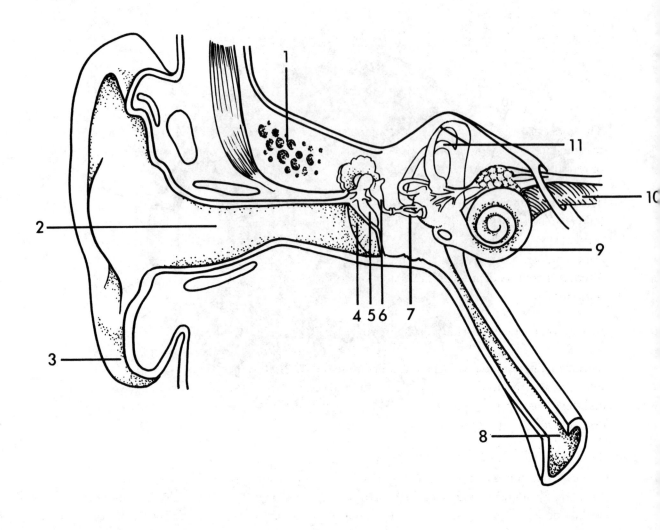

1. _____   7. _____

2. _____   8. _____

3. _____   9. _____

4. _____   10. _____

5. _____   11. _____

6. _____

CHAPTER **10** **The Endocrine System**

The endocrine system has often been compared to a fine concert symphony. When all instruments are playing properly, the sound is melodious. If one instrument plays too loud or too soft, however, it affects the overall quality of the entire performance.

The endocrine system is a ductless system that releases hormones into the bloodstream to help regulate body functions. The pituitary gland may be considered the conductor of the orchestra, as it stimulates many of the endocrine glands to secrete their powerful hormones. All hormones, whether stimulated in this manner or by other control mechanisms, are interdependent. A change in the level of one hormone may affect the level of many other hormones.

In addition to the endocrine glands, prostaglandins, or "tissue hormones," are powerful substances similar to hormones that have been found in a variety of body tissues. These hormones are often produced in a tissue and diffuse only a short distance to act on cells within that area. Prostaglandins influence respiration, blood pressure, gastrointestinal secretions, and the reproductive system, and may some day play an important role in the treatment of diseases such as hypertension, asthma, and ulcers.

The endocrine system is a system of communication and control. It differs from the nervous system in that hormones provide a slower, longer lasting effect than do nerve stimuli and responses. Your understanding of the "system of hormones" will alert you to the mechanism of our emotions, response to stress, growth, chemical balances, and many other body functions.

TOPICS FOR REVIEW

Before progressing to Chapter 11, you should be able to identify and locate the primary endocrine glands of the body. Your understanding should include the hormones that are produced by these glands and the method by which these secretions are regulated. Your study will conclude with the pathological conditions that result from the malfunctioning of this system.

MECHANISMS OF HORMONE ACTION
REGULATION OF HORMONE SECRETION
MECHANISMS OF ENDOCRINE DISEASE
PROSTAGLANDINS

Match the term on the left with the proper selection on the right.

Group A

_____ 1. Pituitary
_____ 2. Parathyroids
_____ 3. Adrenals
_____ 4. Ovaries
_____ 5. Thymus

A. Pelvic cavity
B. Mediastinum
C. Neck
D. Cranial cavity
E. Abdominal cavity

Group B

_____ 6. Negative feedback
_____ 7. Tissue hormones
_____ 8. Second messenger hypothesis
_____ 9. Exocrine glands
_____ 10. Target organ cells

A. Explanation for hormone organ recognition
B. Respond to a particular hormone
C. Prostaglandins
D. Discharge secretions into ducts
E. Specialized homeostatic mechanism that regulates release of hormones

Fill in the blanks.

The (11) _____ _____ hypothesis is a

theory that attempts to explain why hormones cause specific effects in target organs but do not

(12) _____ or act on other organs of the body. Protein hormones serve as

(13) _____ _____, providing communication

between endocrine glands and (14) _____ _____.

A second messenger, (15) such as _____ _____

provides communication within a hormone's (16) _____

_____. (17) _____ _____

disrupts the normal negative feedback control of hormones throughout the body, and may result in tis-

sue damage, sterility, mental imbalance, and a host of life-threatening metabolic problems.

▶ *If you have had difficulty with this section, review pages 263-270.*

PITUITARY GLAND
HYPOTHALAMUS

Circle the correct choice.

18. The pituitary gland lies in the _____ bone.
    A. Ethmoid
    B. Sphenoid
    C. Temporal
    D. Frontal
    E. Occipital

19. Which one of the following structures would <u>not</u> be stimulated by a tropic hormone from the anterior pituitary?
    A. Ovaries
    B. Testes
    C. Thyroid
    D. Adrenals
    E. Uterus

20. Which one of the following is <u>not</u> a function of FSH?
    A. Stimulates the growth of follicles
    B. Stimulates the production of estrogens
    C. Stimulates the growth of seminiferous tubules
    D. Stimulates the interstitial cells of the testes

21. Which one of the following is <u>not</u> a function of LH?
    A. Stimulates maturation of a developing follicle
    B. Stimulates the production of estrogens
    C. Stimulates the formation of a corpus luteum
    D. Stimulates sperm cells to mature in the male
    E. Causes ovulation to occur

22. Which one of the following is <u>not</u> a function of GH?
    A. Increases glucose catabolism
    B. Increases fat catabolism
    C. Speeds up the movement of amino acids into cells from the bloodstream.
    D. All of the above are functions of GH

23. Which one of the following hormones is <u>not</u> released by the anterior pituitary gland?
    A. ACTH
    B. TSH
    C. ADH
    D. FSH
    E. LH

24. Which one of the following is <u>not</u> a function of prolactin?
    A. Stimulates breast development during pregnancy
    B. Stimulates milk secretion after delivery
    C. Causes the release of milk from glandular cells of the breast
    D. All of the above are functions of prolactin

25. The anterior pituitary gland:
    A. Secretes eight major hormones
    B. Secretes tropic hormones that stimulate other endocrine glands to grow and secrete
    C. Secretes ADH
    D. Secretes oxytocin

26. TSH acts on the:
    A. Thyroid   C. Pineal
    B. Thymus   D. Testes

27. ACTH stimulates the:
    A. Adrenal cortex   C. Hypothalamus
    B. Adrenal medulla   D. Ovaries

28. Which hormone is secreted by the posterior pituitary gland?
    A. MSH   C. GH
    B. LH   D. ADH

29. ADH serves the body by:
    A. Initiating labor
    B. Accelerating water reabsorption from urine into the blood
    C. Stimulating the pineal gland
    D. Regulating the calcium/phosphorus levels in the blood

30. The disease caused by hyposecretion of ADH is:
    A. Diabetes insipidus   C. Acromegaly
    B. Diabetes mellitus   D. Myxedema

31. The actual production of ADH and oxytocin takes place in which area?
    A. Anterior pituitary   C. Hypothalamus
    B. Posterior pituitary   D. Pineal

32. Inhibiting hormones are produced by the:
    A. Anterior pituitary   C. Hypothalamus
    B. Posterior pituitary   D. Pineal

Select the best answer from the choices given and insert the letter in the answer blank.
(a) Anterior pituitary   (b) Posterior pituitary   (c) Hypothalamus

_____ 33. Adenohypophysis   _____ 38. Body temperature

_____ 34. Neurohypophysis   _____ 39. Sex hormones

_____ 35. Induced labor   _____ 40. Tropic hormones

_____ 36. Appetite   _____ 41. Gigantism

_____ 37. Acromegaly   _____ 42. Releasing hormones

▶ *If you have had difficulty with this section, review pages 271-274.*

THYROID GLAND
PARATHYROID GLANDS

Circle the correct answer.

43. The thyroid gland lies (above or below) the larynx.

44. The thyroid gland secretes (calcitonin or glucagon).

45. For thyroxine to be produced in adequate amounts, the diet must contain sufficient (calcium or iodine).

46. Most endocrine glands (do or do not) store their hormones.

47. Colloid is a storage medium for the (thyroid hormone or parathyroid hormone).

48. Calcitonin (increases or decreases) the concentration of calcium in the blood.

49. Simple goiter results from (hyperthyroidism or hypothyroidism).

50. Hyposecretion of thyroid hormones during the formative years leads to (cretinism or myxedema).

51. The parathyroid glands secrete the hormone (PTH or PTA).

52. Parathyroid hormone tends to (increase or decrease) the concentration of calcium in the blood.

▷ *If you have had difficulty with this section, review pages 274-277.*

ADRENAL GLANDS

Fill in the blanks.

53. The adrenal gland is actually two separate endocrine glands, the _____

    _____ and the _____

    _____.

54. Hormones secreted by the adrenal cortex are known as _____.

55. The outer zone of the adrenal cortex, the zona glomerulosa, secretes

    _____.

56. The middle zone, the zona fasciculata, secretes _____.

57. The innermost zone, the zona reticularis, secretes _____

_____.

58. Glucocorticoids act in several ways to increase _____.

59. Glucocorticoids also play an essential part in maintaining _____

_____.

60. The adrenal medulla secretes the hormones _____ and

_____.

61. The adrenal medulla may help the body resist _____.

62. The term _____ _____

_____ is often used to describe how the body mobilizes a number of dif-

ferent defense mechanisms when threatened by harmful stimuli.

Select the best response from the choices given and insert the letter in the answer blank.

      (a) Adrenal cortex   (b) Adrenal medulla

_____ 63. Addison's disease

_____ 64. Anti-immunity

_____ 65. Adrenaline

_____ 66. Cushing's syndrome

_____ 67. Fight or flight syndrome

_____ 68. Aldosterone

_____ 69. Androgens

▶ *If you have had difficulty with this section, review pages 278-282.*

PANCREATIC ISLETS
SEX GLANDS
THYMUS
PLACENTA
PINEAL GLAND

Circle the term that does not belong.

70. Alpha cells   Glucagon   Beta cells   Glycogenolysis

71. Insulin   Glucagon   Beta cells   Diabetes mellitus

72. Estrogens   Progesterone   Corpus luteum   Thymosin

73. Chorion   Interstitial cells   Testosterone   Semen

74. Immune system   Mediastinum   Aldosterone   Thymosin

75. Pregnancy   ACTH   Estrogen   Chorion

76. Melatonin   Menstruation   "Third eye"   Semen

Match the term on the left with the proper selection on the right.
Group A

———— 77. Alpha cells   A. Estrogen
———— 78. Beta cells   B. Progesterone
———— 79. Corpus luteum   C. Insulin
———— 80. Interstitial cells   D. Testosterone
———— 81. Ovarian follicles   E. Glucagon

Group B

———— 82. Placenta   A. Melatonin
———— 83. Pineal   B. ANH
———— 84. Heart atria   C. Testosterone
———— 85. Testes   D. Thymosin
———— 86. Thymus   E. Chorionic gonadotropin

▷ *If you have had difficulty with this section, review pages 282-285.*

APPLYING WHAT YOU KNOW

87. Mrs. Fortner made a routine visit to her physician last week. When the laboratory results came back, the report indicated a high level of chorionic gonadotropin in her urine. What did this mean to Mrs. Fortner?

88. Mrs. Wilcox noticed that her daughter was beginning to take on the secondary sex characteristics of a male. The pediatrician diagnosed the condition as a tumor of an endocrine gland. Where specifically was the tumor located?

89. WORD FIND

Can you find 16 terms from the chapter in the box of letters? Words may be spelled top to bottom, bottom to top, right to left, left to right, or diagonally.

```
S  S  I  S  E  R  U  I  D  M  E  S  I  T  W
N  D  N  X  E  B  A  M  E  D  E  X  Y  M  I
I  I  G  O  N  R  S  G  X  T  I  I  Y  V  B
D  O  M  S  I  N  I  T  E  R  C  C  U  Q  D
N  C  X  S  R  T  N  B  O  T  V  M  Y  O  M
A  I  M  E  C  L  A  C  R  E  P  Y  H  I  X
L  T  Y  R  O  I  E  Z  Q  R  T  J  V  K  F
G  R  E  T  D  P  S  N  I  L  D  J  M  X  N
A  O  O  S  N  I  D  K  I  N  K  S  P  P  O
T  C  P  R  E  T  I  O  G  R  I  F  M  X  G
S  L  M  H  Y  P  O  G  L  Y  C  E  M  I  A
O  A  J  L  H  O  R  M  O  N  E  O  T  G  C
R  C  E  L  T  S  E  L  C  N  P  N  X  U  U
P  I  O  S  W  R  T  X  C  G  U  L  O  E  L
G  G  V  Y  H  M  S  H  Y  K  A  K  N  Q  G
```

Corticoids	Glucagon	Myxedema
Cretinism	Goiter	Prostaglandins
Diabetes	Hormone	Steroids
Diuresis	Hypercalcemia	Stress
Endocrine	Hypoglycemia	
Exocrine	Luteinization	

DID YOU KNOW?

The total daily output of the pituitary gland is less than 1/1,000,000 of a gram, yet this small amount is responsible for stimulating the majority of all endocrine functions.

THE ENDOCRINE SYSTEM

ACROSS

1. Secreted by cells in the walls of the heart's atria
4. Adrenal medulla
6. Estrogens
8. Converts amino acids to glucose
9. Melanin
11. Labor

DOWN

2. Hypersecretion of insulin
3. Antagonist to diuresis
5. Increases calcium concentration
7. Hyposecretion of Islands of Langerhans (one word)
8. Hyposecretion of thyroid
10. Adrenal cortex

ENDOCRINE GLANDS

1. _____

2. _____

3. _____

4. _____

5. _____

6. _____

7. _____

8. _____

9. _____

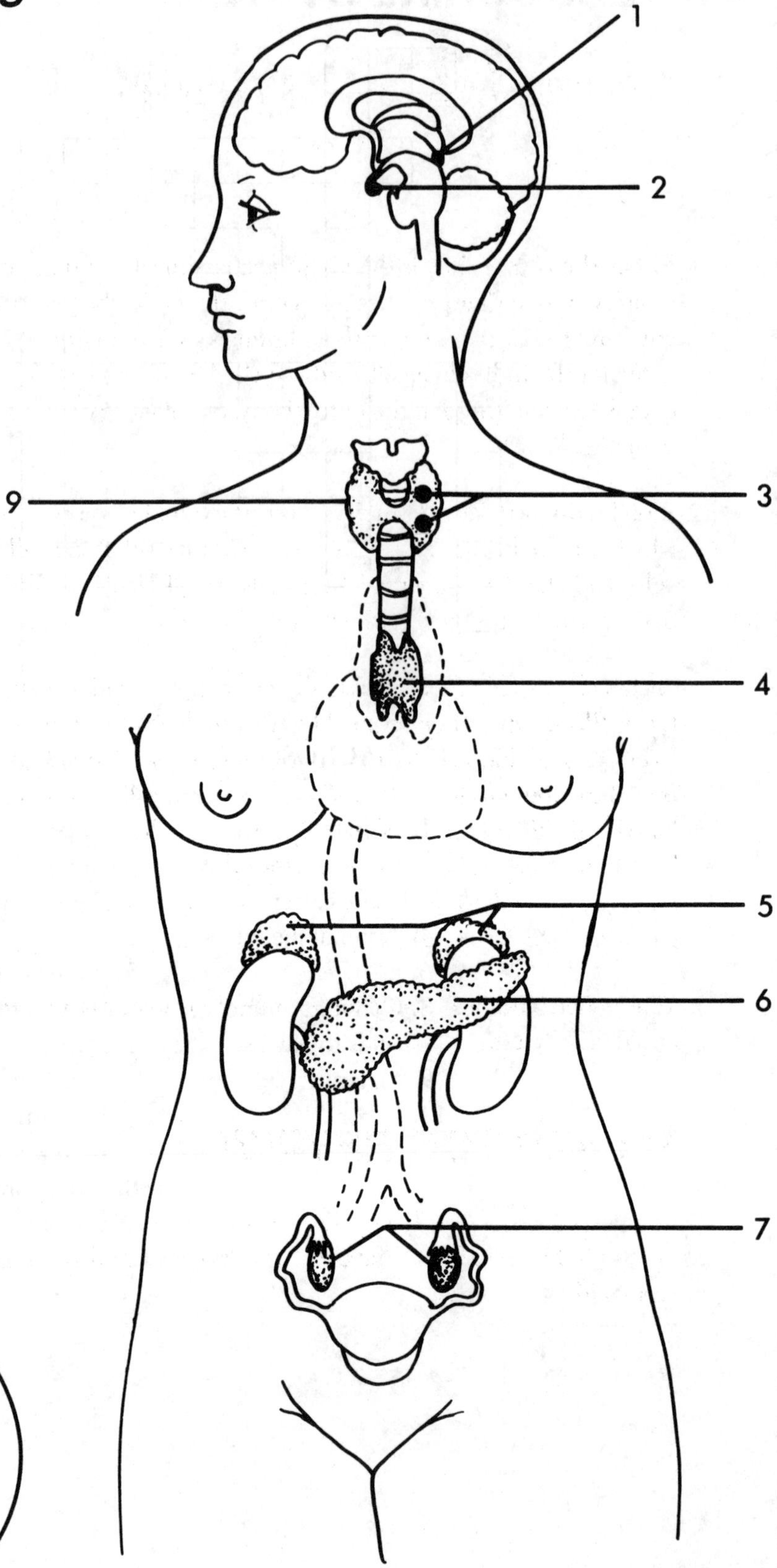

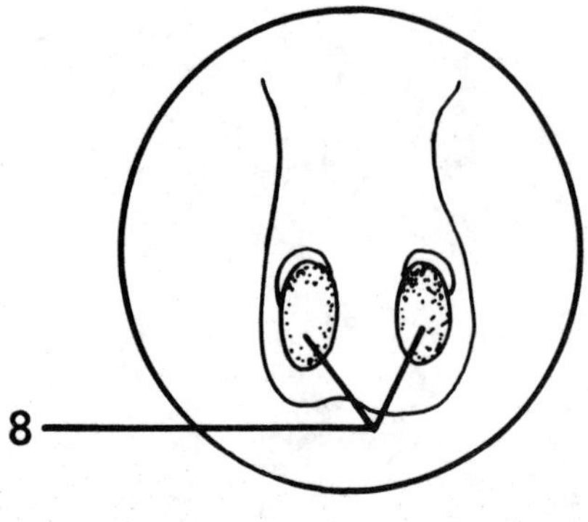

CHAPTER **11**   # Blood

Blood, the river of life, is the body's primary means of transportation. Although it is the respiratory system that provides oxygen for the body, the digestive system that provides nutrients, and the urinary system that eliminates wastes, none of these functions could be provided for the individual cells without the blood. In less than 1 minute, a drop of blood will complete a trip through the entire body, distributing nutrients and collecting the wastes of metabolism.

Blood is divided into plasma, which is the liquid portion of blood, and the formed elements, which are the blood cells. There are three types of blood cells: red blood cells, white blood cells, and platelets. Together these cells and plasma provide a means of transportation that delivers the body's daily necessities.

Although the red blood cells in all of us are of a similar shape, we have different blood types. Blood types are identified by the presence of certain antigens in the red blood cells. Every person's blood belongs to one of four main blood groups: Type A, B, AB, or O. Any one of the four groups or "types" may or may not have the Rh factor present in the red blood cells. If an individual has a specific antigen called the *Rh factor* present in his or her blood, the blood is Rh positive. If this factor is missing, the blood is Rh negative. Approximately, 85% of the population have the Rh factor (Rh positive) and 15% do not have the Rh factor (Rh negative).

Your understanding of this chapter will be necessary to prepare a proper foundation for the circulatory system.

TOPICS FOR REVIEW

Before progressing to Chapter 12, you should have an understanding of the structure and function of blood plasma and cells. Your review should also include a knowledge of blood types and Rh factors.

BLOOD COMPOSITION

Circle the best answer.

1. Which one of the following substances is <u>not</u> a part of the plasma?
   - A. Hormones
   - B. Salts
   - C. Nutrients
   - D. Wastes
   - E. All of the above are part of the plasma

2. The normal volume of blood in an adult is about:
   - A. 2-3 pints
   - B. 2-3 quarts
   - C. 2-3 gallons
   - D. 4-6 liters

3. Blood is normally:
   - A. Very acidic
   - B. Slightly acidic
   - C. Neutral
   - D. Slightly alkaline

4. Another name for white blood cells is:
   - A. Erythrocytes
   - B. Leukocytes
   - C. Thrombocytes
   - D. Platelets

5. Another name for platelets is:
   - A. Neutrophils
   - B. Eosinophils
   - C. Thrombocytes
   - D. Erythrocytes

6. Pernicious anemia is caused by:
   - A. A lack of vitamin B_{12}
   - B. Hemorrhage
   - C. Radiation
   - D. Bleeding ulcers

7. The laboratory test called *hematocrit* tells the physician:
   - A. The volume of white cells in a blood sample
   - B. The volume of red cells in a blood sample
   - C. The volume of platelets in a blood sample
   - D. The volume of plasma in a blood sample

8. An example of a nongranular leukocyte is a/an:
   - A. Platelet
   - B. Erythrocyte
   - C. Eosinophil
   - D. Monocyte

9. An excess of red blood cells is known as:
   - A. Erythropenia
   - B. Erythroplasia
   - C. Polycythemia
   - D. Anemia

10. A critical component of hemoglobin is:
    - A. Potassium
    - B. Calcium
    - C. Vitamin K
    - D. Iron

11. Sickle cell anemia is caused by:
    A. The production of an abnormal type of hemoglobin
    B. The production of excessive neutrophils
    C. The production of excessive platelets
    D. The production of abnormal leukocytes

12. The practice of using blood transfusions to increase oxygen delivery to muscles during athletic events is called:
    A. Blood antigen
    B. Blood doping
    C. Blood agglutination
    D. Blood proofing

13. One of the most useful and frequently performed clinical blood tests is called the:
    A. WBC
    B. CBC
    C. RBC
    D. Hematocrit

14. Which one of the following types of cells is not a granular leukocyte?
    A. Neutrophil
    B. Monocyte
    C. Basophil
    D. Eosinophil

15. If a blood cell has no nucleus and is shaped like a biconcave disc, then the cell most likely is a/an:
    A. Platelet
    B. Lymphocyte
    C. Basophil
    D. Eosinophil
    E. Red blood cell

16. Red bone marrow forms all kinds of blood cells except some:
    A. Platelets and basophils
    B. Lymphocytes and monocytes
    C. Red blood cells
    D. Neutrophils and eosinophils

17. Myeloid tissue is found in all but which one of the following locations?
    A. Sternum
    B. Ribs
    C. Wrist bones
    D. Hip bones
    E. Cranial bones

18. Lymphatic tissue is found in all but which of the following locations?
    A. Lymph nodes
    B. Thymus
    C. Spleen
    D. All of the above contain lymphatic tissue

19. The "buffy coat" layer in a hematocrit tube contains:
    A. Red blood cells and platelets
    B. Plasma only
    C. Platelets only
    D. White blood cells and platelets
    E. None of the above is correct

20. The hematocrit value for red blood cells is _____%.
    A. 75   D. 45
    B. 60   E. 35
    C. 50

21. An unusually low white blood cell count would be termed:
    A. Leukemia   D. Anemia
    B. Leukopenia   E. None of the above is correct
    C. Leukocytosis

22. Most of the oxygen transported in the blood is carried by:
    A. Platelets   D. Red blood cells
    B. Plasma   E. None of the above is correct
    C. White blood cells

23. The most numerous of the phagocytes are the _____.
    A. Lymphocytes   D. Eosinophils
    B. Neutrophils   E. Monocytes
    C. Basophils

24. Which one of the following types of cells is not phagocytic?
    A. Neutrophils   D. Monocytes
    B. Eosinophils   E. All of the above are phagocytic cells
    C. Lymphocytes

25. Which of the following cell types functions in the immune process?
    A. Neutrophils   D. Basophils
    B. Lymphocytes   E. Reticuloendothelial cells
    C. Monocytes

26. Vitamin K stimulates liver cells to increase the synthesis of:
    A. Prothrombin   D. Heparin
    B. Thrombin   E. Calcium
    C. Platelets

27. If part of a clot dislodges and circulates through the bloodstream, the dislodged part is called a/an:
    A. Thrombus   D. Clotting factor
    B. Thrombosis   E. Embolus
    C. Anticoagulant

28. This disease usually occurs as a result of the destruction of bone marrow by toxic chemicals or radiation.
    A. Folate-deficiency anemia   C. Hemolytic anemia
    B. Aplastic anemia   D. Sickle cell anemia

29. An example of a hemolytic anemia is:
    A. Folate-deficiency anemia   C. Sickle cell anemia
    B. Aplastic anemia   D. Pernicious anemia

30. The disease that results from a failure to form blood clotting factor VIII, IX, or XI is:
    A. Hemophilia   C. Thrombophlebitis
    B. Thrombocytopenia   D. None of the above

31. A special type of white blood cell count used as a diagnostic tool is known as a/an:
    A. Leukopenia   C. Differential WBC count
    B. WBC   D. CBC

▷ *If you have had difficulty with this section, review pages 293-303.*

BLOOD TYPES
RH FACTOR

Fill in the blank areas.

32.

Blood Type	Antigen Present in RBC	Antibody Present in Plasma
A	_____	Anti-B
B	B	_____
AB	_____	None
O	None	_____

Fill in the blanks

33. An _____ is a substance that can stimulate the body to make antibodies.

34. An _____ is a substance made by the body in response to stimulation

   by an antigen.

35. Many antibodies react with their antigens to clump or _____ them.

36. If a baby is born to an Rh-negative mother and Rh-positive father, it may develop the disease

   _____ _____.

37. The term "Rh" is used because the antigen was first discovered in the blood of a

   _____ _____.

38. The universal donor blood is _____.

39. The universal recipient blood is _____.

▷ *If you have had difficulty with this section, review pages 304-306.*

APPLYING WHAT YOU KNOW

40. Mrs. Payne's blood type is O positive. Her husband's type is O negative. Her newborn baby's blood type is O negative. Is there any need for concern with this combination?

41. After Mrs. Freund's baby was born, the doctor applied a gauze dressing for a short time on the umbilical cord. He also gave the baby a dose of vitamin K. Why did the doctor perform these two procedures?

42. Colleen was a teenager with a picky appetite. She loved junk food and seldom ate properly. She complained of being tired all the time. A visit to her doctor revealed a hemoglobin of 10 and RBCs that are classified as *hypochromic*. What condition does Colleen have?

43. Mr. Minkin complained of fever and a sore throat. His doctor said that his lymphocyte and monocyte count was elevated and that under the microscope his lymphocytes were irregularly shaped. The tenderness in his spleen led the doctor to believe that he might have a virus. Do you know the name of that virus? HINT: See Appendix B, Table 2.

44. WORD FIND

Can you find 24 terms from this chapter in the box of letters? Words may be spelled top to bottom, bottom to top, right to left, left to right, or diagonally.

```
H S H K L S U L O B M E A E S
K E E V M Z H E P A R I N D N
D T M F A C T O R Y E T I Q P
O Y A O H N B A T Q Y A R A R
N C T J G W E H N P N L B U D
O O O S Q L R M E T I S I P M
R K C E M O O N I H I Q F W W
H U R T C N I B P A S G Z T G
E E I Y O B O O I V E W E T X
S L T C M D S E C N R T U N R
U E Y O Y A I M E K U E L Y S
S T R G B S T H R O M B U S Q
E H Z A M S A L P N D Z P O N
T E N H F P D A P M E E I B W
E W B P H K B O N C K W X V J
```

AIDS	Factor	Phagocytes
Anemia	Fibrin	Plasma
Antibody	Hematocrit	Recipient
Antigen	Hemoglobin	Rhesus
Basophil	Heparin	Serum
Donor	Leukemia	Thrombin
Embolus	Leukocytes	Thrombus
Erythrocytes	Monocyte	Type

DID YOU KNOW?

Blood products are good for approximately 21 days, and fresh frozen plasma is good for at least 6 months.

BLOOD

ACROSS

1. Abnormally high WBC count
4. Final stage of clotting process
6. Oxygen carrying mechanism of blood
9. To engulf and digest microbes
10. Stationary blood clot
12. RBC
13. Circulating blood clot
14. Liquid portion of blood

DOWN

2. Type O (two words)
3. Substances that stimulate the body to make antibodies
5. Type of leukocyte
7. Platelets
8. Prevents clotting of blood
11. Inability of the blood to carry sufficient oxygen

HUMAN BLOOD CELLS

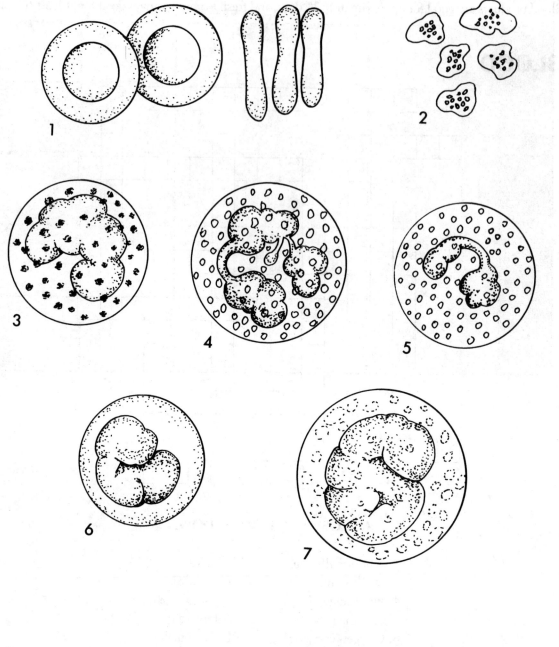

1. _____

2. _____

3. _____

4. _____

5. _____

6. _____

7. _____

BLOOD TYPING

Recipient's blood		Reactions with donor's blood			
RBC antigens	Plasma antibodies	Donor type O	Donor type A	Donor type B	Donor type AB
None (Type O)	Anti-A Anti-B	◯	◯	◯	◯
A (Type A)	Anti-B	◯	◯	◯	◯
B (Type B)	Anti-A	◯	◯	◯	◯
AB (Type AB)	(none)	◯	◯	◯	◯

 Normal blood    Agglutinated blood

CHAPTER 12 The Heart and Heart Disease

The heart is actually two pumps, one to move blood to the lungs, the other to push it out into the body. These two functions seem rather elementary by comparison to the complex and numerous functions performed by most of the other body organs, and yet, if this pump stops, within a few short minutes all life ceases.

The heart is divided into two upper compartments called *atria*, or receiving chambers, and two lower compartments or discharging chambers called *ventricles*. By age 45, approximately 300,000 tons of blood will have passed through these chambers to be circulated to the blood vessels. This closed system of circulation provides distribution of blood to the whole body (systemic circulation) and to specific regions, such as pulmonary circulation or coronary circulation.

The beating of the heart must be coordinated in a rhythmic manner if the heart is to pump effectively. This is achieved by electrical impulses that are stimulated by specialized structures embedded in the walls of the heart. The sinoatrial node, atrioventricular node, bundle of His, and Purkinje fibers combine efforts to produce the tiny electrical currents necessary to contract the heart. Any interruption or failure of this system may result in serious pathology or even death.

A healthy heart is necessary to pump sufficient blood throughout the body to nourish and oxygenate cells continuously. Your review of this chapter will provide you with an understanding of this vital organ necessary for survival.

TOPICS FOR REVIEW

Before progressing to Chapter 13, you should have an understanding of the structure and function of the heart. Your review should include a study of coronary circulation and the conduction system of the heart. Your study should conclude with an understanding of the major coronary diseases and disorders.

LOCATION, SIZE, AND POSITION OF THE HEART
ANATOMY OF THE HEART

Fill in the blanks.

1. The system that supplies our cells' transportation needs is the _____ _____.

2. The _____ or blunt point at the lower edge of the heart lies on the diaphragm, pointing to the left.

3. The _____ _____ divides the heart into right and left sides between the atria.

4. The _____ are the two upper chambers of the heart.

5. The _____ are the two lower chambers of the heart.

6. The cardiac muscle tissue is referred to as the _____.

7. Inflammation of the heart lining is _____.

8. The two AV valves are _____ and _____.

9. The inner layer of the pericardium is called the _____ _____.

10. The outer layer of pericardium is called _____ _____.

11. If the pericardium becomes inflamed, a condition called _____ results.

12. The _____ _____ are located between the two ventricular chambers and the large arteries that carry blood away from the heart when contraction occurs.

13. A _____ _____ _____ is a condition caused when the flaps of this valve extend back into the left atrium, causing leaking of the valve.

14. _____ _____

_____ is cardiac damage resulting from a delayed inflammatory

response to streptococcal infection that occurs most often in children.

▷ *If you have had difficulty with this section, review pages 313-318.*

HEART SOUNDS
BLOOD FLOW THROUGH THE HEART
CORONARY CIRCULATION AND CORONARY
HEART DISEASE
HEART FAILURE

Select the best answer.

A.	Heart murmur	F.	Systemic circulation
B.	Pulmonary circulation	G.	Atherosclerosis
C.	Embolism	H.	Hypertension
D.	Heart attack	I.	Coronary bypass
E.	Angina pectoris	J.	Pulmonary veins

_____ 15. Movement of blood from the left ventricle through the body

_____ 16. Blood clot

_____ 17. Myocardial infarction

_____ 18. Abnormal heart sound often caused by disorders of the valves

_____ 19. Movement of blood from the right ventricle to the lungs

_____ 20. Hardening of the arteries

_____ 21. Severe chest pain

_____ 22. High blood pressure

_____ 23. Blood returns to the left atrium through these structures

_____ 24. Treatment for certain coronary disorders

CARDIAC CYCLE
CONDUCTION SYSTEM OF THE HEART

Circle the best answer.

25. The heart beats at an average rate of _____ beats per minute.
    A. 50
    B. 72
    C. 100
    D. 120

26. Each complete beat of the heart is called :
    A. Cardiac output
    B. Stroke volume
    C. A cardiac cycle
    D. A contraction

27. The pacemaker of the heart is also known as the:
    A. SA node
    B. AV node
    C. AV bundle
    D. Purkinje fibers

28. A rapid heart rhythm, over 100 beats per minutes, is referred to as:
    A. Bradycardia
    B. Sinus arrhythmia
    C. Tachycardia
    D. Premature contractions

29. The term _____ describes the electrical activity that triggers contraction of the heart muscle.
    A. Depolarization
    B. Repolarization
    C. AV node block
    D. Cardiac arrhythmia

30. A diagnostic tool that uses ultrasound to detect valve and heart disorders is known as a/an:
    A. Electrocardiogram
    B. Pacemaker
    C. TPA
    D. Echocardiogram

31. Frequent premature contractions can lead to:
    A. Extrasystoles
    B. Bradycardia
    C. Fibrillation
    D. Heart failure

32. A drug that slows and increases the strength of cardiac contractions is:
    A. Digitalis
    B. Nitroglycerin
    C. Calcium channel blocker
    D. Anticoagulant

33. Congestive heart failure inevitably causes:
    A. Extra systole
    B. Pulmonary edema
    C. Fibrillation
    D. Bradycardia

34. Right-sided heart failure, caused by blockage of pulmonary blood flow, is called:
    A. Cardiomyopathy
    B. Ventricular fibrillation
    C. Cor pulmonale
    D. TPA

35. The Jarvik-7 is a/an:
    A. Artificial heart
    B. Beta-blocker
    C. Demand pacemaker
    D. ECG

36. Coumadin and Dicumarol are examples of commonly used oral:
    A. Beta-blockers
    B. Nitroglycerin
    C. Calcium channel blockers
    D. Anticoagulants

▷ *If you have had difficulty with this section review pages 321-327.*

APPLYING WHAT YOU KNOW

37. Else was experiencing angina pectoris. Her doctor suggested a surgical procedure that would require the removal of a vein from another region of her body. They would then use the vein to bypass a partial blockage in her coronary arteries. What is this procedure called?

38. Mr. Stuckey has heart block. His electrical impulses are being blocked from reaching the ventricles. An electrical device that causes ventricular contractions at a rate necessary to maintain circulation is being considered as possible treatment for his condition. What is this device?

39. Mrs. Haygood was diagnosed with an acute case of endocarditis. What is the real danger of this diagnosis?

40. Jeanne's homework assignment was to be able to demonstrate knowledge of the flow of blood through the heart. Can you help her?

Trace the blood flow through the heart by numbering the following structures in the correct sequence. Start with number 1 for the vena cava and continue until you have numbered all 12 structures.

_____ Tricuspid valve   _____ Pulmonary veins

_____ Pulmonary arteries   _____ Pulmonary semilunar valve

_____ Bicuspid valve   _____ Left ventricle

_____ Vena cava   _____ Right atrium

_____ Right ventricle   _____ Left atrium

_____ Aorta   _____ Aortic semilunar valve

Can you find the 12 terms from this chapter in the box of letters? Words may be spelled top to bottom, bottom to top, right to left, left to right, or diagonally.

```
P  W  S  T  L  W  G  V  F  V  W  Q  U  S  Y
U  T  X  U  L  Q  L  V  M  J  W  O  U  J  D
R  E  S  P  E  B  S  W  Z  W  K  N  X  Q  Y
K  V  Y  T  E  V  E  N  T  R  I  C  L  E  S
I  F  K  U  O  E  L  O  T  S  Y  S  X  V  R
N  G  Z  O  A  R  G  A  Y  C  M  X  F  K  H
J  B  B  C  U  J  T  R  V  K  P  Y  P  W  Y
E  V  L  A  V  R  A  N  U  L  I  M  E  S  T
F  D  T  I  Z  N  H  I  Y  A  A  D  U  T  H
I  T  B  D  O  D  S  H  Y  P  U  R  W  I  M
B  P  E  R  I  C  A  R  D  I  U  M  T  D  I
E  M  O  A  B  R  A  D  Y  C  A  R  D  I  A
R  C  U  C  E  N  D  O  C  A  R  D  I  U  M
S  A  I  D  R  A  C  Y  H  C  A  T  B  Y  P
```

Bradycardia	Endocardium	Semilunar valve
Cardiac output	Mitral valve	Systole
Coronary sinus	Pericardium	Tachycardia
Dysrhythmia	Purkinje fibers	Ventricle

DID YOU KNOW?

Your heart pumps more than 5 quarts of blood every minute, or 2000 gallons a day.

Sudden cardiac arrest strikes more than 350,000 people per year, or nearly 1000 per day, making it the single leading cause of death in the United States.

THE HEART AND HEART DISEASE

ACROSS

1. Inflammation of the pericardium
3. A condition in which muscle fibers contract out of step with each other
6. Disease of the myocardial tissue
8. Also known as the visceral pericardium
9. Relaxation of the heart
10. Upper chambers of the heart

DOWN

2. Heart specialist
4. Also known as the sinoatrial node
5. Complex that occurs as a result of depolarization of the ventricles
7. Also known as the mitral valve
8. Graphic record of the heart's electrical activity

THE HEART

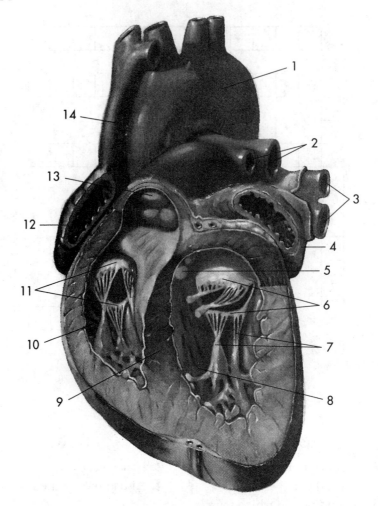

1. _____   8. _____

2. _____   9. _____

3. _____   10. _____

4. _____   11. _____

5. _____   12. _____

6. _____   13. _____

7. _____   14. _____

CONDUCTION SYSTEM OF THE HEART

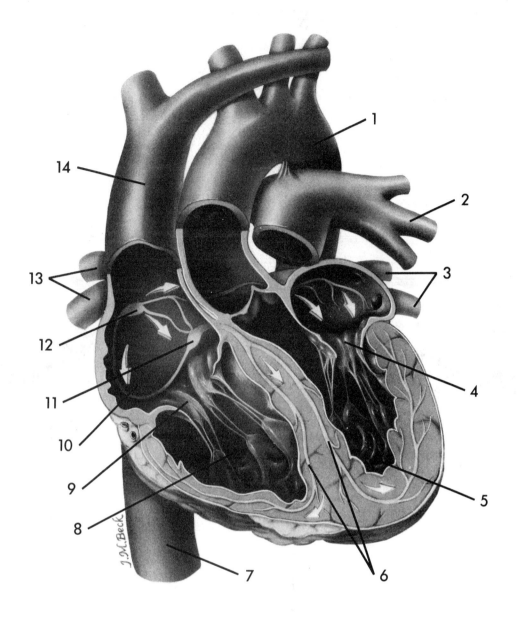

1. _____   8. _____

2. _____   9. _____

3. _____   10. _____

4. _____   11. _____

5. _____   12. _____

6. _____   13. _____

7. _____   14. _____

NORMAL ECG DEFLECTIONS

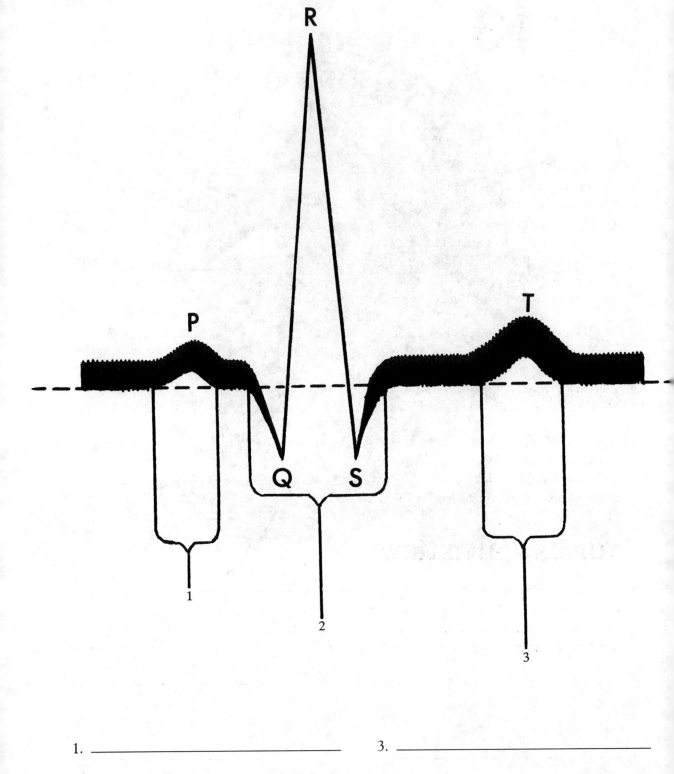

1. _____   3. _____

2. _____

CHAPTER 13

Circulation of
the Blood

One hundred thousand miles of blood vessels make up the elaborate transportation system that circulates materials for energy, growth, and repair, and eliminates wastes for your body. These vessels, called *arteries*, *veins*, and *capillaries*, serve different functions. Arteries carry blood from the heart, veins carry blood to the heart, and capillaries are exchange vessels or connecting links between the arteries and veins. The pumping action of the heart keeps blood moving through the closed system of vessels. This closed system of circulation provides distribution of blood to the whole body (systemic circulation) and to specific regions, such as pulmonary circulation, or hepatic portal circulation.

Blood pressure is the force of blood in the vessels. This force is highest in arteries and lowest in veins. Normal blood pressure varies among individuals and depends on the volume of blood in the arteries. The larger the volume of blood in the arteries, the more pressure is exerted on the walls of the arteries, and the higher the arterial pressure. Conversely, the less blood in the arteries, the lower the blood pressure.

A functional cardiovascular system is vital for survival because without circulation, tissues would lack a supply of oxygen and nutrients. Waste products would begin to accumulate and could become toxic. Your review of this system will provide you with an understanding of the complex transportation mechanism of the body necessary for survival.

TOPICS FOR REVIEW

Before progressing to Chapter 14, you should have an understanding of the structure and function of the blood vessels. Your review should include a study of systemic, pulmonary, hepatic portal, and fetal circulations, and should conclude with a thorough understanding of blood pressure, pulse, and circulatory shock.

BLOOD VESSELS

Match the term on the left with the proper selection on the right.

_____ 1. Arteries
_____ 2. Veins
_____ 3. Capillaries
_____ 4. Tunica adventitia
_____ 5. Precapillary sphincters
_____ 6. Superior vena cava
_____ 7. Aorta

A. Smooth muscle cells that guard entrance to capillaries
B. Carry blood to the heart
C. Carry blood into venules
D. Carry blood away from the heart
E. Largest vein
F. Largest artery
G. Outermost layer of arteries and veins

▶ *If you have had difficulty with this section, review pages 333-335.*

DISORDERS OF BLOOD VESSELS

Match the term on the left with the proper selection on the right.

_____ 8. Hardening of the arteries
_____ 9. Decreased blood supply to a tissue
_____ 10. Tissue death
_____ 11. Necrosis that has progressed to decay
_____ 12. A type of arteriosclerosis caused by lipids
_____ 13. A section of an artery that has become abnormally widened
_____ 14. Varicose veins in the rectum
_____ 15. Vein inflammation
_____ 16. Clot formation
_____ 17. Cerebrovascular accident

A. Atherosclerosis
B. Ischemia
C. Aneurysm
D. Necrosis
E. Gangrene
F. Hemorrhoids
G. Phlebitis
H. Stroke
I. Arteriosclerosis
J. Thrombus

▶ *If you have had difficulty with this section, review pages 335-341.*

CIRCULATION OF BLOOD

Circle the best answer.

18. The aorta carries blood out of the:
    A. Right atrium
    B. Left atrium
    C. Right ventricle
    D. Left ventricle
    E. None of the above is correct

19. The superior vena cava returns blood to the:
    A. Left atrium
    B. Left ventricle
    C. Right atrium
    D. Right ventricle
    E. None of the above is correct

20. The _____ function as exchange vessels.
   A. Venules
   B. Capillaries
   C. Arteries
   D. Arterioles
   E. Veins

21. Blood returns from the lungs during pulmonary circulation via the:
   A. Pulmonary artery
   B. Pulmonary veins
   C. Aorta
   D. Inferior vena cava

22. The hepatic portal circulation serves the body by:
   A. Removing excess glucose and storing it in the liver as glycogen
   B. Detoxifying blood
   C. Removing various poisonous substances present in blood
   D. All of the above

23. The structure used to bypass the liver in fetal circulation is the:
   A. Foramen ovale
   B. Ductus venosus
   C. Ductus arteriosus
   D. Umbilical vein

24. The foramen ovale serves the fetal circulation by:
   A. Connecting the aorta and the pulmonary artery
   B. Shunting blood from the right atrium directly into the left atrium
   C. Bypassing the liver
   D. Bypassing the lungs

25. The structure used to connect the aorta and pulmonary artery in fetal circulation is the:
   A. Ductus arteriosus
   B. Ductus venosus
   C. Aorta
   D. Foramen ovale

26. Which of the following is not an artery?
   A. Femoral
   B. Popliteal
   C. Coronary
   D. Inferior vena cava

▷ *If you have had difficulty with this section, review pages 341-345 and Figures 13-8 and 13-9.*

BLOOD PRESSURE
PULSE

Mark "T" if the answer is true. If the answer is false, circle the wrong word(s) and correct the statement by inserting the proper word(s) in the answer blank.

_____ 27. Blood pressure is highest in the veins and lowest in the arteries.

_____ 28. The difference between two blood pressures is referred to as *blood pressure deficit*.

_____ 29. If the blood pressure in the arteries were to decrease so that it became equal to the average pressure in the arterioles, circulation would increase.

_____ 30. A stroke is often the result of low blood pressure.

_____ 31. Massive hemorrhage increases blood pressure.

_____ 32. Blood pressure is the volume of blood in the vessels.

_____ 33. Both the strength and the rate of heartbeat affect cardiac output and blood pressure.

_____ 34. The diameter of the arterioles helps to determine how much blood drains out of arteries into arterioles.

_____ 35. A stronger heartbeat tends to decrease blood pressure and a weaker heartbeat tends to increase it.

_____ 36. The systolic pressure is the pressure while the ventricles relax.

_____ 37. The diastolic pressure is the pressure while the ventricles contract.

_____ 38. A device called a _sphygmomanometer_ is used to measure blood pressures in clinical situations.

_____ 39. Loud, tapping Korotkoff sounds suddenly begin when the cuff pressure measured by the mercury column equals the systolic pressure.

_____ 40. The venous blood pressure within the left atrium is called the _central venous pressure_.

_____ 41. The pulse is a vein expanding and then recoiling.

_____ 42. The radial artery is located at the wrist.

_____ 43. The common carotid artery is located in the neck along the front edge of the sternocleidomastoid muscle.

_____ 44. The artery located at the bend of the elbow and used for locating the pulse is the dorsalis pedis.

▶ _If you have had difficulty with this section, review pages 345-349._

CIRCULATORY SHOCK

Fill in the blanks.

45. Complications of septicemia may result in _____

_____.

46. _____ _____ results from any type of

heart failure.

47. An acute type of allergic reaction called _____ results in

_____ _____

_____.

48. _____ _____ results from widespread dilation

of blood vessels caused by an imbalance in autonomic stimulation of smooth muscles in vessel walls.

49. Hypovolemia means "_____ _____

_____."

50. A type of septic shock that results from staphylococcal infections that begin in the vagina of

menstruating women and spread to the blood is _____

_____ _____.

▷ *If you have had difficulty with this section, review page 350.*

WORD SCRAMBLE

Unscramble the words.

51. STMESYCI

52. NULVEE

53. RYTREA

54. USLEP

Take the circled letters, unscramble them, and fill in the statement.

How Noah survived the flood.

55.

APPLY WHAT YOU KNOW

56. Mrs. Levin was enjoying a picnic lunch one day when a bee suddenly flew down and stung her. Within seconds Mrs. Levin began to experience difficulty with breathing, tachycardia, a decrease in blood pressure, and cyanosis. What is Mrs. Levin experiencing?

57. Mr. Attanas was scheduled to undergo extensive surgery. His surgeon, Dr. Berger, requested that two units of blood be available for Mr. Attanas should he require them. What complication of surgery was Dr. Berger hoping to avoid?

58. Rochelle is a hair stylist and works long hours. Lately she has noticed that her feet are sore and edematous. What might be the cause of these symptoms? What advice could offer Rochelle some relief from these symptoms?

59. Mr. Philbrick returned from surgery in stable condition. The nurse noted that each time she took Mr. Philbrick's pulse and blood pressure, the pulse became higher and the blood pressure lower than the last time. What might be the cause?

60. WORD FIND

Can you find the 15 terms from this chapter in the box of letters? Words may be spelled top to bottom, bottom to top, right to left, left to right, or diagonally.

```
Y H Y S I S O B M O R H T A R
L A C I L I B M U O A Y N I Y
E E S Y S T E M I C C G D E U
M V E N U L E D D C I X M D I
E Y M U I R T A R N L E C G Y
N O I T A Z I R A L O P E D N
U D L A T R O P C I T A P E H
S I U K M U E T O E S L U P U
R P N F Y C B E D R A L Z P J
D S A H T I T V N L I I B D W
Q U R O I V A Q E O D A K R K
K C R M P G A I G N D D Z Y J
Y I Y R I N E A F Z L Q S P X
S R M I C C Q O A W U N H O K
P T A V H H Z L H I J J X K Z
```

Angina pectoris	ECG	Systemic
Apex	Endocardium	Thrombosis
Atrium	Hepatic portal	Tricuspid
Depolarization	Pulse	Umbilical
Diastolic	Semilunar	Venule

DID YOU KNOW?

Every pound of excess fat contains some 200 miles of additional capillaries to push blood through.

CIRCULATION OF THE BLOOD

ACROSS

2. Inflammation of the lining of the heart
3. Bicuspid valve (2 words)
5. Inner layer of pericardium
7. Cardiopulmonary resuscitation (abbreviation)
10. Carries blood away from the heart
11. Upper chamber of heart
12. Lower chambers of the heart
13. SA node

DOWN

1. Unique blood circulation through the liver (2 words)
3. Muscular layer of the heart
4. Carries blood to the heart
6. Tiny artery
8. Heart rate
9. Carries blood from arterioles into venules

FETAL CIRCULATION

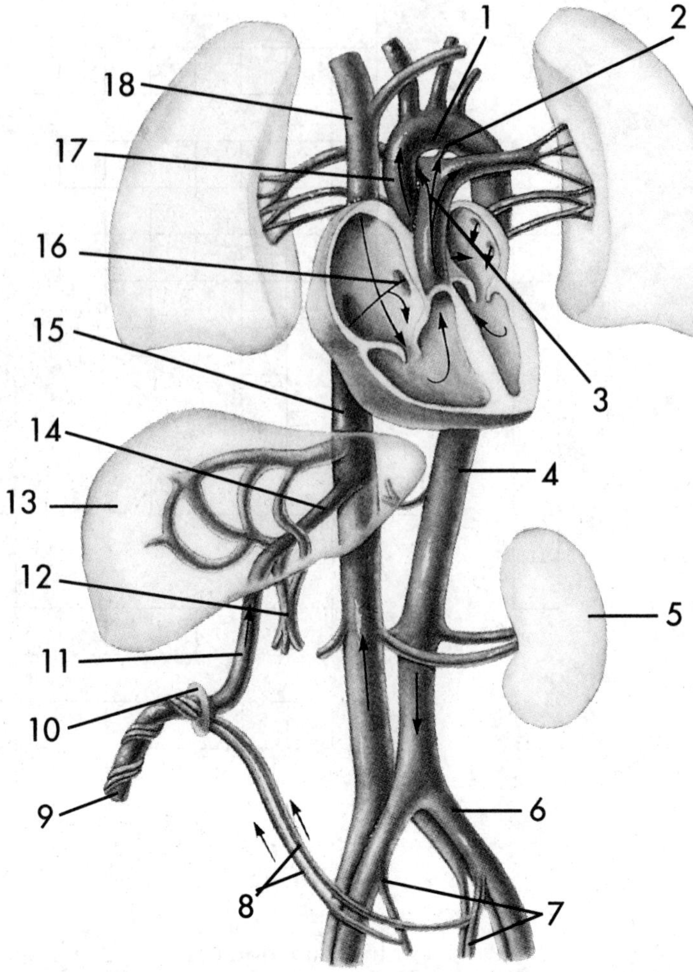

1. _____

2. _____

3. _____

4. _____

5. _____

6. _____

7. _____

8. _____

9. _____

10. _____

11. _____

12. _____

13. _____

14. _____

14. _____

15. _____

16. _____

17. _____

18. _____

HEPATIC PORTAL CIRCULATION

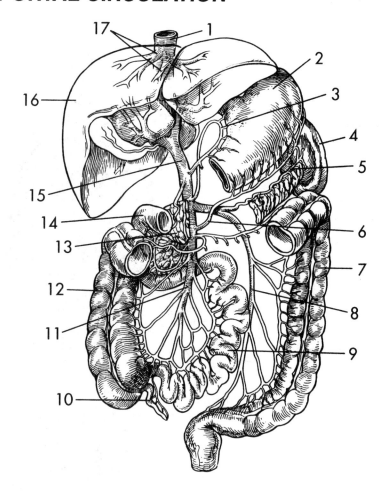

1. _____

2. _____

3. _____

4. _____

5. _____

6. _____

7. _____

8. _____

9. _____

10. _____

11. _____

12. _____

13. _____

14. _____

15. _____

16. _____

17. _____

PRINCIPAL ARTERIES OF THE BODY

1. _____

2. _____

3. _____

4. _____

5. _____

6. _____

7. _____

8. _____

9. _____

10. _____

11. _____

12. _____

13. _____

14. _____

15. _____

16. _____

17. _____

18. _____

19. _____

20. _____

21. _____

22. _____

23. _____

24. _____

25. _____

26. _____

27. _____

28. _____

29. _____

30. _____

PRINCIPAL VEINS OF THE BODY

1. _____

2. _____

3. _____

4. _____

5. _____

6. _____

7. _____

8. _____

9. _____

10. _____

11. _____

12. _____

13. _____

14. _____

15. _____

16. _____

17. _____

18. _____

19. _____

20. _____   25. _____   30. _____

21. _____   26. _____   31. _____

22. _____   27. _____   32. _____

23. _____   28. _____   33. _____

24. _____   29. _____   34. _____

CHAPTER **14**   # The Lymphatic System and Immunity

The lymphatic system is a system similar to the circulatory system. Lymph, like blood, flows through an elaborate route of vessels. In addition to lymphatic vessels, the lymphatic system consists of lymph nodes, lymph, and the spleen. Unlike the circulatory system, the lymphatic vessels do not form a closed circuit. Lymph flows only once through the vessels before draining into the general blood circulation. This system is a filtering mechanism for microorganisms and serves as a protective device against foreign invaders, such as cancer.

The immune system is the armed forces division of the body. Ready to attack at a moment's notice, the immune system defends us against the major enemies of the body: microorganisms, foreign transplanted tissue cells, and our own cells that have turned malignant.

The most numerous cells of the immune system are the lymphocytes. These cells circulate in the body's fluids, seeking invading organisms and destroying them with powerful lymphotoxins, lymphokines, or antibodies.

Phagocytes, another large group of immune system cells, assist with the destruction of foreign invaders by a process known as *phagocytosis*. Neutrophils, monocytes, and connective tissue cells called *macrophages* use this process to surround unwanted microorganisms and then ingest and digest them, rendering them harmless to the body.

Another weapon that the immune system possesses is complement. Normally a group of inactive enzymes present in the blood, complement can be activated to kill invading cells by drilling holes in their cytoplasmic membranes, allowing fluid to enter the cell until it bursts.

Your review of this chapter will give you an understanding of how the body defends itself from the daily invasion of destructive substances.

TOPICS FOR REVIEW

Before progressing to Chapter 15, you should familiarize yourself with the functions of the lymphatic system, the immune system, and the major structures that make up these systems. Your review should include knowledge of lymphatic vessels, lymph nodes, lymph, antibodies, complement, and the development of B and T cells. Your study should also include the differences in humoral and cell-mediated immunity. Finally, an understanding of the excessive responses of the immune system and immune system deficiencies is necessary to complete your review of this chapter.

THE LYMPHATIC SYSTEM

Fill in the blanks.

1. _____ is a specialized fluid formed in the tissue spaces that will be

   transported by way of specialized vessels to eventually reenter the circulatory system.

2. Blood plasma that has filtered out of capillaries into microscopic spaces between cells is called

   _____ _____.

3. The network of tiny blind-ended tubes distributed in the tissue spaces is called

   _____ _____.

4. Lymph eventually empties into two terminal vessels called the _____

   _____ _____ and the _____

   _____.

5. The thoracic duct has an enlarged pouchlike structure called the _____

   _____.

6. Lymph is filtered by moving through _____ _____

   which are located in clusters along the pathway of lymphatic vessels.

7. Lymph enters the node through four _____ lymph vessels.

8. Lymph exits from the node through a single _____ lymph vessel.

9. An abnormal condition in which tissues exhibit edema because of the accumulation of lymph is

   _____.

10. Hodgkin's disease is an example of _____.

▶ *If you have had difficulty with this section, review pages 355-359.*

THYMUS
TONSILS
SPLEEN

Choose the correct response.

        (a) Thymus   (b) Tonsils   (c) Spleen

_____ 11. Palatine, pharyngeal, and lingual are examples

_____ 12. Largest lymphoid organ in the body

_____ 13. Destroys worn-out red blood cells

_____ 14. Located in the mediastinum

_____ 15. Serves as a reservoir for blood

_____ 16. T-lymphocytes

_____ 17. Largest at puberty

▷ *If you have had difficulty with this section, review pages 359-360.*

THE IMMUNE SYSTEM

Match the term on the left with the proper selection on the right.

_____ 18. Nonspecific immunity   A. Inborn immunity

_____ 19. Inherited immunity   B. Natural immunity

_____ 20. Specific immunity   C. General protection

_____ 21. Acquired immunity   D. Artificial exposure

_____ 22. Immunization   E. Memory

IMMUNE SYSTEM MOLECULES

Choose the term that applies to each of the following descriptions. Place the letter for the term in the appropriate answer blank.

    A. Antibodies   E. Complement

    B. Antigen   F. Humoral

    C. Monoclonal   G. Combining site

    D. Complement fixation   H. Hybridomas

_____ 23. Type of very specific antibodies produced from a population of identical cells

_____ 24. Protein compounds normally present in the body

_____ 25. Also known as antibody-mediated immunity

_____ 26. Combines with antibody to produce humoral immunity

_____ 27. Antibody

_____ 28. Process of changing antibody molecule shape slightly to expose binding sites

_____ 29. Capable of producing large quantities of very specific antibodies

_____ 30. Inactive proteins in blood

▷ *If you have had difficulty with this section, review pages 362-363 and 366.*

IMMUNE SYSTEM CELLS

Circle the best answer.

31. The most numerous cells of the immune system are the:
    A. Monocytes
    B. Eosinophils
    C. Neutrophils
    D. Lymphocytes
    E. Complement

32. The second stage of B cell development changes an immature B cell into a/an:
    A. Plasma cell
    B. Stem cell
    C. Antibody
    D. Activated B cell
    E. Immature B cell

33. Which one of the terms listed below occurs last in the immune process?
    A. Plasma cells
    B. Stem cells
    C. Antibodies
    D. Activated B cells
    E. Immature B cells

34. Which one of the following is part of the cell membrane of B cells?
    A. Complement
    B. Antigens
    C. Antibodies
    D. Epitopes
    E. None of the above

35. Immature B cells have:
    A. Four types of defense mechanisms on their cell membrane
    B. Several kinds of defense mechanisms on their cell membrane
    C. One specific kind of defense mechanism on their cell membrane
    D. No defense mechanisms on their cell membrane

36. Development of an immature B cell depends on the B cell coming in contact with:
    A. Complement
    B. Antibodies
    C. Lymphotoxins
    D. Lymphokines
    E. Antigens

37. The kind of cell that produces large numbers of antibodies is the:
    A. B cell
    B. Stem cell
    C. T cell
    D. Memory cell
    E. Plasma cell

38. Just one of these short-lived cells that make antibodies can produce _____ of them per second.
    A. 20
    B. 200
    C. 2000
    D. 20,000

39. Which of the following statements is <u>not</u> true of memory cells?
    A. They can secrete antibodies
    B. They are found in lymph nodes
    C. They develop into plasma cells
    D. They can react with antigens
    E. All of the above are true of memory cells

40. T cell development begins in the:
   A. Lymph nodes   D. Spleen
   B. Liver   E. Thymus
   C. Pancreas

41. B cells function indirectly to produce:
   A. Humoral immunity   C. Lymphotoxins
   B. Cell-mediated immunity   D. Lymphokines

42. T cells function to produce:
   A. Humoral immunity   C. Antibodies
   B. Cell-mediated immunity   D. Memory cells

▷ *If you have had difficulty with this section, review pages 365-369.*

HYPERSENSITIVITY OF THE IMMUNE SYSTEM

Circle the correct answer.

43. The term *allergy* is used to describe (hypersensitivity or hyposensitivity) of the immune system to relatively harmless environmental antigens.

44. Antigens that trigger an allergic response are often called (*antibodies* or *allergens*).

45. (Anaphylactic shock or urticaria) is a life-threatening condition.

46. A common autoimmune disease is (lupus or SCID).

47. Erythroblastosis fetalis is an example of (isoimmunity or autoimmunity).

48. The antigens most commonly involved in transplant rejection are called (SCIDs or HLAs).

▷ *If you have had difficulty with this section, review pages 370-371.*

IMMUNE SYSTEM DEFICIENCY

Select the correct response.
        (a) Congenital   (b) Acquired (after birth)
_____ 49. AIDS
_____ 50. SCID
_____ 51. Improper B cell development before birth
_____ 52. Viral infection
_____ 53. Genetic defect

▷ *If you have had difficulty with this section, review pages 372-373.*

Unscramble the words.

54. NTCMPEOLEM

55. MTMYIUNI

56. OENCLS

57. FNROERTENI

...and please, don't let me forget to remember!

Take the circled letters, unscramble them, and fill in the statement.

What the student was praying for the night before exams.

58.

APPLYING WHAT YOU KNOW

59. Two-year old baby Metcalfe was exposed to chickenpox and subsequently developed the disease. What type of immunity will be developed as a result of this?

60. Marcia was a bisexual and an intravenous drug user. She has developed a type of skin cancer known as Kaposi's sarcoma. What is Marcia's primary diagnosis?

61. Baby Easton was born without a thymus gland. Immediate plans were made for a transplant to be performed. In the meantime, baby Easton was placed in strict isolation. For what reason was he placed in isolation?

Can you find the 14 terms from this chapter in the box of letters? Words may be spelled top to bottom, bottom to top, right to left, left to right, or diagonally.

```
I N F L A M M A T O R Y F C G
Q N L O Y Z O C C P A O F S X
M W T A A M N J X Q K R N P H
U R L E R M P X B R U I A L C
C M A C R O P H A G E I E D Z
X M N D K F M N O T U C R N M
A E O R E Z U O C F B Y E B
Y P L E B G G R H T Y T S E D
Y S C R I S P J O E I T M L A
Z M O T J X E T O N A E E P X
T O N S I L S S U M Y H T S Y
W A O C J N I M W K O Z E N D
D W M K W R M O I P S H Y B G
F H W U J I Z F V D Z L Y T X
```

Acquired	Interferon	Proteins
Antigen	Lymph	Spleen
Humoral	Lymphocytes	Thymus
Immunity	Macrophage	Tonsils
Inflammatory	Monoclonal	

DID YOU KNOW?

In the United States, the HIV infection rate is increasing four times faster in women than in men. Women tend to underestimate their risk.

Ten percent of all HIV/AIDS cases are individuals 50 years of age and older.

LYMPH AND IMMUNITY

ACROSS

1. Largest lymphoid organ in the body
3. Connective tissue cells that are phagocytes
4. Protein compounds normally present in the body
5. Remain in reserve then turn into plasma cells when needed (2 words)
9. Synthetically produced to fight certain diseases
10. Lymph exits the node through this lymph vessel
11. Lymph enters the node through these lymph vessels

DOWN

2. Secretes a copious amount of antibodies into the blood (2 words)
6. Inactive proteins
7. Family of identical cells descended from one cell
8. Type of lymphocyte (humoral immunity – 2 words)
11. Immune deficiency disorder
12. Type of lymphocyte (cell-mediated immunity – 2 words)

PRINCIPAL ORGANS OF THE LYMPHATIC SYSTEM

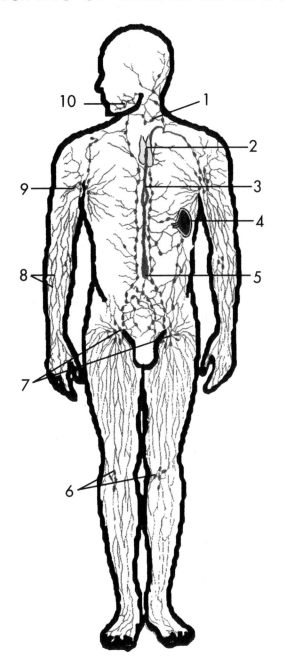

1. _____

2. _____

3. _____

4. _____

5. _____

6. _____

7. _____

8. _____

9. _____

10. _____

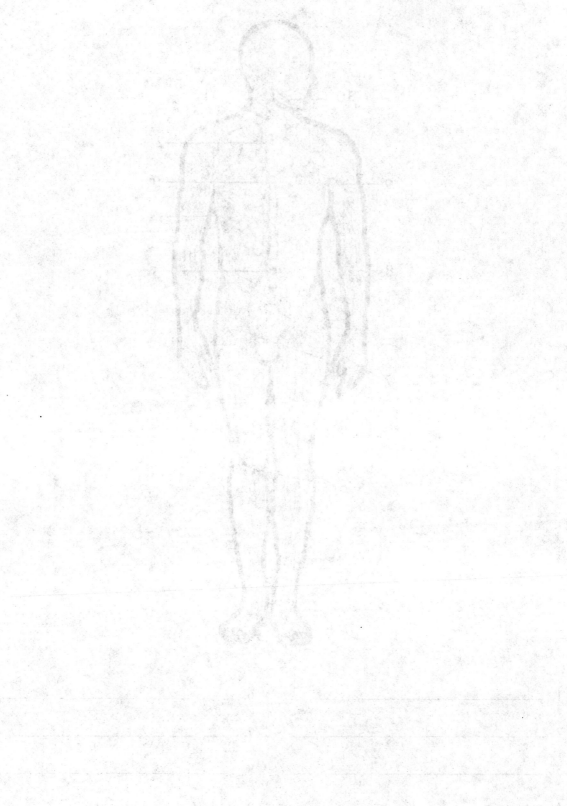

CHAPTER 15

The Respiratory System

As you sit reviewing this system, your body needs 16 quarts of air per minute. Walking requires 24 quarts of air, and running requires 50 quarts per minute. The respiratory system provides the air necessary for you to perform your daily activities and eliminates the waste gases from the air that you breathe. Take a deep breath, and think of the air as entering some 250 million tiny air sacs similar in appearance to clusters of grapes. These microscopic air sacs expand to let air in and contract to force it out. These tiny sacs, or alveoli, are the functioning units of the respiratory system. They provide the necessary volume of oxygen and eliminate carbon dioxide 24 hours a day.

Air enters either through the mouth or the nasal cavity. It next passes through the pharynx and past the epiglottis, through the glottis, and the rest of the larynx. It then continues down the trachea, into the bronchi to the bronchioles, and finally through the alveoli. The reverse occurs for expelled air.

The exchange of gases between air in the lungs and in the blood is known as *external respiration*. The exchange of gases that occurs between the blood and the cells of the body is known as *internal respiration*. By constantly supplying adequate oxygen and by removing carbon dioxide as it forms, the respiratory system helps to maintain an environment conducive to maximum cell efficiency.

Your review of this system is necessary to provide you with an understanding of this essential homeostatic mechanism.

TOPICS FOR REVIEW

Before progressing to Chapter 16, you should have an understanding of the structure and function of the organs of the respiratory system. Your review should include knowledge of the mechanisms responsible for both internal and external respiration. Your study should conclude with a knowledge of the volumes of air exchanged in pulmonary ventilation, an understanding of how respiration is regulated, and the common disorders of the respiratory tract.

STRUCTURAL PLAN
RESPIRATORY TRACTS
RESPIRATORY MUCOSA

Match the term with the definition.

A. Diffusion
B. Respiratory membrane
C. Alveoli
D. Capillaries
E. Respiration

F. Respiratory mucosa
G. Upper respiratory tract
H. Lower respiratory tract
I. Cilia
J. Air distributor

_____ 1. Function of respiratory system

_____ 2. Pharynx

_____ 3. Passive transport process responsible for actual exchange of gases

_____ 4. Assists with the movement of mucus toward the pharynx

_____ 5. Barrier between the blood in the capillaries and the air in the alveolus

_____ 6. Lines the tubes of the respiratory tree

_____ 7. Terminal air sacs

_____ 8. Trachea

_____ 9. Surround alveoli

_____ 10. Homeostatic mechanism

Fill in the blanks.

The organs of the respiratory system are designed to perform two basic functions. They serve

as an: (11) _____ _____ and as a

(12) _____ _____ . In addition to the above, the

respiratory system (13) _____, (14) _____, and

(15) _____ the air we breathe. Respiratory organs include the

(16) _____, (17) _____,

(18) _____, (19) _____,

(20) _____, and the (21) _____. The respiratory

system ends in millions of tiny, thin-walled sacs called (22) _____.

(23) _____ of gases takes place in these sacs. Two aspects of the structure of

these sacs assist them in the exchange of gases. First, an extremely thin membrane, the

(24)_____ _____ , allows for easy exchange, and

second, the large number of air sacs makes an enormous (25) _____ area.

▷ *If you have had difficulty with this section, review pages 379-382.*

NOSE
PHARYNX
LARYNX
DISORDERS OF UPPER RESPIRATORY TRACT

Circle the word or phrase that does not belong.

26. Nares	Septum	Oropharynx	Conchae
27. Conchae	Frontal	Maxillary	Sphenoidal
28. Oropharynx	Throat	5 inches	Epiglottis
29. Pharyngeal	Adenoids	Uvula	Nasopharynx
30. Middle ear	Tubes	Nasopharynx	Larynx
31. Voice box	Thyroid cartilage	Tonsils	Vocal cords
32. Palatine	Eustachian tube	Tonsils	Oropharynx
33. Pharynx	Epiglottis	Adam's apple	Voice box

Choose the correct response.

              (a) Nose   (b) Pharynx   (c) Larynx

_____ 34. Warms and humidifies air

_____ 35. Air and food pass through here

_____ 36. Sinuses

_____ 37. Conchae

_____ 38. Septum

_____ 39. Tonsils

_____ 40. Middle ear infections

_____ 41. Epiglottis

_____ 42. Rhinitis

_____ 43. Sore throat

_____ 44. Epistaxis

▷ *If you have had difficulty with this section, review pages 382-388.*

TRACHEA
BRONCHI, BRONCHIOLES, AND ALVEOLI
LUNGS AND PLEURA

Fill in the blanks.

45. The windpipe is more properly referred to as the _____.

46. _____ keep the framework of the trachea almost noncollapsible.

47. A lifesaving technique designed to free the trachea of ingested food or foreign objects is the

    _____ _____.

48. The first branch or division of the trachea leading to the lungs is the

    _____ _____.

49. Each alveolar duct ends in several _____ _____.

50. The narrow part of each lung, up under the collarbone, is its _____.

51. The _____ covers the outer surface of the lungs and lines the inner surface of the rib cage.

52. Inflammation of the lining of the thoracic cavity is _____.

53. The presence of air in the pleural space on one side of the chest is a

    _____.

▷ *If you have had difficulty with this section, review pages 387-392.*

RESPIRATION

Mark "T" if the answer is true. If the answer is false, circle the incorrect word(s) and correct the statement.

_____ 54. Diffusion is the process that moves air into and out of the lungs.

_____ 55. For inspiration to take place, the diaphragm and other respiratory muscles relax.

_____ 56. Diffusion is a passive process that results in movement up a concentration gradient.

_____ 57. The exchange of gases that occurs between blood in tissue capillaries and the body cells is external respiration.

_____ 58. Many pulmonary volumes can be measured as a person breathes into a spirometer.

_____ 59. Ordinarily we take about 2 pints of air into our lungs.

_____ 60. The amount of air normally breathed in and out with each breath is called *tidal volume*.

_____ 61. The largest amount of air that one can breathe out in one expiration is called *residual volume*.

_____ 62. The inspiratory reserve volume is the amount of air that can be forcibly inhaled after a normal inspiration.

▷ *If you have had difficulty with this section, review pages 388-396.*

Circle the best answer.

63. The term that means the same thing as breathing is:
    A. Gas exchange
    B. Respiration
    C. Inspiration
    D. Expiration
    E. Pulmonary ventilation

64. Carbaminohemoglobin is formed when _____ bind(s) to hemoglobin.
    A. Oxygen
    B. Amino acids
    C. Carbon dioxide
    D. Nitrogen
    E. None of the above is correct

65. Most of the oxygen transported by the blood is:
    A. Dissolved to white blood cells
    B. Bound to white blood cells
    C. Bound to hemoglobin
    D. Bound to carbaminohemoglobin
    E. None of the above is correct

66. Which of the following does <u>not</u> occur during inspiration?
    A. Elevation of the ribs
    B. Elevation of the diaphragm
    C. Contraction of the diaphragm
    D. Chest cavity becomes longer from top to bottom

67. A young adult male would have a vital capacity of about _____ ml.
    A. 500
    B. 1200
    C. 3300
    D. 4800
    E. 6200

68. The amount of air that can be forcibly exhaled after expiring the tidal volume is known as the:
    A. Total lung capacity
    B. Vital capacity
    C. Inspiratory reserve volume
    D. Expiratory reserve volume
    E. None of the above is correct

69. Which one of the following is correct?
    A. VC = TV − IRV + ERV
    B. VC = TV + IRV − ERV
    C. VC = TV + IRV × ERV
    D. VC = TV + IRV + ERV
    E. None of the above is correct

▷ *If you have had difficulty with this section, review pages 393-398.*

REGULATION OF RESPIRATION
RECEPTORS INFLUENCING RESPIRATION
TYPES OF BREATHING

Match the term on the left with the proper selection on the right.

———— 70. Inspiratory center
———— 71. Chemoreceptors
———— 72. Pulmonary stretch receptors
———— 73. Dyspnea
———— 74. Respiratory arrest
———— 75. Eupnea
———— 76. Hypoventilation

A. Difficult breathing
B. Located in carotid bodies
C. Slow and shallow respirations
D. Normal respiratory rate
E. Located in the medulla
F. Failure to resume breathing following a period of apnea
G. Located throughout pulmonary airways and in the alveoli

▷ *If you have had difficulty with this section, review pages 398-401.*

DISORDERS OF THE LOWER RESPIRATORY TRACT

Fill in the blanks.

77. ———————————————— is an acute inflammation of the lungs in which the alveoli and

bronchi become plugged with thick fluid.

78. Still a major cause of death in many poor, densely populated regions of the world, it has recently

reemerged as an important health problem in some major U.S. cities. It is

————————————————.

79. ———————————————— may result from the progression of chronic bronchitis or other

conditions as air becomes trapped within alveoli, causing them to enlarge and eventually rupture.

80. ———————————————— is an obstructive disorder characterized by recurring spasms of

the smooth muscle in the walls of the bronchial air passages.

▷ *If you have had difficulty with this section, review pages 402-403.*

Unscramble the words.

81. SPUELIRY

82. CRNBOSITHI

83. SESXPTIAI

84. DDNEAOIS

Take the circled letters, unscramble them, and fill in the statement.

What Mona Lisa was to DaVinci.

85.

APPLYING WHAT YOU KNOW

86. Mr. Gorski is a heavy smoker. Recently he has noticed that when he gets up in the morning, he has a bothersome cough that brings up a large accumulation of mucus. This cough persists for several minutes and then leaves until the next morning. What is an explanation for this problem?

87. Kim was 5 years old and was a mouth breather. She had repeated episodes of tonsillitis and the pediatrician, Dr. Smith, suggested removal of her tonsils and adenoids. He further suggested that the surgery would probably cure her mouth breathing problem. Why is this a possibility?

88. Ms. Peace developed emphysema. This disease reduces the capacity of the lungs to recoil elastically. Which respiratory air volumes will this condition affect? Why?

89. WORD FIND

Can you find the 14 terms from this chapter in the box of letters? Words may be spelled top to bottom, bottom to top, right to left, left to right, or diagonally.

```
N  K  S  A  Q  B  I  L  V  A  D  T  I  X  D
O  X  O  O  B  F  I  F  G  I  M  N  R  G  Y
I  G  N  X  W  D  E  E  F  L  B  A  U  T  S
T  B  K  Y  N  H  E  F  O  I  U  T  I  R  P
A  T  M  H  E  O  U  T  R  C  C  C  P  V  N
L  L  A  E  P  S  I  R  I  Z  A  A  N  F  E
I  P  T  M  I  H  G  T  I  P  R  F  P  C  A
T  U  B  O  G  Q  E  V  A  Q  O  R  V  N  W
N  L  N  G  L  R  J  C  C  R  T  U  P  D  C
E  M  U  L  O  V  L  A  U  D  I  S  E  R  E
V  O  V  O  T  A  N  G  J  E  D  P  Z  U  U
O  N  K  B  T  C  N  U  U  E  B  O  S  J  S
P  A  L  I  I  K  E  U  C  N  O  Z  K  N  A
Y  R  V  N  S  D  I  O  N  E  D  A  M  F  I
H  Y  O  M  L  O  A  Z  D  T  Y  M  N  L  K
```

Adenoids   Epiglottis   Residual volume
Carotid body   Hypoventilation   Surfactant
Cilia   Inspiration   URI
Diffusion   Oxyhemoglobin   Vital capacity
Dyspnea   Pulmonary

DID YOU KNOW?

If the alveoli in our lungs were flattened out, they would cover one half of a tennis court.

Eighty percent of lung cancer cases are caused by cigarette smoking.

RESPIRATORY SYSTEM

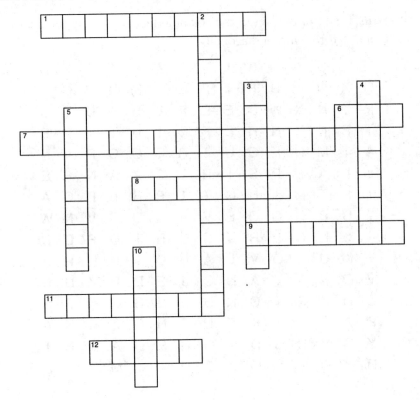

ACROSS

1. Device used to measure the amount of air exchanged in breathing
6. Expiratory reserve volume (abbreviation)
7. Sphenoidal (two words)
8. Terminal air sacs
9. Shelf-like structures that protrude into the nasal cavity
11. Inflammation of pleura
12. Respirations stop

DOWN

2. Surgical procedure to remove tonsils
3. Doctor who developed lifesaving technique
4. Windpipe
5. Trachea branches into right and left structures
10. Voice box

SAGITTAL VIEW OF FACE AND NECK

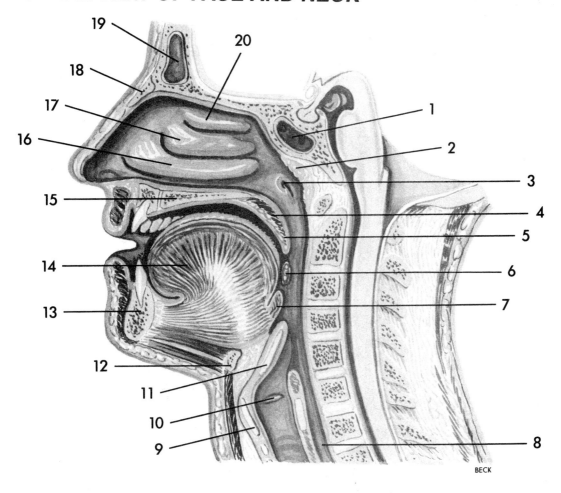

BECK

1. _____   11. _____

2. _____   12. _____

3. _____   13. _____

4. _____   14. _____

5. _____   15. _____

6. _____   16. _____

7. _____   17. _____

8. _____   18. _____

9. _____   19. _____

10. _____   20. _____

RESPIRATORY ORGANS

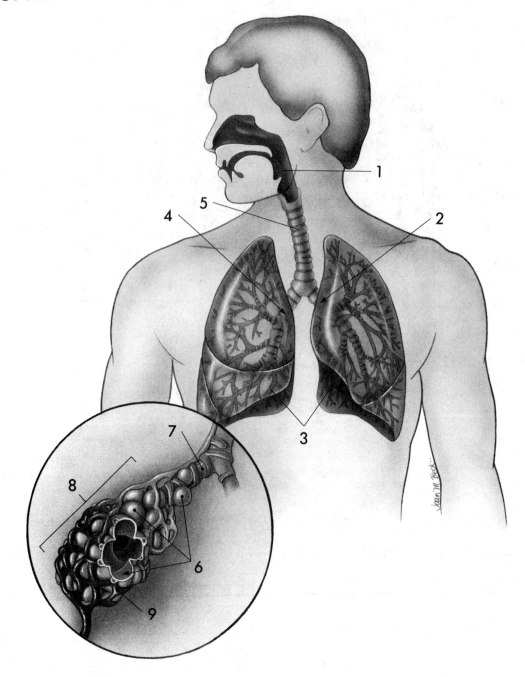

1. _____   6. _____

2. _____   7. _____

3. _____   8. _____

4. _____   9. _____

5. _____

PULMONARY VENTILATION VOLUMES

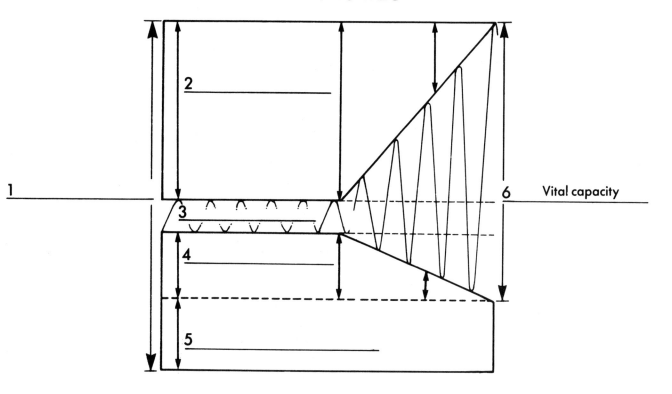

1. _____

2. _____

3. _____

4. _____

5. _____

CHAPTER 16 The Digestive System

Think of the last meal you ate. The different shapes, sizes, tastes, and textures that you so recently enjoyed. Think of those items circulating in your bloodstream in those same original shapes and sizes. Impossible? Of course. And because of this impossibility you will begin to understand and marvel at the close relationship of the digestive system to the circulatory system. It is the digestive system that changes our food, both mechanically and chemically, into a form that is acceptable to the blood and the body.

This change begins the moment you take the very first bite. Digestion starts in the mouth, where food is chewed and mixed with saliva. It then moves down the pharynx and esophagus by peristalsis and enters the stomach. In the stomach it is churned and mixed with gastric juices to become chyme. The chyme goes from the stomach into the duodenum where it is further broken down chemically by intestinal fluids, bile, and pancreatic juice. Those secretions prepare the food for absorption all along the course of the small intestine. Products that are not absorbed pass through the entire length of the small intestine (duodenum, jejunum, ileum). From there they enter into the cecum of the large intestine, the ascending colon, transverse colon, descending colon, sigmoid colon, into the rectum, and out the anus.

Products that are used in the cells undergo absorption. Absorption allows newly processed nutrients to pass through the walls of the digestive tract and into the bloodstream to be distributed to the cells.

Your review of this system will help you understand the mechanical and chemical processes necessary to convert food into energy sources and compounds necessary for survival.

TOPICS FOR REVIEW

Before progressing to Chapter 17, you should review the structure and function of all the organs of digestion. You should have an understanding of the process of digestion, both chemical and mechanical, and of the processes of absorption and metabolism.

WALL OF THE DIGESTIVE SYSTEM

Fill in the blanks.

1. The organs of the digestive system form an irregular-shaped tube called the *alimentary canal* or

   _____ _____ .

2. The churning of food in the stomach is an example of the _____ break-

   down of food.

3. _____ breakdown occurs when digestive enzymes act on food as it

   passes through the digestive tract.

4. Waste material resulting from the digestive process is known as _____ .

5. Foods undergo three kinds of processing in the body: _____ ,

   _____ , and _____ .

6. The serosa of the digestive tube is composed of the _____

   _____ in the abdominal cavity.

7. The digestive tract extends from the _____ to the

   _____ .

8. The inside or hollow space within the alimentary canal is called the

   _____ .

9. The inside layer of the digestive tract is the _____ .

10. The connective tissue layer that lies beneath the lining of the digestive tract is the

    _____ .

11. The muscularis contracts and moves food through the gastrointestinal tract by a process known as

    _____ .

12. The outermost covering of the digestive tube is the _____ .

13. The loops of the digestive tract are anchored to the posterior wall of the abdominal cavity by the

_____.

Select the correct response from the two choices given and insert the letter in the answer blank.

(a) Main organ   (b) Accessory organ

_____ 14. Mouth

_____ 15. Parotids

_____ 16. Liver

_____ 17. Stomach

_____ 18. Cecum

_____ 19. Esophagus

_____ 20. Rectum

_____ 21. Pharynx

_____ 22. Appendix

_____ 23. Teeth

_____ 24. Gallbladder

_____ 25. Pancreas

▷ *If you have had difficulty with this section, review pages 411-413.*

MOUTH
TEETH
SALIVARY GLANDS

Circle the best answer.

26. Which one of the following is <u>not</u> a part of the roof of the mouth?
    A. Uvula
    B. Palatine bones
    C. Maxillary bones
    D. Soft palate
    E. All of the above are part of the
       roof of the mouth

27. The largest of the papillae on the surface of the tongue are the:
    A. Filiform
    B. Fungiform
    C. Vallate
    D. Taste buds

28. The first baby tooth, on an average, appears at:
    A. 2 months
    B. 1 year
    C. 3 months
    D. 1 month
    E. 6 months

29. The portion of the tooth that is covered with enamel is the:
    A. Pulp cavity
    B. Neck
    C. Root
    D. Crown
    E. None of the above is correct

30. The wall of the pulp cavity is surrounded by:
    A. Enamel
    B. Dentin
    C. Cementum
    D. Connective tissue
    E. Blood and lymphatic vessels

31. Which of the following teeth is missing from the deciduous arch?
    A. Central incisor
    B. Canine
    C. Second premolar
    D. First molar
    E. Second molar

32. The permanent central incisor erupts between the ages of _____.
    A. 9-13
    B. 5-6
    C. 7-10
    D. 7-8
    E. None of the above is correct

33. The third molar appears between the ages of _____.
    A. 10-14
    B. 5-8
    C. 11-16
    D. 17-24
    E. None of the above is correct

34. A general term for infection of the gums is known as:
    A. Dental caries
    B. Leukoplakia
    C. Vincent's angina
    D. Gingivitis

35. The ducts of the _____ glands open into the floor of the mouth.
    A. Sublingual
    B. Submandibular
    C. Parotid
    D. Carotid

36. The volume of saliva secreted per day is about:
    A. One half pint
    B. One pint
    C. One liter
    D. One gallon

37. Mumps are an infection of the:
    A. Parotid gland
    B. Sublingual gland
    C. Submandibular gland
    D. Tonsils

38. Incisors are used during mastication to:
    A. Cut
    B. Piece
    C. Tear
    D. Grind

39. Another name for the third molar is:
    A. Central incisor
    B. Wisdom tooth
    C. Canine
    D. Lateral incisor

40. After food has been chewed, it is formed into a small rounded mass called a:
    A. Moat
    B. Chyme
    C. Bolus
    D. Protease

▷ *If you have had difficulty with this section, review pages 412-418.*

PHARYNX
ESOPHAGUS
STOMACH

Fill in the blanks.

The (41) _____ is a tubelike structure that functions as part of both respiratory

and digestive systems. It connects the mouth with the (42) _____.

The esophagus serves as a passageway for movement of food from the pharynx to the

(43) _____. Food enters the stomach by passing through the muscular

(44) _____ _____ at the end of the esophagus.

Contraction of the stomach mixes the food thoroughly with the gastric juices and breaks it down into

a semisolid mixture called (45) _____. The three divisions of the stomach

are the (46) _____, (47) _____, and

(48) _____. Food is held in the stomach by the

(49) _____ _____ muscle long enough for

partial digestion to occur. After food has been in the stomach for approximately 3 hours, the chyme

will enter the (50) _____ _____.

Match the term with the correct definition.

A. Esophagus   F. Greater curvature
B. Chyme   G. Emesis
C. Peristalsis   H. Tagamet
D. Rugae   I. Hiatal hernia
E. Ulcer   J. Lesser curvature

_____ 51. Stomach folds

_____ 52. Upper right border of stomach

_____ 53. Total emptying of stomach contents back through the cardiac sphincter, up the esophagus, and out of the mouth

_____ 54. 10-inch passageway

_____ 55. Drug used to treat heartburn by suppressing the stomach's secretion of acid

_____ 56. Semisolid mixture of stomach contents

_____ 57. Muscle contractions of the digestive system

_____ 58. Open wound in digestive system that is acted on by acidic gastric juice

_____ 59. Stomach pushes through the gap in the diaphragm

_____ 60. Lower left border of stomach

▶ *If you have had difficulty with this section, review pages 418-420.*

SMALL INTESTINE
LIVER AND GALLBLADDER
PANCREAS

Circle the best answer.

61. Which one is <u>not</u> part of the small intestine?
 A. Jejunum   C. Cecum
 B. Ileum   D. Duodenum

62. Which one of the following structures does <u>not</u> increase the surface area of the intestine for absorption?
 A. Plicae   C. Villi
 B. Rugae   D. Brush border

63. The union of the cystic duct and hepatic duct form the:
    A. Common bile duct
    B. Major duodenal papilla
    C. Minor duodenal papilla
    D. Pancreatic duct

64. Obstruction of the _____ will lead to jaundice.
    A. Hepatic duct
    B. Pancreatic duct
    C. Cystic duct
    D. None of the above

65. Each villus in the intestine contains a lymphatic vessel or _____ that serves to absorb lipid or fat materials from the chyme.
    A. Plica
    B. Lacteal
    C. Villa
    D. Microvilli

66. The middle third of the duodenum contains the:
    A. Islets
    B. Fundus
    C. Body
    D. Rugae
    E. Major duodenal papilla

67. *Cholelithiasis* is the term used to describe:
    A. Biliary colic
    B. Jaundice
    C. Portal hypertension
    D. Gall stones

68. The liver is an:
    A. Enzyme
    B. Endocrine organ
    C. Endocrine gland
    D. Exocrine gland

69. Fats in chyme stimulate the secretion of the hormone:
    A. Lipase
    B. Cholecystokinin
    C. Protease
    D. Amylase

70. The largest gland in the body is the:
    A. Pituitary
    B. Thyroid
    C. Liver
    D. Thymus

▷ *If you have had difficulty with this section, review pages 421-425.*

LARGE INTESTINE
APPENDIX
PERITONEUM

If the statement is true, mark "T" next to the answer. If the statement is false, circle the incorrect word(s) and write the correct term in the blank next to the statement.

_____ 71. Bacteria in the large intestine are responsible for the synthesis of vitamin E needed for normal blood clotting.

_____ 72. Villi in the large intestine absorb salts and water.

_____ 73. If waste products pass rapidly through the large intestine, constipation results.

_____ 74. The ileocecal valve opens into the sigmoid colon.

_____ 75. The splenic flexure is the bend between the ascending colon and the transverse colon.

_____ 76. The splenic colon is the **S**-shaped segment that terminates in the rectum.

_____ 77. The appendix serves no important digestive function in humans.

_____ 78. For patients with suspected appendicitis, a physician will often evaluate the appendix by a digital rectal examination.

_____ 79. The visceral layer of the peritoneum lines the abdominal cavity.

_____ 80. The greater omentum is shaped like a fan and serves to anchor the small intestine to the posterior abdominal wall.

_____ 81. Diarrhea is an inflammation of abnormal saclike outpouchings of the intestinal wall.

_____ 82. Crohn's disease is a type of autoimmune colitis.

_____ 83. A colostomy is a surgical procedure in which an artificial anus is created on the abdominal wall.

_____ 84. Peritonitis is the abnormal accumulation of fluid in the peritoneal space.

▷ *If you have had difficulty with this section, review pages 426-432.*

DIGESTION ABSORPTION METABOLISM

Circle the best answer.

85. Which one of the following substances does <u>not</u> contain any enzymes?
    A. Saliva
    B. Bile
    C. Gastric juice
    D. Pancreatic juice
    E. Intestinal juice

86. Which one of the following is a simple sugar?
    A. Maltose
    B. Sucrose
    C. Lactose
    D. Glucose
    E. Starch

87. Cane sugar is the same as:
   A. Maltose
   B. Lactose
   C. Sucrose
   D. Glucose
   E. None of the above is correct

88. Most of the digestion of carbohydrates takes place in the:
   A. Mouth
   B. Stomach
   C. Small intestine
   D. Large intestine

89. Fats are broken down into:
   A. Amino acids
   B. Simple sugars
   C. Fatty acids
   D. Disaccharides

▷ *If you have had difficulty with this section, review pages 432-434.*

CHEMICAL DIGESTION

90. *Fill in the blank areas on the chart below.*

DIGESTIVE JUICES AND ENZYMES	SUBSTANCE DIGESTED (OR HYDROLYZED)	RESULTING PRODUCT
SALIVA		
1. Amylase	1. _____	1. Maltose
GASTRIC JUICE		
2. Protease (pepsin) plus hydrochloric acid	2. Proteins	2. _____
PANCREATIC JUICE		
3. Protease (trypsin)	3. Proteins (intact or partially digested)	3. _____
4. Lipase	4. _____	4. Fatty acids, monoglycerides, and glycerol
5. Amylase	5. _____	5. Maltose
INTESTINAL JUICE		
6. Peptidase	6. _____	6. Amino acids
7. _____	7. Sucrose	7. Glucose and fructose
8. Lactase	8. _____	8. Glucose and galactose (simple sugars)
9. Maltase	9. Maltose	9. _____

▷ *If you have had difficulty with this section, review pages 432-434.*

APPLYING WHAT YOU KNOW

91. Mr. Amato was a successful businessman, but he worked too hard and was always under great stress. His doctor cautioned him that if he did not alter his style of living, he would be subject to hyperacidity. What could be the resulting condition of hyperacidity?

92. Baby Askins has been regurgitating his bottle feeding at every meal. The milk is curdled, but does not appear to be digested. He has become dehydrated, and so his mother, Erika, is taking him to the pediatrician. What is a possible diagnosis from your textbook reading?

93. Mr. Wampler has gained a great deal of weight suddenly. He also noticed that he was sluggish and always tired. What test might his physician order for him and for what reason?

94. WORD FIND

Can you find 22 terms in the box of letters? Words may be spelled top to bottom, bottom to top, right to left, left to right, or diagonally.

```
X  M  E  T  A  B  O  L  I  S  M  X  X  W
R  S  D  P  E  R  I  S  T  A  L  S  I  S
E  V  A  M  N  O  I  T  S  E  G  I  D  R
E  D  E  E  U  O  Q  T  W  Q  O  H  N  Q
Q  Z  H  S  R  N  I  N  T  F  E  C  E  S
D  H  R  E  C  C  I  T  K  C  J  A  P  E
Q  W  R  N  A  T  N  V  P  Y  R  M  P  C
O  C  A  T  N  R  B  A  P  R  H  O  A  I
U  Y  I  E  O  W  T  A  P  A  O  T  W  D
B  O  D  R  L  N  P  B  F  Q  J  S  V  N
N  T  S  Y  F  I  S  L  U  M  E  E  B  U
W  G  J  A  L  U  V  U  N  R  N  W  O  A
Q  S  N  L  X  D  U  O  D  E  N  U  M  J
H  C  A  V  I  T  Y  M  U  C  O  S  A  D
Y  E  A  A  P  H  V  W  S  V  C  Q  J  C
```

Absorption	Emulsify	Mucosa
Appendix	Feces	Pancreas
Cavity	Fundus	Papillae
Crown	Heartburn	Peristalsis
Dentin	Jaundice	Stomach
Diarrhea	Mastication	Uvula
Digestion	Mesentery	
Duodenum	Metabolism	

DID YOU KNOW?

The liver performs over 500 functions and produces over 1000 enzymes to handle the chemical conversions necessary for survival.

DIGESTIVE SYSTEM

ACROSS

5. Digested food moves from intestine to blood
8. Semisolid mixture
9. Inflammation of the appendix
11. Rounded mass of food
13. Stomach folds

DOWN

1. Yellowish skin discoloration
2. Process of chewing
3. Fluid stools
4. Movement of food through digestive tract
6. Vomitus
7. Waste product of digestion
10. Intestinal folds
12. Open wound in digestive area acted on by acid juices
14. Prevents food from entering nasal cavities

LOCATION OF DIGESTIVE ORGANS

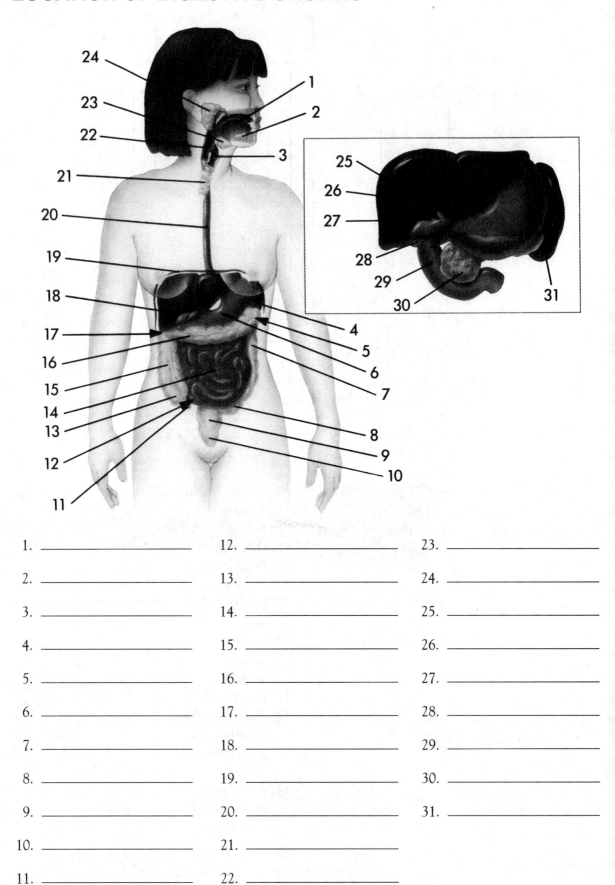

1. _____

2. _____

3. _____

4. _____

5. _____

6. _____

7. _____

8. _____

9. _____

10. _____

11. _____

12. _____

13. _____

14. _____

15. _____

16. _____

17. _____

18. _____

19. _____

20. _____

21. _____

22. _____

23. _____

24. _____

25. _____

26. _____

27. _____

28. _____

29. _____

30. _____

31. _____

TOOTH

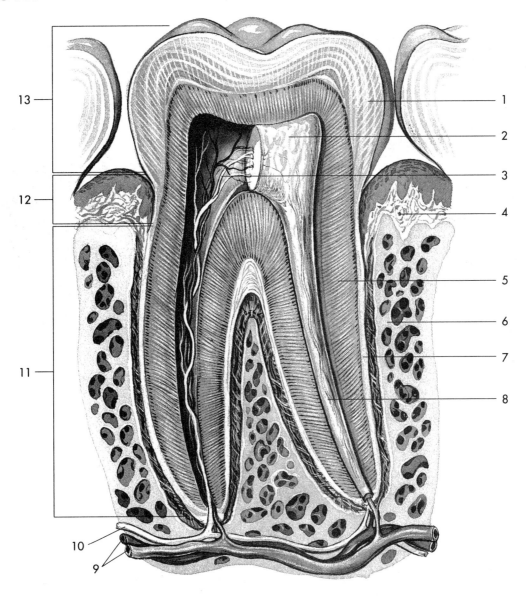

1. _____   8. _____

2. _____   9. _____

3. _____   10. _____

4. _____   11. _____

5. _____   12. _____

6. _____   13. _____

7. _____

THE SALIVARY GLANDS

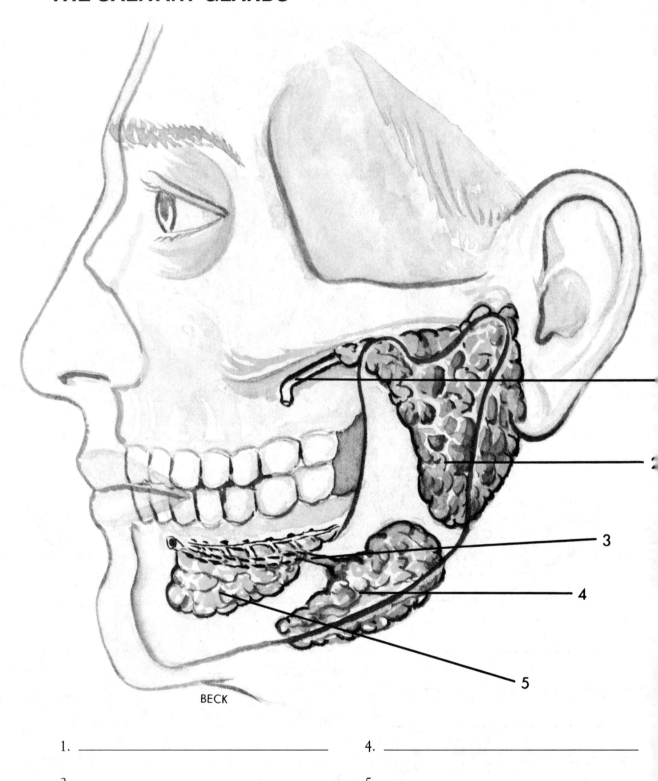

BECK

1. _____   4. _____

2. _____   5. _____

3. _____

STOMACH

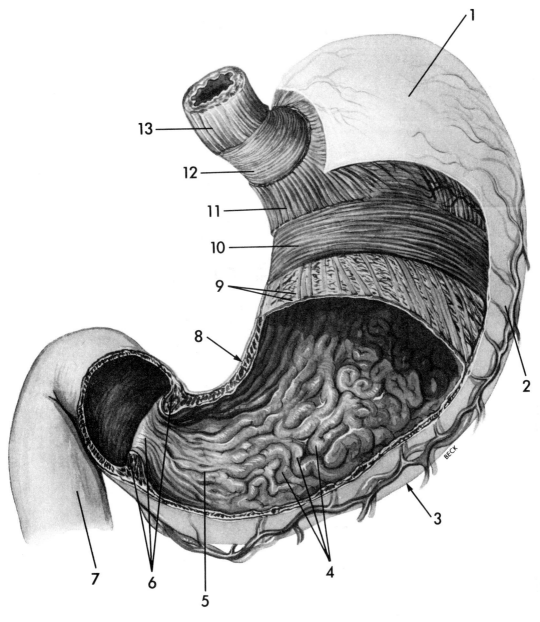

1. _____   8. _____

2. _____   9. _____

3. ._____   10. _____

4. _____   11. _____

5. _____   12. _____

6. _____   13. _____

7. _____

GALLBLADDER AND BILE DUCTS

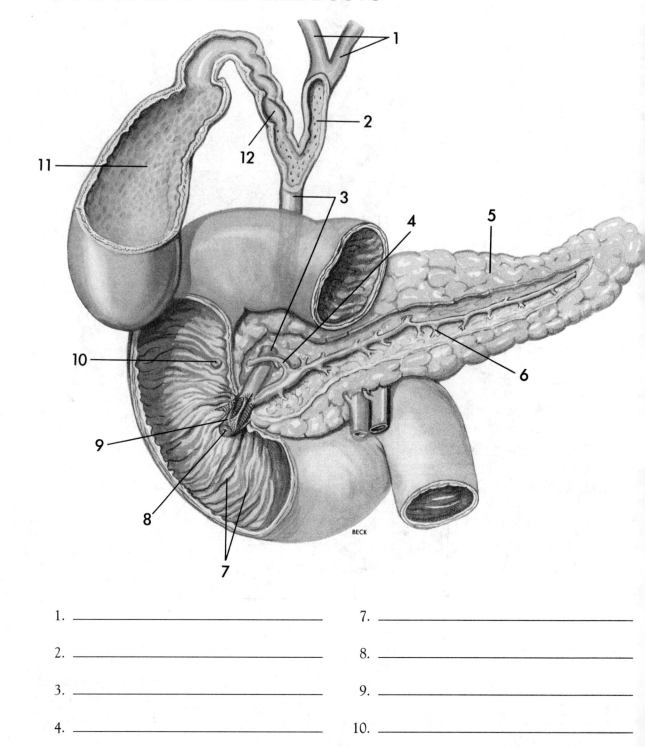

BECK

1. _____   7. _____

2. _____   8. _____

3. _____   9. _____

4. _____   10. _____

5. _____   11. _____

6. _____   12. _____

THE SMALL INTESTINE

SEGMENT OF JEJUNUM

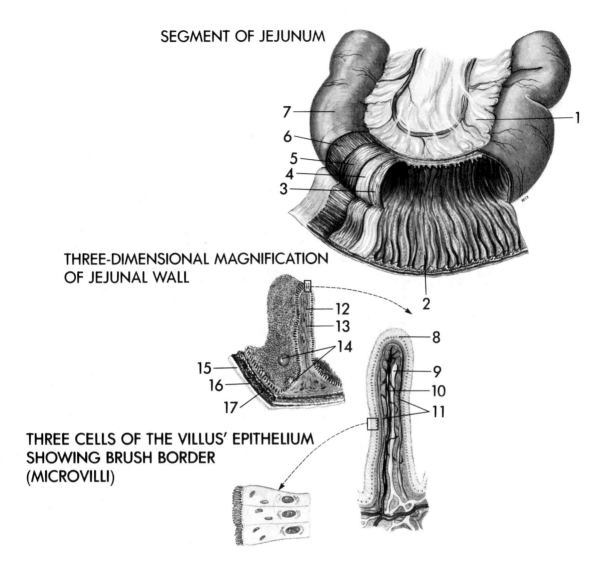

THREE-DIMENSIONAL MAGNIFICATION
OF JEJUNAL WALL

THREE CELLS OF THE VILLUS' EPITHELIUM
SHOWING BRUSH BORDER
(MICROVILLI)

1. _____

2. _____

3. _____

4. _____

5. _____

6. _____

7. _____

8. _____

9. _____

10. _____

11. _____

12. _____

13. _____

14. _____

15. _____

16. _____

17. _____

THE LARGE INTESTINE

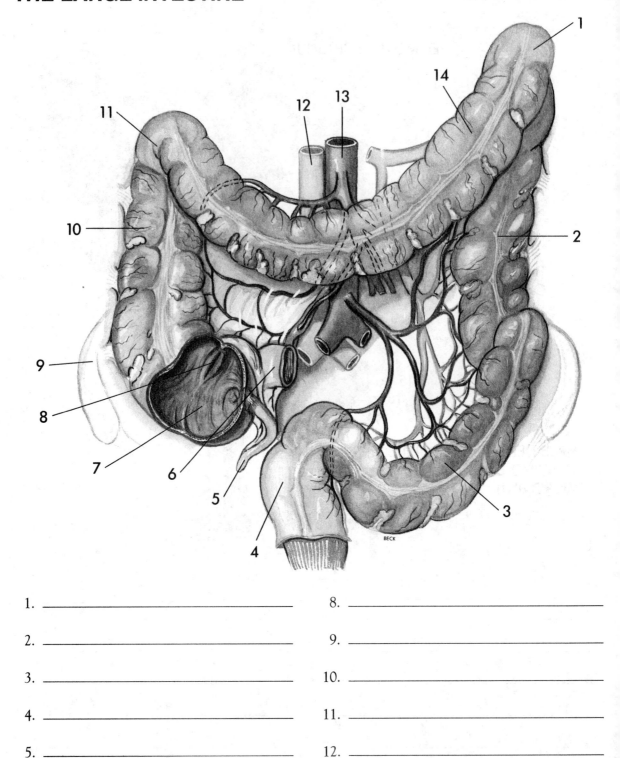

1. _____   8. _____

2. _____   9. _____

3. _____   10. _____

4. _____   11. _____

5. _____   12. _____

6. _____   13. _____

7. _____   14. _____

Nutrition and Metabolism

Most of us love to eat, but do the foods we enjoy provide us with the basic food types necessary for good nutrition? The body, a finely tuned machine, requires a balance of carbohydrates, fats, proteins, vitamins, and minerals to function properly. These nutrients must be digested, absorbed, and circulated to cells constantly to accommodate the numerous activities that occur throughout the body. The use the body makes of foods once these processes are completed is called *metabolism*.

The liver plays a major role in the metabolism of food. It helps maintain a normal blood glucose level, removes toxins from the blood, processes blood immediately after it leaves the gastrointestinal tract, and initiates the first steps of protein and fat metabolism.

This chapter also discusses basal metabolic rate (BMR). The BMR is the rate at which food is catabolized under basal conditions. This test and the protein-bound iodine (PBI) are indirect measures of thyroid gland functioning. The total metabolic rate (TMR) is the amount of energy, expressed in calories, used by the body each day.

Finally, maintaining a constant body temperature is a function of the hypothalamus and a challenge for the metabolic factors of the body. Review of this chapter is necessary to provide you with an understanding of the "fuel" or nutrition necessary to maintain your complex homeostatic machine—the body.

TOPICS FOR REVIEW

Before progressing to Chapter 18, you should be able to define and contrast catabolism and anabolism. Your review should include the metabolic roles of carbohydrates, fats, proteins, vitamins, and minerals. Your study should conclude with an understanding of the basal metabolic rate, physiological mechanisms that regulate body temperature, and the common metabolic and eating disorders.

THE ROLE OF THE LIVER

Fill in the blanks.

The liver plays an important role in the mechanical digestion of lipids because it secretes

(1) _____. It also produces two of the plasma proteins that

play an essential role in blood clotting. These two proteins are (2) _____

and (3) _____. Additionally, liver cells store several substances, notably vit-

amins A, D, K, and (4) _____. Finally, the liver is assisted by a unique

structural feature of the blood vessels that supply it. This arrangement, known as the

(5) _____ _____ _____,

allows toxins to be removed from the bloodstream before nutrients are distributed throughout

the body.

NUTRIENT METABOLISM

Match the term with the definition.

    (a) Carbohydrate   (d) Vitamins
    (b) Fat   (e) Minerals
    (c) Protein

_____ 6. Used if cells have inadequate amounts of glucose to catabolize

_____ 7. Preferred energy food

_____ 8. Amino acids

_____ 9. Fat soluble

_____ 10. Required for nerve conduction

_____ 11. Glycolysis

_____ 12. Inorganic elements found naturally in the earth

_____ 13. Pyruvic acid

Circle the word or phrase that does not belong.

14. Glycolysis   Citric acid cycle   ATP   Bile

15. Adipose   Amino acids   Triglycerides   Lipid

16. A   D   M   K

17. Iron   Proteins   Amino acids   Essential

18. Hydrocortisone   Insulin   Growth hormone   Epinephrine

19. Sodium   Calcium   Zinc   Folic acid

20. Thiamine   Niacin   Ascorbic acid   Riboflavin

▷ *If you have had difficulty with this section, review pages 441-447.*

METABOLIC RATES
BODY TEMPERATURE

Circle the correct choice.

21. The rate at which food is catabolized under basal conditions is the:
    A. TMR   C. BMR
    B. PBI   D. ATP

22. The total amount of energy used by the body per day is the:
    A. TMR   C. BMR
    B. PBI   D. ATP

23. Over _____ of the energy released from food molecules during catabolism is converted to heat rather than being transferred to ATP.
    A. 20%   C. 60%
    B. 40%   D. 80%

24. Maintaining thermoregulation is a function of the:
    A. Thalamus   C. Thyroid
    B. Hypothalamus   D. Parathyroids

25. Transfer of heat energy to the skin and then to the external environment is known as:
    A. Radiation   C. Convection
    B. Conduction   D. Evaporation

26. A flow of heat waves away from the blood is known as:
   A. Radiation
   B. Conduction
   C. Convection
   D. Evaporation

27. A transfer of heat energy to air that is continually flowing away from the skin is known as:
   A. Radiation
   B. Conduction
   C. Convection
   D. Evaporation

28. Heat that is absorbed by the process of water vaporization is called:
   A. Radiation
   B. Conduction
   C. Convection
   D. Evaporation

29. Heat can be lost from the blood and skin by means of:
   A. Radiation
   B. Conduction
   C. Convection
   D. All of the above

▷ *If you have had difficulty with this section, review pages 447-451.*

ABNORMAL BODY TEMPERATURE

Mark "T" if the answer is true. If the answer is false, circle the wrong word(s) and correct the statement by inserting the proper word(s) in the answer blank.

_____ 30. Pyrogens cause the thermostatic control centers of the hypothalamus to produce a fever.

_____ 31. Malignant hyperthermia is the inability to maintain a normal body temperature in extremely cold environments.

_____ 32. Frostbite is local damage to tissues caused by extremely low temperatures.

_____ 33. Heat exhaustion is characterized by body temperatures of 41 degrees Celsius or higher.

_____ 34. Dantrium is used to prevent or relieve the effects of frostbite.

▷ *If you have had difficulty with this section, review page 452.*

METABOLIC AND EATING DISORDERS

Choose the correct response.

    A. BMR   E. Obesity

    B. Diabetes mellitus   F. PCM

    C. Anorexia nervosa   G. Marasmus

    D. Bulimia   H. Ascites

_____ 35. Insulin deficiency is a symptom of this disorder

_____ 36. Behavioral disorder characterized by chronic refusal to eat

_____ 37. An advanced form of PCM

_____ 38. Results from a deficiency of calories in general and protein in particular

_____ 39. Hypothyroidism will affect this measurement

_____ 40. Abdominal bloating

_____ 41. Symptom of chronic overeating behavior

_____ 42. Behavioral disorder characterized by insatiable craving for food alternating with periods of self-deprivation.

▷ *If you have had difficulty with this section, review pages 444-450.*

Unscramble the words.

43. LRIEV

44. TAOBALICMS

45. OMNIA

46. YPURCVI

abracadabra!

Take the circled letters, unscramble them, and fill in the statement.

How the magician paid his bills.

47.

APPLYING WHAT YOU KNOW

48. Dr. Carey was concerned about Deborrah. Her daily food intake provided fewer calories than her TMR. If this trend continues, what will be the result? If it continues over a long period of time, what eating disorder might Deborrah develop?

49. Kathryn Arce was experiencing fatigue and a blood test revealed that she was slightly anemic. What mineral will her doctor most likely prescribe? What dietary sources might you suggest that she emphasize in her daily intake?

50. Mr. Mobley was training daily for an upcoming marathon. Three days before the 25-mile event, he suddenly quit his daily routine of jogging and switched to a diet high in carbohydrates. Why did Mr. Mobley suddenly switch his training routine?

51. WORD FIND

Can you find 18 nutrition terms below in the box of letters? Words may be spelled top to bottom, bottom to top, right to left, left to right, or diagonally.

```
C C C B W E F F L J V G G S
A T N L W E U O Z I E L I B
R K K P Z F R I T P O Y K L
B Q M I N E R A L S J C C P
O S S N C X M I D B D O W P
H S I Y O I T X H I N L S N
Y E L N N I K W W D S Y N S
D G O S O W T I U E H S C N
R M B Y T I W C Z N N I A A
A R A Q W A T B E I G S J M
T E T F N I F A E V E W T Y
E V A P O R A T I O N D T E
S I C N E S O P I D A O F E
H L Y K I R E B V P A H C J
I W E E P A D F T E A R G G
```

ATP	Conduction	Liver
Adipose	Convection	Minerals
BMR	Evaporation	Proteins
Bile	Fats	Radiation
Carbohydrates	Glycerol	TMR
Catabolism	Glycolysis	Vitamins

DID YOU KNOW?

The amount of energy required to raise a 200 lb man 15 feet is about the amount of energy in one large calorie.

NUTRITION/METABOLISM

ACROSS

4. A unit of measure for heat, also known as a large calorie

6. Breaks food molecules down releasing stored energy

7. Occurs when food molecules enter cells and undergo many chemical changes there

9. Oxygen-using

10. Organic molecule needed in small quantities for normal metabolism throughout the body

DOWN

1. Takes place in the cytoplasm of a cell and changes glucose to pyruvic acid

2. A series of reactions that join glucose molecules together to form glycogen

3. Builds food molecules into complex substances

5. Rate of metabolism when a person is lying down, but awake (abbreviation)

8. Amount of energy needed to raise the temperature of one gram of water one degree Celsius

CHAPTER **18**   **The Urinary System**

Living produces wastes. Wherever people live or work or play, wastes accumulate. To keep these areas healthy, there must be a method of disposing of these wastes, such as a sanitation department.

Wastes accumulate in your body also. The conversion of food and gases into substances and energy necessary for survival results in waste products. A large percentage of these wastes is removed by the urinary system.

Two vital organs, the kidneys, cleanse the blood of the many waste products that are continually produced as a result of the metabolism of food in the body cells. They eliminate these wastes in the form of urine.

Urine formation is the result of three processes: filtration, reabsorption, and secretion. These processes occur in successive portions of the microscopic units of the kidneys known as *nephrons*. The amount of urine produced by the nephrons is controlled primarily by the hormones ADH and aldosterone.

After urine is produced, it is drained from the renal pelvis by the ureters to flow into the bladder. The bladder then stores the urine until it is voided through the urethra.

If waste products are allowed to accumulate in the body, they soon become poisonous, a condition called *uremia*. A knowledge of the urinary system is necessary to understand how the body rids itself of waste and avoids toxicity.

TOPICS FOR REVIEW

Before progressing to Chapter 19, you should have an understanding of the structure and function of the organs of the urinary system. Your review should include knowledge of the nephron and its role in urine production. Your study should conclude with a review of the three main processes involved in urine production, the mechanisms that control urine volume, and the major renal and urinary disorders.

KIDNEYS
FORMATION OF URINE

Circle the correct choice.

1. The outermost portion of the kidney is known as the:
   A. Medulla
   B. Papilla
   C. Pelvis
   D. Pyramid
   E. Cortex

2. The saclike structure that surrounds the glomerulus is the:
   A. Renal pelvis
   B. Calyx
   C. Bowman's capsule
   D. Cortex
   E. None of the above is correct

3. The renal corpuscle is made up of the:
   A. Bowman's capsule and proximal convoluted tubule
   B. Glomerulus and proximal convoluted tubule
   C. Bowman's capsule and the distal convoluted tubule
   D. Glomerulus and the distal convoluted tubule
   E. Bowman's capsule and the glomerulus

4. Which of the following functions is <u>not</u> performed by the kidneys?
   A. Help maintain homeostasis
   B. Remove wastes from the blood
   C. Produce ADH
   D. Remove electrolytes from the blood

5. _____% of the glomerular filtrate is reabsorbed.
   A. 20
   B. 40
   C. 75
   D. 85
   E. 99

6. The glomerular filtration rate is _____ ml per minute.
   A. 1.25
   B. 12.5
   C. 125.0
   D. 1250.0
   E. None of the above is correct

7. Glucose is reabsorbed in the:
   A. Loop of Henle
   B. Proximal convoluted tubule
   C. Distal convoluted tubule
   D. Glomerulus
   E. None of the above is correct

8. Reabsorption does not occur in the:
   A. Loop of Henle
   B. Proximal convoluted tubule
   C. Distal convoluted tubule
   D. Collecting tubules
   E. Calyx

9. The greater the amount of salt intake the:
   A. Less salt excreted in the urine
   B. More salt is reabsorbed
   C. The more salt excreted in the urine
   D. None of the above is correct

10. Which one of the following substances is secreted by diffusion?
    A. Sodium ions
    B. Certain drugs
    C. Ammonia
    D. Hydrogen ions
    E. Potassium ions

11. Which of the following statements about ADH is not correct?
    A. It is stored by the pituitary gland
    B. It makes the collecting tubules less permeable to water
    C. It makes the distal convoluted tubules more permeable
    D. It is produced by the hypothalamus

12. Which of the following statements about aldosterone is not correct?
    A. It is secreted by the adrenal cortex
    B. It is a water-retaining hormone
    C. It is a salt-retaining hormone
    D. All of the above are correct

Choose the correct term and write the letter in the space next to the appropriate definition below.

A.	Medulla	H.	Creatinine
B.	Cortex	I.	Albumin
C.	Pyramids	J.	Bowman's capsule
D.	Papilla	K.	Glomerulus
E.	Pelvis	L.	Loop of Henle
F.	Calyx		
G.	Nephrons		

_____ 13. Functioning unit of urinary system

_____ 14. Abnormal characteristic of urine

_____ 15. Normal characteristic of urine

_____ 16. Outer part of kidney

_____ 17. Together with Bowman's capsule forms renal corpuscle

_____ 18. Division of the renal pelvis

_____ 19. Cup-shaped top of a nephron

_____ 20. Innermost end of a pyramid

_____ 21. Extension of proximal tubule

_____ 22. Triangular-shaped divisions of the medulla of the kidney

_____ 23. An expansion of the upper end of a ureter

_____ 24. Inner portion of kidney

▷ If you have had difficulty with this section, review pages 457-463.

URETERS
URINARY BLADDER
URETHRA

Indicate which organ is identified by the following descriptions by inserting the appropriate letter in the answer blank.

(a) Ureters (b) Bladder (c) Urethra

_____ 25. Between urinary meatus and bladder

_____ 26. Rugae

_____ 27. Lower-most part of urinary tract

_____ 28. Lining membrane richly supplied with sensory nerve endings

_____ 29. Lies behind pubic symphysis

_____ 30. Dual function in male

_____ 31. 1½ inches long in female

_____ 32. Drain renal pelvis

_____ 33. Surrounded by prostate in male

_____ 34. Elastic fibers and involuntary muscle fibers

_____ 35. 10 to 12 inches long

_____ 36. Trigone

Fill in the blanks.

37. The physical, chemical, and microscopic examination of urine is termed

_____.

38. The urinary tract is lined with _____ - _____.

39. Urine specimens are often spun in a _____ to force suspended particles

to the bottom of a test tube.

40. The absence of urine is known as _____.

41. Clinical studies have proven that improper catheterization techniques cause

_____ in hospitalized patients.

42. In the male, the urethra serves a dual function: a passageway for urine and

_____.

43. The external opening of the urethra is the _____

_____.

▷ *If you have had difficulty with this section, review pages 466-468.*

MICTURITION

Fill in the blanks.

The terms (44) _____, (45) _____, and

(46) _____ all refer to the passage of urine from the body or the emptying

of the bladder. The sphincters guard the bladder. The (47) _____

_____ _____ is the sphincter located at the

bladder (48) _____ and is involuntary. The external urethral sphincter

encircles the (49) _____ and is under (50) _____

control. As the bladder fills, nervous impulses are transmitted to the spinal cord and an

(51) _____ _____ is initiated. Urine then

enters the (52) _____ to be eliminated. Urinary

(53) _____ is a condition in which no urine is voided. Urinary

(54) _____ is when the kidneys do not produce any urine, but the bladder

retains its ability to empty itself. Complete destruction or transection of the sacral cord produces an

(55) _____ _____.

▷ *If you have had difficulty with this section, review pages 468-469.*

RENAL AND URINARY DISORDERS

Select the correct disorder from the clues that are provided.

A. Pyelonephritis	G. Neurogenic bladder
B. Renal colic	H. Acute renal failure
C. Renal calculi	I. Hydronephrosis
D. Acute glomerulonephritis	J. Chronic renal failure
E. Proteinuria	K. Cystitis
F. Hematuria	L. Urethritis

_____ 56. Urine backs up into the kidneys causing swelling of renal pelvis and calyces

_____ 57. Kidney stones

_____ 58. Involuntary retention of urine with subsequent distention of the bladder

_____ 59. Blood in the urine

_____ 60. Inflammation of the bladder

_____ 61. Inflammation of the renal pelvis and connective tissues of the kidney

_____ 62. An abrupt reduction in kidney function characterized by oliguria and a sharp rise in nitrogenous compounds in the blood

_____ 63. Progressive condition resulting from gradual loss of nephrons

_____ 64. Intense kidney pain caused by obstruction of the ureters by large kidney stones

_____ 65. Most common form of kidney disease, caused by a delayed immune response to streptococcal infection

_____ 66. Albumin in the urine

_____ 67. Inflammation of the urethra that commonly results from bacterial infection

▶ *If you have had difficulty with this section, review pages 469-471.*

APPLYING WHAT YOU KNOW

68. John suffered from low levels of ADH. What primary urinary symptom would he notice?

69. Bud was in a diving accident and his spinal cord was severed. He was paralyzed from the waist down and as a result was incontinent. His physician, Dr. Welch, was concerned about the continuous residual urine buildup. What was the reason for concern?

70. Mrs. Lynch had a prolonged surgical procedure and experienced problems with urinary retention post operatively. A urinary catheter was inserted into her bladder for the elimination of urine. Several days later Mrs. Lynch developed cystitis. What might be a possible cause of this diagnosis?

71. Mr. Dietz, an accident victim, was admitted to the hospital several hours ago. His chart indicates that he had been hemorrhaging at the scene of the accident. Nurse Petersen has been closely monitoring his urinary output and has noted that it has dropped to 10 ml/hr. (The normal urine output for a healthy adult is approximately 30 to 60 ml/hr.) What might explain this drop in urine output?

72. WORD FIND

Can you find the 18 terms in the box of letters? Words may be spelled top to bottom, bottom to top, right to left, left to right, or diagonally.

```
H  N  O  I  T  I  R  U  T  C  I  M  N  M  Y
V  E  Q  N  G  A  L  L  I  P  A  P  S  E  S
T  P  M  C  O  L  D  U  J  Y  S  I  N  D  D
L  H  G  O  X  I  O  W  C  G  V  D  I  U  J
C  R  F  N  D  B  T  M  T  L  I  M  B  K  L
P  O  O  T  X  I  C  A  E  K  A  P  X  L  D
Q  N  U  I  E  G  A  P  R  R  T  C  W  A  O
B  J  R  N  T  T  L  L  Y  T  U  Y  G  D  M
S  D  E  E  R  G  Y  P  Y  V  L  L  P  H  Z
I  H  T  N  O  U  X  W  D  S  X  I  U  J  G
M  X  E  C  C  Y  S  T  I  T  I  S  F  S  Q
J  O  R  E  D  D  A  L  B  U  E  S  G  B  S
Y  I  S  E  B  V  L  L  B  H  V  Q  L  U  L
```

ADH	Filtration	Micturition
Bladder	Glomerulus	Nephron
Calculi	Hemodialysis	Papilla
Calyx	Incontinence	Pelvis
Cortex	Kidney	Pyramids
Cystitis	Medulla	Ureters

DID YOU KNOW?

If the tubules in a kidney were stretched out and untangled, there would be 70 miles of them.

One out of every eight men will develop prostate cancer in his lifetime.

URINARY SYSTEM

ACROSS

3. Bladder infection
7. Absence of urine
8. Passage of a tube into the bladder to withdraw urine
11. Network of blood capillaries tucked into Bowman's capsule

DOWN

1. Urination
2. Ultrasound generator used to break up kidney stones
3. Division of the renal pelvis
4. Voiding involuntarily
5. Area on posterior bladder wall free of rugae
6. Glucose in the urine
9. Large amount of urine
10. Scanty urine

URINARY SYSTEM

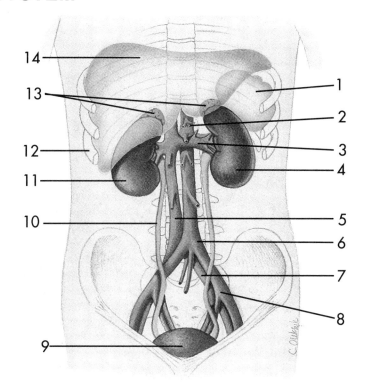

1. _____

2. _____

3. _____

4. _____

5. _____

6. _____

7. _____

8. _____

9. _____

10. _____

11. _____

12. _____

13. _____

14. _____

KIDNEY

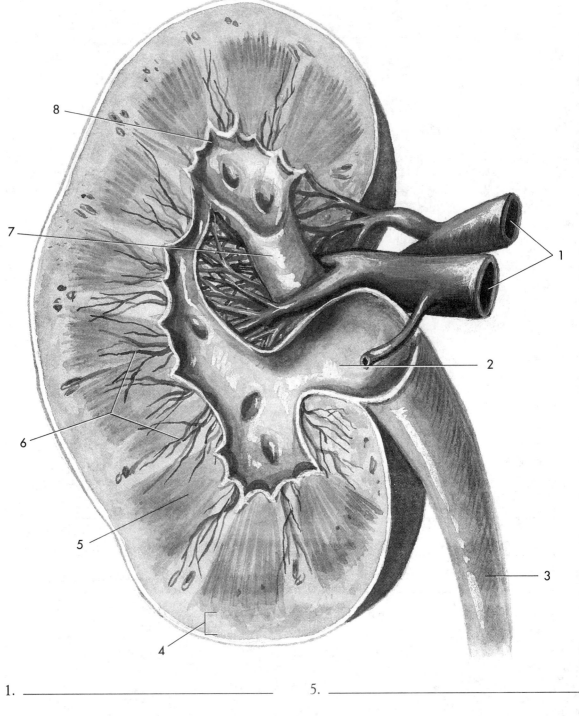

1. _____   5. _____

2. _____   6. _____

3. _____   7. _____

4. _____   8. _____

NEPHRON

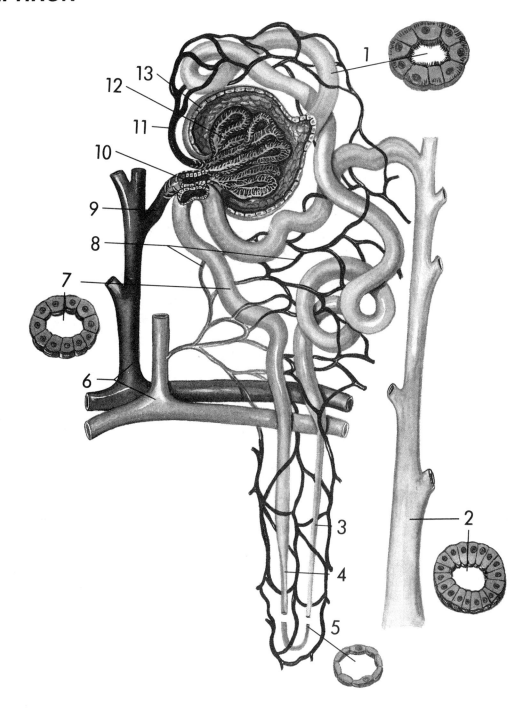

1. _____
2. _____
3. _____
4. _____
5. _____
6. _____
7. _____

8. _____
9. _____
10. _____
11. _____
12. _____
13. _____

Fluid and Electrolyte Balance

Referring to the very first chapter in your text, you will recall that survival depends on the body's ability to maintain or restore homeostasis. Specifically, homeostasis means that the body fluids remain constant within very narrow limits. These fluids are classified as either *intracellular fluid (ICF)* or *extracellular fluid (ECF)*. As their names imply, intracellular fluid lies within the cells and extracellular fluid is located outside the cells. A balance between these two fluids is maintained by certain body mechanisms. They are: (1) the adjustment of fluid output to fluid intake under normal circumstances, (2) the concentration of electrolytes in the extracellular fluid, (3) the capillary blood pressure, and (4) the concentration of proteins in the blood.

Comprehension of how these mechanisms maintain and restore fluid balance is necessary for an understanding of the complexities of homeostasis and its relationship to the survival of the individual.

TOPICS FOR REVIEW

Before progressing to Chapter 20, you should review the types of body fluids and their subdivisions. Your study should include the mechanisms that maintain fluid balance and the nature and importance of electrolytes in body fluids. You should be able to give examples of common fluid imbalances, and have an understanding of the role of fluid and electrolyte balance in the maintenance of homeostasis.

BODY FLUIDS

Circle the correct answer.

1. The largest volume of water by far lies (inside or outside) cells.

2. Interstitial fluid is (intracellular or extracellular).

3. Plasma is (intracellular or extracellular).

4. Obese people have a (lower or higher) water content per pound of body weight than thin people.

5. Infants have (more or less) water in comparison to body weight than adults of either sex.

6. There is a rapid (increase or decline) in the proportion of body water to body weight during the first year of life.

7. The female body contains slightly (more or less) water per pound of weight.

8. In general, as age increases, the amount of water per pound of body weight (increases or decreases).

9. Excluding adipose tissue, approximately (55% or 85%) of body weight is water.

10. The term (fluid balance or fluid compartments) means the volumes of ICF, IF, plasma, and the total volume of water in the body all remain relatively constant.

▶ *If you have had difficulty with this section, review page 481.*

MECHANISMS THAT MAINTAIN FLUID BALANCE

Circle the correct choice.

11. Which one of the following is a positively charged ion?
    A. Chloride
    B. Calcium
    C. Sodium
    D. Potassium

12. Which one of the following is a negatively charged ion?
    A. Chloride
    B. Bicarbonate
    C. Phosphate
    D. Sodium

13. The most abundant electrolyte in blood plasma is:
    A. NaCl
    B. KMg
    C. HCO_3
    D. HPO_4
    E. $CaPO_4$

14. The smallest amount of water comes from:
    A. Water in foods that are eaten
    B. Ingested liquids
    C. Water formed from catabolism
    D. None of the above is correct

15. The greatest amount of water lost from the body is from the:
    A. Lungs
    B. Skin by diffusion
    C. Skin by sweat
    D. Feces
    E. Kidneys

16. Which one of the following is <u>not</u> a major factor that influences extracellular and intracellular fluid volumes?
    A. The concentration of electrolytes in the extracellular fluid
    B. The capillary blood pressure
    C. The concentration of proteins in blood
    D. All of the above are important factors

17. The type of fluid output that changes the most is:
    A. Water loss in the feces
    B. Water loss across the skin
    C. Water loss via the lungs
    D. Water loss in the urine
    E. None of the above is correct

18. The chief regulators of sodium within the body are the:
    A. Lungs
    B. Sweat glands
    C. Kidneys
    D. Large intestine
    E. None of the above is correct

19. Which of the following is <u>not</u> correct?
    A. Fluid output must equal fluid intake
    B. ADH controls salt reabsorption in the kidney
    C. Water follows sodium
    D. Renal tubule regulation of salt and water is the most important factor in determining urine volume
    E. All of the above are correct

20. Diuretics work on all but which one of the following?
    A. Proximal tubule
    B. Loop of Henle
    C. Distal tubule
    D. Collecting ducts
    E. Diuretics work on all of the above

21. Of all the sodium-containing secretions, the one with the largest volume is:
    A. Saliva
    B. Gastric secretions
    C. Bile
    D. Pancreatic juice
    E. Intestinal secretions

22. The higher the capillary blood pressure, the _____ the amount of interstitial fluid.
    A. Smaller
    B. Larger
    C. There is no relationship between capillary blood pressure and volume of interstitial fluid

23. An increase in capillary blood pressure will lead to _____ in blood volume.
    A. An increase
    B. A decrease
    C. No change
    D. None of the above is correct

24. Which one of the fluid compartments varies the most in volume?
   A. Intracellular
   B. Interstitial
   C. Extracellular
   D. Plasma

If the following statements are true, insert "T" in the answer blanks. If any of the statements are false, circle the incorrect word(s) and write the correct word in the answer blank.

_____ 25. The three sources of fluid intake are: the liquids we drink, the foods we eat, and water formed by the anabolism of foods.

_____ 26. The body maintains fluid balance mainly by changing the volume of urine excreted to match changes in the volume of fluid intake.

_____ 27. Some output of fluid will occur as long as life continues.

_____ 28. Glucose is an example of an electrolyte.

_____ 29. Where sodium goes, water soon follows.

_____ 30. Excess aldosterone leads to hypovolemia.

_____ 31. Diuretics have their effect on glomerular function.

_____ 32. Typical daily water intake and output totals should be approximately 1200 ml.

_____ 33. Bile is a sodium-containing internal secretion.

_____ 34. The average daily diet contains about 500 mEq of sodium.

▷ *If you have had difficulty with this section, review pages 484-488.*

FLUID IMBALANCES

Fill in the blanks.

(35) _____ is the fluid imbalance seen most often. In this condition,

interstitial fluid volume (36) _____ first, but eventually, if treatment has

not been given, intracellular fluid and plasma volumes (37) _____.

(38) _____ can also occur, but is much less common. Giving

(39) _____ too rapidly or in too large amounts can put too heavy a burden

on the (40) _____.

▷ *If you have had difficulty with this section, review page 488.*

APPLYING WHAT YOU KNOW

41. Mrs. Titus was asked to keep an accurate record of her fluid intake and output. She was concerned because the two did not balance. What is a possible explanation for this?

42. Nurse Briker was caring for a patient who was receiving diuretics. What special nursing implications should be followed for patients on this therapy?

43. Jack Sprat was 6′5″ and weighted 185 lbs. His wife was 5′6″ and weighed 185 lbs. Whose body contained more water?

44. WORD FIND

Can you find 12 terms from this chapter in the box of letters? Words may be spelled top to bottom, bottom to top, right to left, left to right, or diagonally.

```
S  T  V  H  O  M  E  O  S  T  A  S  I  S  H
I  E  D  E  M  A  S  Q  A  L  P  U  E  G  L
M  M  L  U  F  L  U  I  D  O  Y  O  I  S  L
W  S  B  E  A  E  C  O  L  D  P  N  I  E  R
L  I  T  A  C  V  S  H  Q  O  C  E  H  B  C
L  L  X  J  L  T  E  A  W  Y  B  V  Q  Q  O
I  O  O  P  E  A  R  U  C  T  C  A  A  R  I
N  B  H  R  X  S  N  O  I  I  P  R  T  C  N
S  A  O  X  M  G  J  C  L  N  J  T  B  A  H
I  N  X  X  D  V  U  D  E  Y  K  N  Y  O  C
E  A  A  J  Q  D  I  U  R  E  T  I  C  S  X
I  F  C  J  A  M  P  V  E  N  B  E  Y  F  W
V  F  K  T  Q  X  R  M  D  D  S  I  V  O  T
E  T  T  Z  N  T  R  P  X  I  M  L  J  F  I
S  W  Y  A  P  V  Q  N  S  K  T  K  W  B  P
```

Aldosterone	Edema	Imbalance
Anabolism	Electrolyte	Intravenous
Catabolism	Fluid	Ions
Diuretics	Homeostasis	Kidney

DID YOU KNOW?

The best fluid replacement drink is to add 1/4 tsp. of table salt to one quart of water.

FLUIDS/ELECTROLYTES

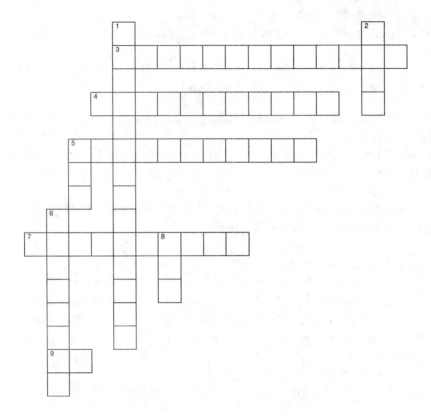

ACROSS

3. Result of rapidly given intravenous fluids
4. Result of large loss of body fluids
5. Compound that dissociates in solution into ions
7. To break up
9. A subdivision of extracellular fluid (abbreviation)

DOWN

1. Organic substance that doesn't dissociate in solution
2. Dissociated particles of an electrolyte that carry an electrical charge
5. Fluid outside cells (abbreviation)
6. "Causing urine"
8. Fluid inside cells (abbreviation)

CHAPTER 20

Acid-Base Balance

It has been established in previous chapters that an equilibrium between intracellular and extracellular fluid volume must exist for homeostasis. Equally important to homeostasis is the chemical acid-base balance of the body fluids. The degree of acidity or alkalinity of a body fluid is expressed in pH value. The neutral point, where a fluid would be neither acid nor alkaline, is pH 7. Increasing acidity is expressed as less than 7, and increasing alkalinity as greater than 7. Examples of body fluids that are acidic are gastric juice (1.6) and urine (6.0). Blood, on the other hand, is considered alkaline with a pH of 7.45.

Buffers are substances that prevent a sharp change in the pH of a fluid when an acid or base is added to it. They are one of several mechanisms that are constantly monitoring the pH of fluids in the body. If, for any reason, these mechanisms do not function properly, a pH imbalance occurs. These two kinds of imbalances are known as *alkalosis* and *acidosis*.

Maintaining the acid-base balance of body fluids is a matter of vital importance. If this balance varies even slightly, necessary chemical and cellular reactions cannot occur. Your review of this chapter is necessary to understand the delicate fluid balance necessary for survival.

TOPICS FOR REVIEW

Before progressing to Chapter 21, you should have an understanding of the pH of body fluids and the mechanisms that control the pH of these fluids in the body. Your study should conclude with a review of the metabolic and respiratory types of pH imbalances.

pH OF THE BODY

Write the letter of the correct term on the blank next to the appropriate statement.

    (a) Acid   (b) Base

_____ 1. Lower concentration of hydrogen ions than hydroxide ions

_____ 2. Higher concentration of hydrogen ions than hydroxide ions

_____ 3. Gastric juice

_____ 4. Saliva

_____ 5. Arterial blood

_____ 6. Venous blood

_____ 7. Baking soda

_____ 8. Milk

_____ 9. Ammonia

_____ 10. Egg white

▷ *If you have had difficulty with this section, review pages 495-496.*

MECHANISMS THAT CONTROL pH OF BODY FLUIDS

Circle the correct choice.

11. When carbon dioxide enters the blood it reacts with the enzyme carbonic anhydrase to form:
    A. Sodium bicarbonate   D. Bicarbonate ion
    B. Water and carbon dioxide   E. Carbonic acid
    C. Ammonium chloride

12. The lungs remove _____ liters of carbonic acid each day.
    A. 10.0   D. 25.0
    B. 15.0   E. 30.0
    C. 20.0

13. When a buffer reacts with a strong acid it changes the strong acid to a:
    A. Weak acid   D. Water
    B. Strong base   E. None of the above is correct
    C. Weak base

14. Which one of the following is <u>not</u> a change in the blood that results from the buffering of fixed acids in tissue capillaries?
    A. The amount of carbonic acid increases slightly
    B. The amount of bicarbonate in blood decreases
    C. The hydrogen ion concentration of blood increases slightly
    D. The blood pH decreases slightly
    E. All of the above are changes that result from the buffering of fixed acids in tissue capillaries

15. The most abundant acid in body fluids is:
    A. HCl
    B. Lactic acid
    C. Carbonic acid
    D. Acetic acid
    E. Sulfuric acid

16. The normal ratio of sodium bicarbonate to carbonic acid in arterial blood is:
    A. 5:1
    B. 10:1
    C. 15:1
    D. 20:1
    E. None of the above is correct

17. Which of the following would <u>not</u> be a consequence of holding your breath?
    A. The amount of carbonic acid in the blood would increase.
    B. The blood pH would decrease.
    C. The body would develop an alkalosis.
    D. No carbon dioxide could leave the body.

18. The most effective regulators of blood pH are:
    A. The lungs
    B. The kidneys
    C. Buffers
    D. None of the above

19. The pH of the urine may be as low as:
    A. 1.6
    B. 2.5
    C. 3.2
    D. 4.8
    E. 7.4

20. In the distal tubule cells the product of the reaction aided by carbonic anhydrase is:
    A. Water
    B. Carbon dioxide
    C. Water and carbon dioxide
    D. Hydrogen ions
    E. Carbonic acid

21. In the distal tubule, _____ leaves the tubule cells and enters the blood capillaries.
    A. Carbon dioxide
    B. Water
    C. HCO_3
    D. NaH_2PO_4
    E. $NaHCO_3$

Mark "T" in the answer blank if the statement is true. If the statement is false, circle the incorrect word(s) and correct the statement on the answer blank.

_____ 22. The body has three mechanisms for regulating the pH of its fluids. They are the heart mechanism, the respiratory mechanism, and the urinary mechanism.

_____ 23. Buffers consist of two kinds of substances and are therefore often called *duobuffers*.

_____ 24. Wine and orange juice are acidic on the pH scale.

_____ 25. Some athletes have adopted a technique called *bicarbonate loading*, ingesting large amounts of sodium bicarbonate ($NaHCO_3$) to counteract the effects of lactic acid buildup.

_____ 26. Anything that causes an excessive increase in respiration will in time produce acidosis.

_____ 27. Venous blood has a higher pH than arterial blood.

_____ 28. More acids than bases are usually excreted by the kidneys because more acids than bases usually enter the blood.

_____ 29. Blood levels of sodium bicarbonate can be regulated by the lungs.

_____ 30. Blood levels of carbonic acid can be regulated by the kidneys.

▷ *If you have had difficulty with this section, review pages 495-502.*

METABOLIC AND RESPIRATORY DISTURBANCES

Write the letter of the correct term on the blank next to the appropriate definition.

A. Metabolic acidosis
B. Metabolic alkalosis
C. Respiratory acidosis
D. Respiratory alkalosis
E. Vomiting

F. Normal saline
G. Uncompensated metabolic acidosis
H. Hyperventilation
I. HCl loss
J. Ipecac

_____ 31. Emesis

_____ 32. Result of untreated diabetes

_____ 33. Chloride-containing solution

_____ 34. Bicarbonate deficit

_____ 35. Occurs during emesis and may result in metabolic alkalosis

_____ 36. Bicarbonate excess

_____ 37. Rapid breathing

_____ 38. Carbonic acid excess

_____ 39. Carbonic acid deficit

_____ 40. Emetic

▷ *If you have had difficulty with this section, review pages 501-502.*

APPLYING WHAT YOU KNOW

41. Holly was pregnant and was experiencing repeated vomiting episodes for several days. Her doctor became concerned, admitted her to the hospital, and began intravenous administrations of normal saline. How will this help Holly?

42. Cara had a minor bladder infection. She had heard that this is often the result of the urine being less acidic than necessary, and that she should drink cranberry juice to correct the acid problem. She had no cranberry juice, so she decided to substitute orange juice. What was wrong with this substitution?

43. Mr. Tuttle has frequent bouts of hyperacidity of the stomach. Which will assist in neutralizing the acid more promptly: milk or milk of magnesia?

44. WORD FIND

Can you find the 18 acid-base balance terms from this chapter in the box of letters? Words may be spelled top to bottom, bottom to top, right to left, left to right, or diagonally.

```
S  I  S  A  T  S  O  E  M  O  H  P  R  G
E  C  N  A  L  A  B  D  I  U  L  F  E  F
T  S  Y  E  N  D  I  K  W  T  I  K  A  J
Y  D  M  N  D  E  J  W  L  P  T  D  J  I
L  D  N  O  L  H  V  W  O  U  H  D  O  I
O  V  E  R  H  Y  D  R  A  T  I  O  N  S
R  E  I  E  E  D  E  M  A  U  R  O  R  Q
T  L  M  T  C  R  U  L  R  F  S  E  O  Y
C  C  U  S  Z  A  W  E  K  A  T  N  I  X
E  O  Z  O  T  T  A  N  A  U  N  M  F
L  F  K  D  P  I  O  I  W  W  Q  L  G  Q
E  N  I  L  C  O  O  H  O  W  S  B  X  S
N  J  X  A  L  N  F  S  U  N  L  J  J  J
O  C  U  V  S  A  L  G  T  I  S  C  Z  X
N  I  Z  L  L  D  Y  X  Q  Q  K  D  C  D
```

ADH	Edema	Nonelectrolytes
Aldosterone	Electrolytes	Output
Anions	Fluid balance	Overhydration
Cations	Homeostasis	Sodium
Dehydration	Intake	Thirst
Diuretic	Kidneys	Water

DID YOU KNOW?

The brain is a 3-lb organ that demands 17% of all cardiac output and 20% of all available oxygen.

ACID/BASE BALANCE

ACROSS

1. Substance with a pH lower than 7.0
2. Acid-base imbalance
6. Results from the excessive metabolism of fats in uncontrolled diabetics (2 words)
7. Vomitus

DOWN

1. Substance with a pH higher than 7.0
2. Serious complication of vomiting
3. Emetic
4. Prevents a sharp change in the pH of fluids
5. Released as a waste product from working muscles (2 words)

CHAPTER 21 The Reproductive Systems

The reproductive system consists of those organs that participate in perpetuating the species. It is a unique body system in that its organs differ between the two sexes, and yet the goal of creating a new being is the same. Of interest also is the fact that this system is the only one not necessary to the survival of the individual, and yet survival of the species depends on the proper functioning of the reproductive organs. The male reproductive system is divided into the external genitals, testes, duct system, and accessory glands. The testes, or gonads, are considered essential organs because they produce the sex cells—sperm—that join with the female sex cells—ova—to form a new human being. They also secrete the male sex hormone testosterone, which is responsible for the physical transformation of a boy to a man.

Sperm are formed in the testes by the seminiferous tubules. From there they enter a long, narrow duct, the epididymis. They continue onward through the vas deferens into the ejaculatory duct, down the urethra, and out of the body. Throughout this journey, various glands secrete substances that add motility to the sperm and create a chemical environment conducive to reproduction.

The female reproductive system is truly extraordinary and diverse. It produces ova, receives the penis and sperm during intercourse, is the site of conception, houses and nourishes the embryo during prenatal development, and nourishes the infant after birth.

Because of its diversity, the physiology of the female is generally considered to be more complex than that of the male. Much of the activity of this system revolves around the menstrual cycle and the monthly preparation that the female undergoes for a possible pregnancy.

The organs of this system are divided into essential organs and accessory organs of reproduction. The essential organs of the female are the ovaries. Just as with the male, the essential organs of the female are referred to as the gonads. The gonads of both sexes produce the sex cells. In the male, the gonads produce the sperm and in the female they produce the ova. The gonads are also responsible for producing the hormones in each sex necessary for the appearance of the secondary sex characteristics.

The menstrual cycle of the female typically covers a period of 28 days. Each cycle consists of three phases: the menstrual period, the postmenstrual phase, and the premenstrual phase. Changes in the blood levels of the hormones that are responsible for the menstrual cycle also cause physical and emotional changes in the female. A knowledge of these phenomena and this system, in both the male and the female, are necessary to complete your understanding of the reproductive system.

TOPICS FOR REVIEW

Before progressing to Chapter 22, you should familiarize yourself with the structure and function of the organs of the male and female reproductive systems. Your review should include emphasis on the gross and microscopic structure of the testes and the production of sperm and testosterone. Your study should continue by tracing the pathway of a sperm cell from formation to expulsion from the body.

You should then familiarize yourself with the structure and function of the organs of the female reproductive system. Your review should include emphasis on the development of a mature ova from ovarian follicles, and should additionally concentrate on the phases and occurrences in a typical 28-day menstrual cycle. Finally, a review of the common disorders occurring in both male and female reproductive systems is necessary to complete the study of this chapter.

MALE REPRODUCTIVE SYSTEM STRUCTURAL PLAN

Match the term on the left with the proper selection on the right.

Group A

_____ 1. Testes   A. Fertilized ovum
_____ 2. Spermatozoa   B. Accessory organ
_____ 3. Ova   C. Male sex cell
_____ 4. Penis   D. Gonads
_____ 5. Zygote   E. Gamete

Group B

_____ 6. Testes   A. Cowper's gland
_____ 7. Bulbourethral   B. Scrotum
_____ 8. Asexual   C. Essential organ
_____ 9. External genital   D. Single parent
_____ 10. Prostate   E. Accessory organ

▷ *If you have had difficulty with this section, review pages 507-508.*

TESTES

Circle the correct choice.

11. The testes are surrounded by a tough membrane called:
    A. Ductus deferens   C. Septum
    B. Tunica albuginea   D. Seminiferous membrane

12. The _____ lie near the septa that separate the lobules.
    A. Ductus deferens   C. Interstitial cells
    B. Sperm   D. Nerves

13. Sperm are found in the walls of the _____.
    A. Seminiferous tubule
    B. Interstitial cells
    C. Septum
    D. Blood vessels

14. The scrotum provides an environment approximately _____ for the testes.
    A. The same as body temperature
    B. 5 degrees warmer than body temperature
    C. 3 degrees warmer than body temperature
    D. 3 degrees cooler than body temperature

15. The structure(s) that produce(s) testosterone is (are) the:
    A. Seminiferous tubules
    B. Prostate gland
    C. Bulbourethral gland
    D. Pituitary gland
    E. Interstitial cells

16. The part of the sperm that contains genetic information that will be inherited is the:
    A. Tail
    B. Neck
    C. Middle piece
    D. Head
    E. Acrosome

17. Which one of the following is not a function of testosterone?
    A. It causes a deepening of the voice
    B. It promotes the development of the male accessory glands
    C. It has a stimulatory effect on protein catabolism
    D. It causes greater muscular development and strength

18. Sperm production is called:
    A. Spermatogonia
    B. Spermatids
    C. Spermatogenesis
    D. Spermatocyte

19. The section of the sperm that contains enzymes that enable it to break down the covering of the ovum and permit entry should contact occur is the:
    A. Acrosome
    B. Midpiece
    C. Tail
    D. Stem

Fill in the blanks.

The (20) _____ are the gonads of the male. From puberty on, the seminiferous

tubules are continuously forming (21) _____. Any of these cells may join with

the female sex cell, the (22) _____ to become a new human being. Another func-

tion of the testes is to secrete the male hormone (23) _____ that transforms a boy

to a man. This hormone is secreted by the (24) _____ _____

of the testes. A good way to remember testosterone's functions is to think of it as "the

(25) _____ hormone" and "the (26) _____ hormone."

▷ *If you have had difficulty with this section, review pages 508-512.*

REPRODUCTIVE DUCTS
ACCESSORY OR SUPPORTIVE SEX GLANDS
EXTERNAL GENITALS

Choose the correct term and write its letter in the space next to the appropriate definition below.

A.	Epididymis	F.	Prostate gland
B.	Vas deferens	G.	Cowper's gland
C.	Ejaculatory duct	H.	Corpus spongiosum
D.	Prepuce	I.	Semen
E.	Seminal vesicles	J.	Scrotum

_____ 27. Continuation of ducts that start in epididymis

_____ 28. Erectile tissue

_____ 29. Also known as *bulbourethral*

_____ 30. Narrow tube that lies along the top and behind the testes

_____ 31. Doughnut-shaped gland beneath bladder

_____ 32. Continuation of vas deferens

_____ 33. Mixture of sperm and secretions of accessory sex glands

_____ 34. Contributes 60% of the seminal fluid volume

_____ 35. Removed during circumcision

_____ 36. External genitalia

▷ *If you have had difficulty with this section, review pages 512-513.*

DISORDERS OF THE MALE
REPRODUCTIVE SYSTEM

Fill in the blanks.

37. Decreased sperm production is called _____.

38. Testes normally descend into the scrotum about _____

_____ before birth.

39. If a baby is born with undescended testes, a condition called _____ results.

40. A common noncancerous condition of the prostate in older men is known as

_____ _____ _____.

41. _____ is a condition in which the foreskin fits so tightly over the glans

that it cannot retract.

42. Failure to achieve an erection of the penis is called _____.

43. An accumulation of fluid in the scrotum is known as a _____.

44. An _____ _____ results when the intestines

push through the weak area of the abdominal wall that separates the abdominopelvic cavity from

the scrotum.

45. The PSA test is a screening test for cancer of the _____.

▷ *If you have had difficulty with this section, review pages 515-516.*

FEMALE REPRODUCTIVE SYSTEM STRUCTURAL PLAN

Match the term on the left with the proper selection on the right.

_____	46. Ovaries	A. Genitals
_____	47. Vagina	B. Accessory sex gland
_____	48. Bartholin	C. Accessory duct
_____	49. Vulva	D. Gonads
_____	50. Ova	E. Sex cell

Write the letter of the correct description in the blank next to the appropriate structure.

    (a) External structure   (b) Internal structure

_____ 51. Mons pubis   _____ 55. Vestibule

_____ 52. Vagina   _____ 56. Clitoris

_____ 53. Labia majora   _____ 57. Labia minora

_____ 54. Uterine tubes   _____ 58. Ovaries

▷ *If you have had difficulty with this section, review pages 516-521.*

OVARIES

Fill in the blanks.

The ovaries are the (59) _____ of the female. They have two main functions. The

first is the production of the female sex cell. This process is called (60) _____.

The specialized type of cell division that occurs during sexual cell reproduction is known as

(61) _____. The ovum is the body's largest cell and has (62) _____

_____ the number of chromosomes found in other body cells. At the time of

(63) _____, the sex cells from both parents fuse and (64) _____

chromosomes are united.

The second major function of the ovaries is to secrete the sex hormones (65) _____

and (66) _____. Estrogen is the sex hormone that causes the development and

maintenance of the female (67) _____ _____

_____. Progesterone acts with estrogen to help initiate the (68)

_____ _____ in girls entering (69) _____.

▶ *If you have had difficulty with this section, review pages 516-521.*

FEMALE REPRODUCTIVE DUCTS

Write the letter of the correct structure in the blank next to the appropriate definition.

     (a) Uterine tubes   (b) Uterus   (c) Vagina

_____ 70. Ectopic pregnancy

_____ 71. Lining known as endometrium

_____ 72. Terminal end of birth canal

_____ 73. Site of menstruation

_____ 74. Fringelike projections called
        fimbriae

_____ 75. Consists of body, fundus, and
        cervix

_____ 76. Site of fertilization

_____ 77. Also known as oviduct

_____ 78. Entranceway for sperm

▶ *If you have had difficulty with this section, review pages 519-521.*

ACCESSORY OR SUPPORTIVE SEX GLANDS EXTERNAL GENITALS

Match the term on the left with the proper selection on the right.

Group A

_____ 79. Bartholin's gland   A. Colored area around nipple
_____ 80. Breasts   B. Grapelike clusters of milk-secreting cells
_____ 81. Alveoli   C. Drain alveoli
_____ 82. Lactiferous ducts   D. Secretes lubricating fluid
_____ 83. Areola   E. Primarily fat tissue

Group B

_____ 84. Mons pubis   A. "Large lips"
_____ 85. Labia majora   B. Area between labia minora
_____ 86. Clitoris   C. Surgical procedure
_____ 87. Vestibule   D. Composed of erectile tissue
_____ 88. Episiotomy   E. Pad of fat over the symphysis pubis

▷ *If you have had difficulty with this section, review pages 521-522.*

MENSTRUAL CYCLE

If the following statement is true, insert "T" in the answer blank. If the statement is false, circle the incorrect word(s) and insert the correct word(s) in the answer blank.

_____ 89. *Climacteric* is the scientific name for the beginning of the menses.

_____ 90. As a general rule, several ovum mature each month during the 30-40 years that a woman has menstrual periods.

_____ 91. Ovulation occurs 28 days before the next menstrual period begins.

_____ 92. The first day of ovulation is considered the first day of the cycle.

_____ 93. A woman's fertile period lasts only a few days out of each month.

_____ 94. The control of the menstrual cycle lies in the posterior pituitary gland.

Write the letter of the correct hormone in the blank next to the appropriate description.
   (a) FSH   (b) LH

_____ 95. Ovulating hormone   _____ 98. Causes final maturation of
                                                               follicle and ovum
_____ 96. Secreted during first days of
               menstrual cycle   _____ 99. Birth control pills suppress
                                                               this one
_____ 97. Secreted after estrogen level of
               blood increases

▷ *If you have had difficulty with this section, review pages 522-524.*

DISORDERS OF THE FEMALE REPRODUCTIVE SYSTEM

Choose the correct response.

A. Toxic shock syndrome
B. Dysmenorrhea
C. Exogenous infections
D. DUB
E. Myoma
F. Vaginitis

G. Sexually transmitted diseases (STDs)
H. Oophorectomy
I. Fibrocystic disease
J. Pap smear
K. Genital herpes
L. Trichomoniasis

_____ 100. Often occurs from STDs or from a "yeast infection"

_____ 101. Benign tumor of smooth muscle and fibrous connective tissue; also known as a *fibroid tumor*

_____ 102. Most often occurs in women who use super-absorbent tampons to absorb the menstrual flow

_____ 103. Removal of ovaries

_____ 104. Benign lumps in one or both breasts

_____ 105. Venereal diseases

_____ 106. Results from pathogenic organisms transmitted from another person; for example, STD

_____ 107. Painful menstruation

_____ 108. Asymptomatic in most women and nearly all men

_____ 109. Results from a hormonal imbalance rather than from an infection or disease condition

_____ 110. Screening test for cervical cancer

_____ 111. Causes blisters on the skin of the genitals; the blisters may disappear temporarily, but reoccur, especially as a result of stress

▷ *If you have had difficulty with this section, review pages 524-530.*

APPLYING WHAT YOU KNOW

112. Mr. Belinki is going into the hospital for the surgical removal of his testes. As a result of this surgery, will Mr. Belinki be impotent?

113. When baby Gaylor was born, the pediatrician, Dr. Self, discovered that his left testicle had not descended into the scrotum. If this situation is not corrected soon, might baby Gaylor be sterile or impotent?

114. Mrs. Gaynes contracted gonorrhea. By the time she made an appointment to see her doctor, it had spread to her abdominal organs. How is this possible when gonorrhea is a disease of the reproductive system?

115. Dr. Sullivan advised Mrs. Harlan to have a bilateral oophorectomy. Is this a sterilization procedure? Will she experience menopause?

116. Mrs. Kelly had a total hysterectomy. Will she experience menopause?

117. WORD FIND

Can you find the 18 reproductive terms from this chapter in the box of letters? Words may be spelled top to bottom, bottom to top, right to left, left to right, or diagonally.

```
M K O V I D U C T S E D H G
S E I R A V O I F U T G L L
I N H Z H M P M K O H I C W
D D V A S D E F E R E N S H
I O A C C I P J V E H Y D S
H M G R R B M N X F G Y I O
C E I O O E Z Y T I C S T E
R T N S T P S D D N O V A D
O R A O U W E B A I J S M Z
T I C M M E Y N E M D L R V
P U A E U D G M I E H I E H
Y M O T C E T A T S O R P B
R P E E R M N E G O R T S E
C O W P E R S I N X K E A P
```

Acrosome	Meiosis	Scrotum
Cowpers	Ovaries	Seminiferous
Cryptorchidism	Oviducts	Sperm
Endometrium	Penis	Spermatids
Epididymis	Pregnancy	Vagina
Estrogen	Prostatectomy	Vas deferens

DID YOU KNOW?

The testes produce approximately 50 million sperm per day. Every 2 to 3 months they produce enough cells to populate the entire earth.

REPRODUCTIVE SYSTEM

ACROSS

2. Female erectile tissue
3. Colored area around nipple
5. Male reproductive fluid
6. Sex cells
7. External genitalia
10. Male sex hormone

DOWN

1. Failure to have a menstrual period
2. Surgical removal of foreskin
4. Foreskin
8. Menstrual period
9. Essential organs of reproduction

MALE REPRODUCTIVE ORGANS

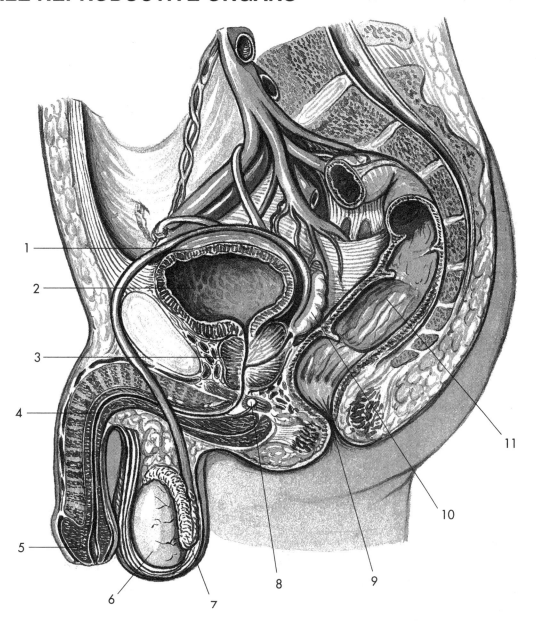

1. _____

2. _____

3. _____

4. _____

5. _____

6. _____

7. _____

8. _____

9. _____

10. _____

11. _____

TUBULES OF TESTIS AND EPIDIDYMIS

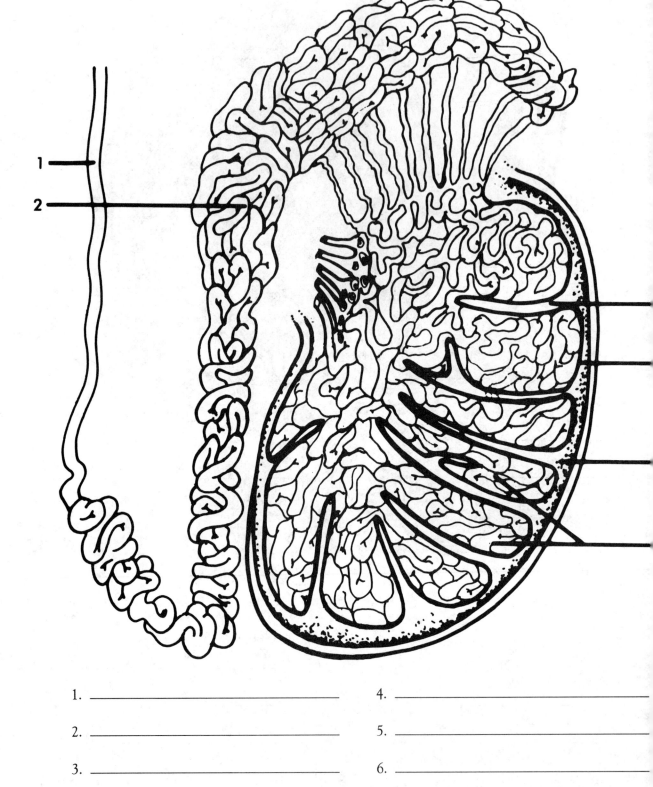

1. _____   4. _____

2. _____   5. _____

3. _____   6. _____

VULVA

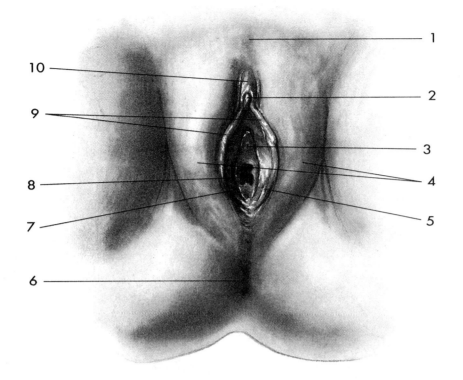

1. _____   6. _____

2. _____   7. _____

3. _____   8. _____

4. _____   9. _____

5. _____   10. _____

BREAST

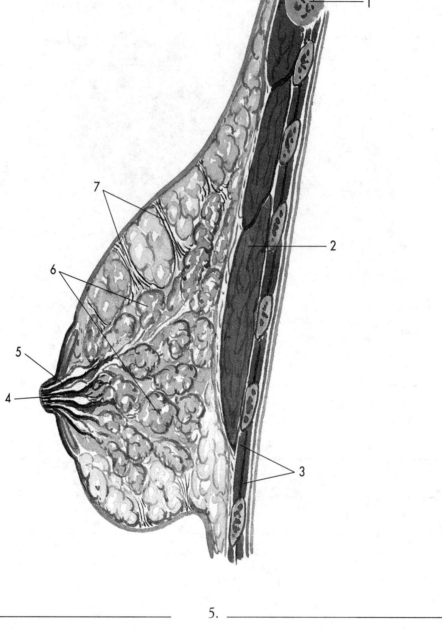

1. _____   5. _____

2. _____   6. _____

3. _____   7. _____

4. _____

FEMALE PELVIS

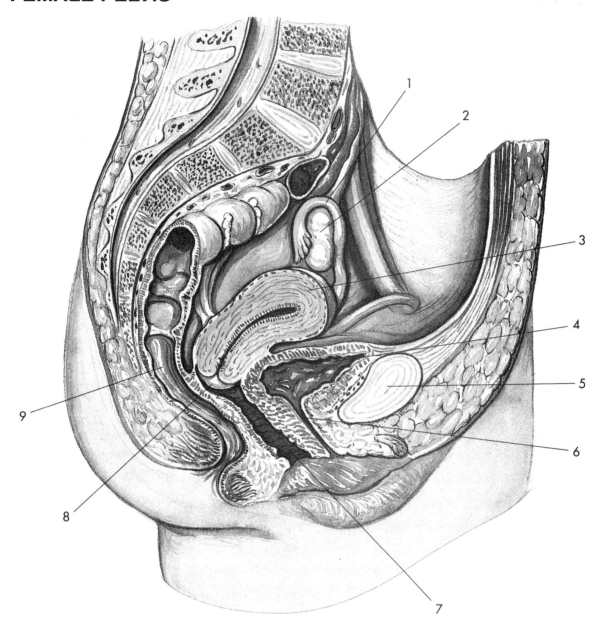

1. _____   6. _____

2. _____   7. _____

3. _____   8. _____

4. _____   9. _____

5. _____

UTERUS AND ADJACENT STRUCTURES

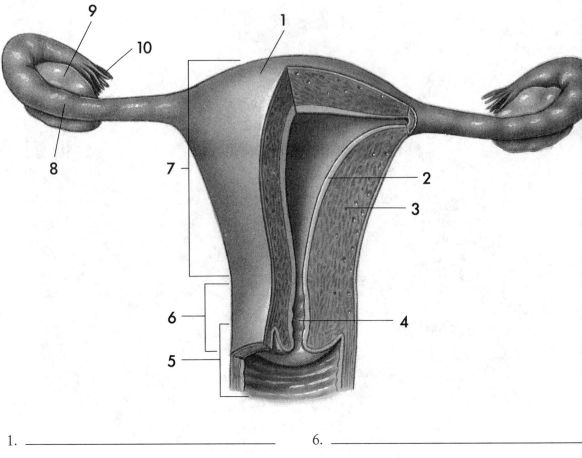

1. _____

2. _____

3. _____

4. _____

5. _____

6. _____

7. _____

8. _____

9. _____

10. _____

CHAPTER 22

Growth and Development

Millions of fragile, microscopic sperm swim against numerous obstacles to reach the ova and create a new life. At birth, the newborn will fill his lungs with air and cry lustily, signaling to the world that he is ready to begin the cycle of life. This cycle will be marked by ongoing changes, periodic physical growth, and continuous development.

This chapter reviews the more significant events that occur in the normal growth and development of an individual from conception to death. Realizing that each individual is unique, we nonetheless can discover amid all the complexities of humanity some constants.

A knowledge of human growth and development is essential in understanding the commonalities that influence individuals as they pass through the cycle of life.

TOPICS FOR REVIEW

Before progressing to Chapter 23, you should have an understanding of the concept of development as a biological process. You should familiarize yourself with the major developmental changes from conception through older adulthood. The disorders of pregnancy should be emphasized as you review the chapter. Finally, your study should conclude with a review of the effects of aging on the body systems.

PRENATAL PERIOD

Fill in the blanks.

The prenatal stage of development begins at the time of (1) _____ and continues

until (2) _____. The science of the development of an individual before birth

is called (3) _____. Fertilization takes place in the outer third of the

(4) _____. The fertilized ovum or (5) _____ begins to divide and

in approximately 3 days forms a solid mass called a (6) _____. By the time it enters

the uterus, it is a hollow ball of cells called a (7) _____. As it continues to develop,

it forms a structure with two cavities. The (8) _____ _____

will become a fluid-filled sac for the embryo. The (9) _____ will develop into an

important fetal membrane in the (10) _____.

Choose the correct term and write its letter in the space next to the appropriate definition below.

A.	Laparoscope	F.	Endoderm
B.	Gestation	G.	In vitro
C.	Antenatal	H.	Parturition
D.	Histogenesis	I.	Embryonic phase
E.	C-section	J.	Ultrasonogram

_____ 11. "Within a glass"

_____ 12. Inside germ layer

_____ 13. Before birth

_____ 14. Length of pregnancy

_____ 15. Optical viewing tube

_____ 16. Process of birth

_____ 17. Surgical procedure in which a newborn is delivered through an incision in the
abdomen and uterine wall

_____ 18. Study of how the primary germ layers develop into many different kinds of tissues

_____ 19. Fertilization until the end of the eighth week of gestation

_____ 20. Monitors progress of developing fetus

▶ *If you have had difficulty with this section, review pages 537-542 and 548.*

DISORDERS OF PREGNANCY

Mark "T" in the answer blank if the statement is true. If the statement is false, circle the incorrect word(s) and correct the statement in the answer blank.

_____ 21. Many offspring are lost before implantation occurs, often for unknown reasons.

_____ 22. The most common type of ectopic pregnancy is a tubal pregnancy.

_____ 23. If the placenta grows too closely to the cervical opening a condition called *abruptio placentae* results.

_____ 24. Separation of the placenta from the uterine wall in a pregnancy of 20 weeks or more is known as *placenta previa*.

_____ 25. Toxemia of pregnancy is also known as *puerperal fever*.

_____ 26. After 20 weeks, delivery of a lifeless infant is termed a *miscarriage*.

_____ 27. Acquired birth defects result from agents called *teratogens* that disrupt normal histogenesis and organogenesis.

▷ *If you have had difficulty with this section, review pages 546-548.*

POSTNATAL PERIOD

Circle the correct choice.

28. During the postnatal period:
    A. The head becomes proportionately smaller
    B. Thoracic and abdominal contours change from round to elliptical
    C. The legs become proportionately longer
    D. The trunk becomes proportionately shorter
    E. All of the above take place during the postnatal period

29. The period of infancy starts at birth and lasts about:
    A. 4 weeks
    B. 4 months
    C. 10 weeks
    D. 12 months
    E. 18 months

30. The lumbar curvature of the spine appears _____ months after birth.
    A. 1-10
    B. 5-8
    C. 8-12
    D. 11-15
    E. 12-18

31. During the first 4 months the birth weight will:
    A. Double
    B. Triple
    C. Quadruple
    D. None of the above is correct

32. At the end of the first year the weight of the baby will have:
    A. Doubled
    B. Tripled
    C. Quadrupled
    D. None of the above is correct

33. The infant is capable of following a moving object with its eyes at:
    A. 2 days
    B. 2 weeks
    C. 2 months
    D. 4 months
    E. 10 months

34. The infant can lift its head and raise its chest at:
    A. 2 months
    B. 3 months
    C. 4 months
    D. 10 months

35. The infant can crawl at:
    A. 2 months
    B. 3 months
    C. 4 months
    D. 10 months
    E. 12 months

36. The infant can stand alone at:
    A. 2 months
    B. 3 months
    C. 4 months
    D. 10 months
    E. 12 months

37. The permanent teeth, with the exception of the third molar, have all erupted by age _____ years.
    A. 6
    B. 8
    C. 12
    D. 14
    E. None of the above is correct

38. Puberty starts at age _____ years in boys.
    A. 10-13
    B. 12-14
    C. 14-16
    D. None of the above is correct

39. Most girls begin breast development at about age:
    A. 8
    B. 9
    C. 10
    D. 11
    E. 12

40. The growth spurt is generally complete by age _____ in males.
    A. 14
    B. 15
    C. 16
    D. 18

41. An average age at which girls begin to menstruate is _____ years.
    A. 10-12
    B. 11-12
    C. 12-13
    D. 13-14
    E. 14-15

42. The first sign of puberty in boys is:
    A. Facial hair
    B. Increased muscle mass
    C. Pubic hair
    D. Deepening of the voice
    E. Enlargement of the testicles

Write the letter of the correct word in the blank next to the appropriate definition.

A. Neonatology   F. Postnatal
B. Neonatal   G. Gerontology
C. Adolescence   H. Childhood
D. Deciduous   I. Senescence
E. Puberty

_____ 43. Begins at birth and lasts until death

_____ 44. Concerned with the diagnosis and treatment of disorders of the newborn

_____ 45. Teenage years

_____ 46. From the end of infancy to puberty

_____ 47. Baby teeth

_____ 48. First 4 weeks of infancy

_____ 49. Secondary sexual characteristics occur

_____ 50. Study of aging

_____ 51. Older adulthood

▷ *If you have had difficulty with this section, review pages 549-555.*

EFFECTS OF AGING

Fill in the blanks.

52. Old bones develop indistinct and shaggy margins with spurs, a process called

_____.

53. A degenerative joint disease common in the aged is _____.

54. The number of _____ units in the kidney decreases by almost 50%

between the ages of 30 and 75.

55. In old age, respiratory efficiency decreases, and a condition known as

_____ _____ results.

56. Fatty deposits accumulate in blood vessels as we age, and the result is

_____, which narrows the passageway for the flow of blood.

57. Hardening of the arteries or _____ occurs during the aging process.

58. Another term for high blood pressure is _____.

59. Hardening of the lens is _____.

60. If the lens becomes cloudy and impairs vision, it is called a _____.

61. _____ causes an increase in the pressure within the eyeball and may

result in blindness.

▶ *If you have had difficulty with this section, review pages 555-556.*

Unscramble the words.

62. ANNFCYI

63. NAALTTSOP

64. OGSSNEGRAONEI

65. GTEYZO

66. HDOOLHCID

The secret is in the bag!

Take the circled letters, unscramble them, and fill in the statement.

The secret to Farmer Brown's prize pumpkin crop.

67. [ ][ ][ ][ ][ ][ ][ ][ ][ ][ ][ ][ ][ ][ ][ ]

APPLYING WHAT YOU KNOW

68. Billy's mother told the pediatrician, Dr. Patrusky, during Billy's 1-year visit that he had tripled his birth weight, was crawling actively, and could stand alone. Is Billy's development normal, retarded, or advanced?

69. John is 70 years old. He has always enjoyed food and has had a hearty appetite. Lately, however, he has complained that food "just doesn't taste as good anymore." What might be a possible explanation?

70. Mr. Keyes has noticed hearing problems, but only under certain circumstances. He has difficulty with certain tones, especially high or low tones, but has no problem with everyday conversation. What might be a possible explanation?

71. Mrs. Dezzi gave birth to twin girls. The obstetrician, Dr. Sullivan, advised Mr. Dezzi that even though the girls looked identical, they were really fraternal twins. How was he able to deduce this?

72. WORD FIND

Can you find 13 terms from this chapter in the box of letters? Words may be spelled top to bottom, bottom to top, right to left, left to right, or diagonally.

```
F  C  M  P  O  D  N  P  P  A  G  M  J  N  Z
K  E  C  N  E  C  S  E  L  O  D  A  G  G  M
I  N  R  B  U  X  T  K  D  A  Y  Q  T  F  R
L  D  L  T  O  M  S  D  W  A  E  Z  B  F  E
Z  O  B  A  I  S  P  M  A  L  C  E  E  R  P
W  D  I  M  P  L  A  N  T  A  T  I  O  N  L
H  E  N  M  K  A  I  T  E  P  D  K  S  X  A
W  R  G  A  S  A  R  Z  R  N  T  Q  P  Y  C
L  M  Q  S  I  J  O  O  A  U  B  F  G  T  E
R  T  N  T  B  N  G  E  S  T  A  T  I  O  N
L  A  T  I  N  E  G  N  O  C  I  T  F  Z  T
D  C  B  T  R  L  A  S  G  C  O  O  R  R  A
E  N  O  I  T  I  R  U  T  R  A  P  N  S  B
N  V  A  S  N  N  E  G  O  T  A  R  E  T  E
```

Adolescence	Implantation	Placenta
Congenital	Laparoscope	Preeclampsia
Endoderm	Mastitis	Progeria
Fertilization	Parturition	Teratogen
Gestation		

DID YOU KNOW?

Brain cells do not regenerate. One beer permanently destroys 10,000 cells.

GROWTH/DEVELOPMENT

ACROSS

7. Old age
9. Fatty deposit buildup on walls of arteries
10. Cloudy lens
11. Name of zygote after 3 days
12. Fertilized ovum

DOWN

1. Process of birth
2. Science of the development of the individual before birth
3. Study of how germ layers develop into tissues
4. Name of zygote after implantation
5. First 4 weeks of infancy
6. Hardening of the lens
8. Eye disease marked by increased pressure in the eyeball
10. Will develop into a fetal membrane in the placenta

FERTILIZATION AND IMPLANTATION

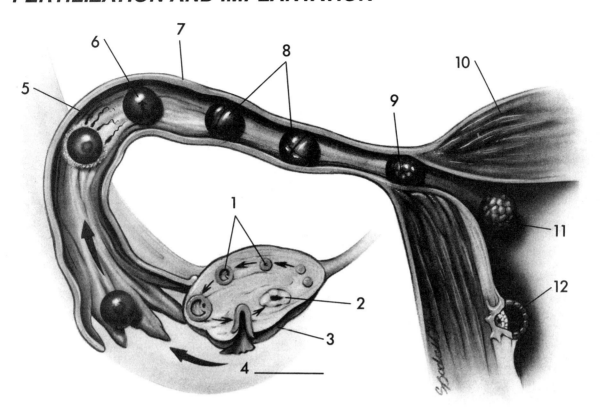

1. _____
2. _____
3. _____
4. _____
5. _____
6. _____

7. _____
8. _____
9. _____
10. _____
11. _____
12. _____

CHAPTER 23 Genetics and Genetic Diseases

Look about your classroom and you will notice various combinations of hair color, eye color, body size, skin tone, hair texture, sex, etc. Everyone has some unique body features and this phenomenon alerts us to the marvel of genetics. Independent units, called *genes*, are responsible for the inheritance of biological traits. Genes determine the structure and function of the human body by producing specific regulatory enzymes. Some genes are dominant and some are recessive. Dominant genes produce traits that appear in the offspring and recessive genes have traits that do not appear in the offspring when they are masked by a dominant gene.

Gene therapy is one of the latest advances of science. This revolutionary branch of medicine combines current technology with genetic research to unlock the secrets of the human body. Daily discoveries into the prevention, diagnosis, treatment, and cure of diseases and disorders are being revealed as a result of genetic therapy. A knowledge of genetics is necessary to understand the basic mechanism by which traits are transmitted from parents to offspring.

TOPICS FOR REVIEW

Your review of this chapter should include an understanding of chromosomes, genes, and gene expression. You should continue your study with a knowledge of common genetic diseases. Finally, your review should conclude with an understanding of the prevention and treatment of genetic diseases.

GENETICS AND HUMAN DISEASE
CHROMOSOMES AND GENES

Match the term on the left with the proper selection on the right.

_____ 1. Gene	A. DNA molecule
_____ 2. Chromosome	B. Male or female reproductive cell
_____ 3. Gamete	C. Special form of nuclear division
_____ 4. Meiosis	D. Formed by union of sperm and ovum at
_____ 5. Zygote	conception
	E. Distinct code within a DNA molecule

▷ *If you have had difficulty with this section, review page 563.*

GENE EXPRESSION

Fill in the blanks.

After experimentation with pea plants, Mendel discovered that each inherited trait is controlled by

two sets of similar (6) _____, one from each parent. He also noted that

some genes are (7) _____ and some are (8) _____.

In the example of albinism, a person with the gene combination of Aa is said to be a genetic

(9) _____. If two different dominant genes occur together, a form of domi-

nance called (10) _____ exists. (11) _____

chromosomes do not have matching structures. If an individual has the sex chromosomes XX,

that person will have the sexual characteristics of a (12) _____.

(13) _____ simply means "change." A (14) _____

_____ is a change in the genetic code.

▷ *If you have had difficulty with this section, review pages 566-569.*

GENETIC DISEASES

Choose the term that applies to each of the following descriptions. Place the letter for the term in the appropriate answer blank.

A. Single-gene disease
B. Nondisjunction
C. Monosomy
D. Leber's hereditary optic neuropathy
E. Cystic fibrosis

F. Phenylketonuria
G. Down syndrome
H. Klinefelter's syndrome
I. Turner's syndrome
J. Genetic predisposition

_____ 15. Caused by recessive genes in chromosome pair 7

_____ 16. Results in total blindness by age 30

_____ 17. Disease conditions that result from the combined effects of inheritance and environmental factors

_____ 18. Results from a failure to produce the enzyme phenylalanine hydroxylase

_____ 19. Presence of only one autosome instead of a pair

_____ 20. Usually caused by trisomy of chromosome 21

_____ 21. Cystic fibrosis is an example

_____ 22. Results from nondisjunction of chromosomes and typically has the XXY pattern

_____ 23. Term used to describe what happens when a pair of chromosomes fails to separate

_____ 24. Sometimes called XO syndrome, it is treated with hormone therapy

▷ *If you have had difficulty with this section, review pages 569-571.*

PREVENTION AND TREATMENT OF GENETIC DISEASES

Circle the best answer.

25. A pedigree is a chart that can be used to determine:
    A. Genetic relationships in a family over several generations
    B. The possibility of producing offspring with certain genetic disorders
    C. The possibility of a person developing a genetic disorder late in life
    D. All of the above are correct
    E. None of the above is correct

26. The Punnett square is a grid used to determine:
    A. Genetic disorders
    B. The probability of inheriting genetic traits
    C. Proper gene replacement therapy
    D. The necessity for amniocentesis

27. Some forms of cancer are thought to be caused, at least in part, by abnormal genes called:
    A. Cancercytes   C. Oncogenes
    B. Trisomy   D. Autosomes

28. When producing a karyotype, the most common source of cells for the sample is the:
    A. Vagina   C. Lining of the cheek
    B. Rectum   D. Throat

29. An ultrasound transducer is used during amniocentesis to:
    A. Create a sharper image
    B. Take measurements during the procedure
    C. Prevent damaging rays during the procedure
    D. Guide the tip of the needle to prevent placental damage

30. Electrophoresis is a process that:
    A. Provides a method for DNA analysis
    B. Means electric separation
    C. Is the basis for DNA fingerprinting
    D. All of the above are correct

31. The use of genetic therapy began in 1990 with a group of young children having:
    A. AIDS   C. Hemophilia
    B. Adenosine deaminase deficiency   D. Cystic fibrosis

If the statement is true, write "T" in the answer blank. If the statement is false, circle the incorrect word(s) and write the correct term in the answer blank.

_____ 32. Chorionic villus sampling is a procedure in which cells that surround a young embryo are collected through the opening of the cervix

_____ 33. Karyotyping is the process used for DNA fingerprinting

_____ 34. In amniocentesis, normal genes are introduced with the hope that they will add to the production of the needed protein

_____ 35. Deficiency of adenosine deaminase results in severe combined immune deficiency

_____ 36. One hypothesis that may explain some forms of cancer is known as the *tumor suppressor gene hypothesis*

▷ *If you have had difficulty with this section, review pages 572-577.*

Unscramble the words.

37. RCRRIEA

38. YTSMOIR

39. EGNE

40. DPEREGIE

41. SOEMCROSHOM

Take the circled letters, unscramble them, and fill in the statement.

How Bill made his fortune.

ANSWER:

42.

APPLYING WHAT YOU KNOW

43. Rubin's mother has a dominant gene for dark skin color. Rubin's father has a dominant gene for light skin color. What color will Rubin's skin most likely be?

44. Mr. and Mrs. Freund both carry recessive genes for cystic fibrosis. Using your knowledge of the Punnett square, estimate the probability of one of their offspring inheriting this condition.

45. Linda is pregnant and is over 40. She fears her age may predispose her baby to genetic disorders and she has sought the advice of a genetic counselor. What tests might the counselor suggest to alleviate Linda's fears?

46. PUNNETT SQUARE

Fill in the Punnett square for the following genetic cases:

Mr. Fortner has two dominant genes for brown eyes and Mrs. Fortner has two recessive genes for blue eyes.

<u>Mr. Fortner PP</u>

	P	P
p		
p		

<u>Mrs. Fortner pp</u>

The offspring of Mr. and Mrs. Fortner have a _____% chance of having brown eyes and a _____% chance of having blue eyes.

Will Mr. and Mrs. Fortner's offspring be carriers of blue eyes?

If Mr. and Mrs. Fortner's offspring mates with another offspring who is a carrier of blue eyes, what is the probability of the resulting offspring having blue eyes?

Draw your own Punnett square to determine your answer

Mr. and Mrs. Rhoades are both carriers for albinism. Using the Punnett square, determine what percentage of Mr. and Mrs. Rhoades' offspring will:
   A. Have normal pigmentation _____
   B. Be carriers _____
   C. Have albinism _____

<u>Mrs. Rhoades Pp</u>

	P	p
P		
p		

<u>Mr. Rhoades Pp</u>

47. WORD FIND

Can you find the 14 genetic terms in the box of letters? Words may be spelled top to bottom, bottom to top, right to left, left to right, or diagonally.

```
N  J  A  T  E  T  O  G  Y  Z  S  F  I  H  Q
M  O  M  D  P  S  I  W  P  L  I  K  Y  E  K
S  M  N  P  E  E  F  Y  A  Z  S  A  X  M  C
F  A  I  D  V  M  M  Z  R  Z  O  R  P  O  L
H  R  O  J  I  O  E  U  E  I  I  Y  D  P  O
I  Q  C  M  S  S  O  L  H  Z  E  O  G  H  X
Y  J  E  O  S  O  J  Z  T  W  M  T  D  I  Q
G  E  N  I  E  M  C  U  E  I  E  Y  X  L  Q
A  O  T  G  C  O  P  K  N  E  J  P  I  I  G
M  P  E  M  E  R  D  A  E  C  P  E  J  A  I
E  D  S  I  R  H  N  C  G  B  T  Z  P  S  Y
T  G  I  D  U  C  G  C  P  X  H  I  F  G  X
E  W  S  R  E  I  R  R  A  C  V  I  O  H  S
S  W  V  B  K  R  C  R  Y  B  V  U  C  N  S
```

Amniocentesis	Gametes	Monosomy
Carrier	Gene therapy	Nondisjunction
Chromosomes	Hemophilia	Recessive
Codominance	Karyotype	Zygote
DNA	Meiosis	

DID YOU KNOW?

Scientists now believe the human body has 50,000 to 100,000 genes packed into just 46 chromosomes.

Genetics

ACROSS

2. Name for the 22 pairs of matched chromosomes
3. Lack of melanin in the skin and eyes
6. Refers to genes that appear in the offspring
7. Chart that illustrates genetic relationships in a family over several generations
8. All genetic material in each cell
9. Scientific study of inheritance

DOWN

1. Trisomy 21 (two words)
4. Agents that cause genetic mutations
5. Triplet of autosomes rather than a pair
7. Excess of phenylketone in the urine (abbreviation)

ANSWER KEY

CHAPTER 1
AN INTRODUCTION TO THE STRUCTURE AND FUNCTION OF THE BODY

Matching

1. D, p. 1
2. E, p. 1
3. A, p. 1
4. C, p. 1
5. B, p. 1

Matching

6. C, p. 3
7. A, p. 3
8. E, p. 3
9. D, p. 3
10. B, p. 3

Crossword

11. Superior
12. Inferior
13. Transverse
14. Ventral
15. Lateral
16. Medial
17. Distal

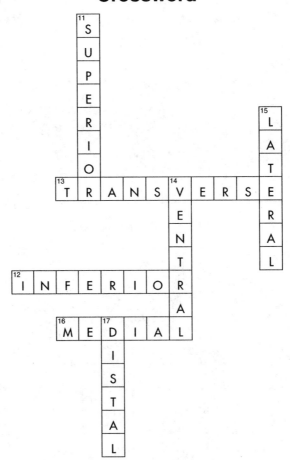

Did you notice that the answers were arranged as they appear on the human body?

Circle the correct answer

18. Inferior, p. 5
19. Anterior, p. 4
20. Lateral, p. 5
21. Proximal, p. 4
22. Superficial, p. 5
23. Equal, p. 5
24. Anterior and posterior, p. 5
25. Upper and lower, p. 5
26. Frontal, p. 5

Select the correct term

27. A, p. 5
28. B, p. 6
29. A, p. 5
30. A, p. 5
31. A, p. 5
32. B, p. 6
33. A, p. 5

Circle the one that does not belong

34. Extremities (all others are part of the axial portions)
35. Cephalic (all others are part of the arm)
36. Plantar (all others are part of the face)
37. Carpal (all others are part of the leg or foot)
38. Tarsal (all others are part of the skull)

True or false

39. T, p. 8
40. F (three stages), p. 8
41. T, p. 8
42. F (they are not usually dissected), p. 8
43. F (during stage 3), p. 8
44. T, p. 8

Fill in the blanks

45. Survival, p. 11
46. Internal environment, p. 11
47. Rise, p. 11
48. Developmental processes, p. 13
49. Aging processes, p. 13
50. Negative, positive, p. 12 - 13
51. Stabilizing, p. 12
52. Stimulatory, p. 13

Applying what you know

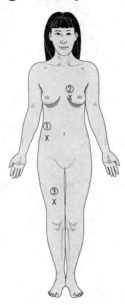

56. WORD FIND

Dorsal and Ventral Body Cavities

1. Cranial cavity
2. Spinal cavity
3. Thoracic cavity
4. Mediastinum
5. Abdominal cavity
6. Pelvic cavity

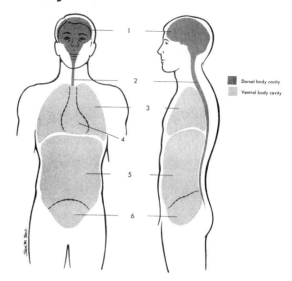

Directions and Planes of Body

1. Superior
2. Proximal
3. Posterior (Dorsal)
4. Anterior (Ventral)
5. Inferior
6. Sagittal plane
7. Frontal plane
8. Lateral

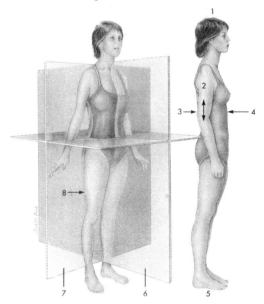

Regions of the Abdomen

1. Epigastric region
2. Left hypochondriac region
3. Umbilical region
4. Left lumbar region
5. Left iliac (inguinal) region
6. Hypogastric region
7. Right iliac (inguinal) region
8. Right lumbar region
9. Right hypochondriac region

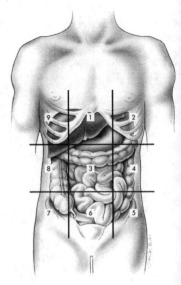

CHAPTER 2
CELLS AND TISSUES

Matching

Group A
1. C, p. 19
2. E, p. 19
3. A, p. 19
4. B, p. 25
5. D, p. 24

Group B
6. D, p. 22
7. E, p. 22
8. A, p. 24
9. B, p. 24
10. C, p. 23

Fill in the blanks

11. Cholesterol, p. 19
12. Tissue typing, p. 20
13. Cilia, p. 24
14. Endoplasmic reticulum, p. 22
15. Ribosomes, p. 22
16. Mitochondria, p. 24
17. Lysosomes, p. 24
18. Golgi apparatus, p. 23
19. Centrioles, p. 24
20. Chromatin granules, p. 25
21. Rejection reaction, p. 23
22. ELISA, p. 23

Multiple choice

23. A, p. 28
24. D, p. 26
25. B, p. 26
26. D, p. 27
27. C, p. 27
28. A, p. 27
29. B, p. 27
30. C, p. 28
31. C, p. 28
32. A, p. 28
33. B, p. 29
34. A, p. 29

Circle the one that does not belong

35. Uracil (RNA contains the base uracil, not DNA)
36. RNA (the others are complementary base pairings of DNA)
37. Anaphase (the others refer to genes and heredity)
38. Thymine (the others refer to RNA)
39. Interphase (the others refer to translation)
40. Prophase (the others refer to anaphase)
41. Prophase (the others refer to interphase)
42. Metaphase (the others refer to telophase)
43. Gene (the others refer to stages of cell division)
44. Fill in the missing area

TISSUE	LOCATION	FUNCTION
Epithelial		
1.	1.	1a. Absorption by diffusion of respiratory gases between alveolar air and blood
		1b. Absorption by diffusion, filtration, and osmosis
2.	2a. Surface of lining of mouth and esophagus	2.
	2b. Surface of skin	
3.	3. Surface layer of lining of stomach, intestines, and parts of respiratory tract	3.
4. Stratified transitional	4.	4.
5.	5. Surface of lining of trachea	5.
6.	6.	6. Secretion; Absorption
Connective		
1.	1. Between other tissues and organs	1.
2. Adipose	2.	2.
3.	3.	3. Flexible but strong connection
4.	4. Skeleton	4.

5.

5. Part of nasal septum, area covering articular surfaces of bones, larynx, rings in trachea and bronchi, disks between vertebrae, external ear

5.

6.

6.

6. Transportation

7. Hemopoietic tissue

7.

7.

Muscle

1.

1. Muscles that attach to bones, eyeball muscles, upper third of esophagus

1.

2. Cardiac

2.

2.

3.

3. Walls of digestive, respiratory, and genitourinary tracts; walls of blood vessels and large lymphatic vessels; ducts of glands; intrinsic eye muscles; arrector muscles of hair

3.

Nervous

1.

1. Brain and spinal cord, nerves

1.

Applying what you know

45.

46. Diffusion
47. Absorption of oxygen into Ms. Bence's blood
48. Merrily may have exceeded the 20% to 22% desirable body fat composition. Fitness depends more on the percentage and ratio of specific tissue types than the overall amount of tissue present.

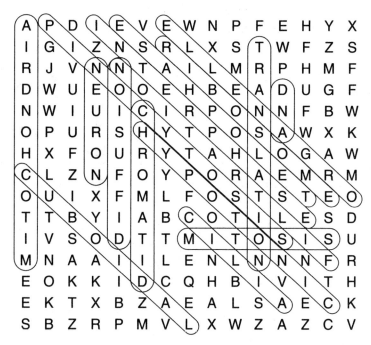

Crossword

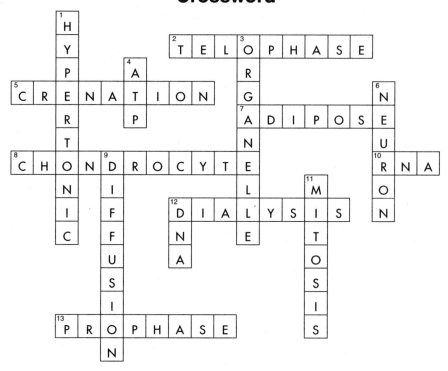

Cell Structure

1. Smooth endoplasmic reticulum
2. Golgi apparatus
3. Nucleolus
4. Nucleus
5. Nuclear envelope
6. Rough endoplasmic reticulum
7. Lysosome
8. Mitochondrion
9. Plasma membrane
10. Smooth endoplasmic reticulum
11. Centrioles
12. Ribosomes

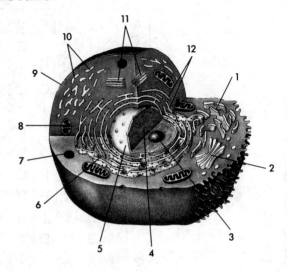

Mitosis

1. Interphase
2. Prophase
3. Metaphase
4. Anaphase
5. Telophase
6. Daughter cells (interphase)

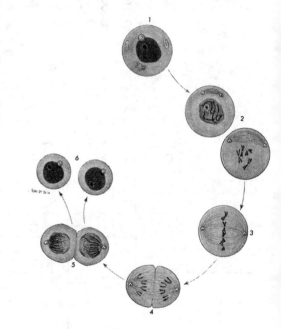

Tissues

1

2

3

4

5

6

7

8

9

10

11

12

1. Stratified squamous epithelium
2. Simple columnar epithelium
3. Stratified transitional epithelium
4. Adipose tissue
5. Dense fibrous connective tissue
6. Bone tissue
7. Cartilage
8. Blood
9. Skeletal muscle
10. Cardiac muscle
11. Smooth muscle
12. Nervous tissue

CHAPTER 3
ORGAN SYSTEMS OF THE BODY

Matching

Group A
1. A, p. 55
2. E, p. 58
3. D, p. 58
4. B, p. 59
5. C, p. 59

Group B
6. F, p. 60
7. E, p. 60
8. B, p. 62
9. A, p. 62
10. C, p. 62
11. D, p. 65

Circle the one that does not belong

12. Mouth (the others refer to the respiratory system)
13. Rectum (the others refer to the reproductive system)
14. Pancreas (the others refer to the circulatory system)
15. Pineal (the others refer to the urinary system)
16. Joints (the others refer to the muscular system)
17. Pituitary (the others refer to the nervous system)
18. Tendons (the others refer to the skeletal system)
19. Appendix (the others refer to the endocrine system)
20. Thymus (the others refer to the integumentary system)
21. Trachea (the others refer to the digestive system)
22. Liver (the others refer to the lymphatic system)

Fill in the missing area

SYSTEM	ORGAN	FUNCTIONS
23.	23.	23. Protection, regulation of body temperature, synthesis of chemicals and hormones, serves as a sense organ
24.	24. Bones, joints	24.
25.	25.	25. Movement, maintains body posture, produces heat
26. Nervous	26.	26.
27.	27. Pituitary, thymus, pineal, adrenal, hypothalamus, thyroid, pancreas, parathyroid, ovaries, testes	27.

28.

29.

30. Urinary

31.

32. Respiratory

33.

28.

29. Lymph nodes, lymph vessels,
    thymus, spleen, tonsils

30.

31. Mouth, pharynx, esophagus,
    stomach, small and large intestine,
    rectum, anal canal, teeth, salivary
    glands, tongue, liver, gallbladder,
    pancreas, appendix

32.

33. a. Gonads: testes and ovaries
    b. Accessory glands (p. 56, 65)
       Supporting structures (p. 56, 65)

28. Transportation, immunity, regulation
    of body temperature

29.

30.

31.

32.

33.

Fill in the blanks

34. Nonvital organ, p. 66
35. Cochlear implants, p. 66
36. Dialysis machine, p. 66
37. Hemopump, p. 68
38. Organ transplantation, p. 68
39. Free-flap surgery, p. 69
40. Rejection, p. 69

Unscramble the words

41. Heart
42. Pineal
43. Nerve
44. Esophagus
45. Nervous

Applying what you know

46. (a) Endocrinology (endocrine system)
    (b) Gynecology (reproductive system)
47. The skin protects the underlying tissue against invasion by harmful bacteria. With a large percentage of Brian's skin destroyed, he was vulnerable to bacteria, and so he was placed in the cleanest environment possible—isolation. Jenny is required to wear special attire so that the risk of a visitor bringing bacteria to the patient is reduced.
48. Free-flap surgery may be considered as an option. A breast can be formed from skin and muscle taken from other parts of Sheila's body.

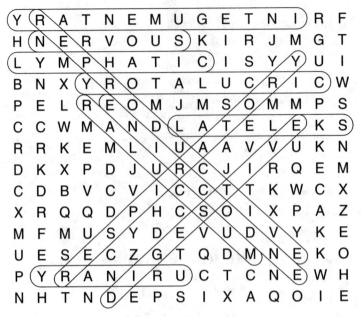

Crossword

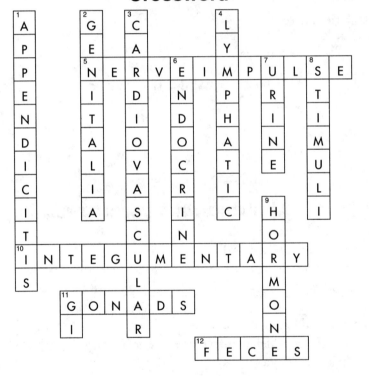

CHAPTER 4
MECHANISMS OF DISEASE

Matching

Group A
1. B, p. 75
2. E, p. 75
3. A, p. 75
4. C, p. 75
5. D, p. 75

Group B
6. C, p. 75
7. A, p. 75
8. D, p. 75
9. B, p. 75
10. E, p. 75

Fill in the blanks

11. Pathophysiology, p. 76
12. Homeostasis, p. 76
13. Mutated, p. 77
14. Parasite, p. 77
15. Neoplasms, p. 77
16. Self-immunity, p. 77
17. Risk factors, p. 78
18. Centers for Disease Control and Prevention, p. 78
19. Psychogenic, p. 78
20. Secondary, p. 78

Multiple choice

21. C, p. 79
22. A, p. 80
23. B, p. 80
24. C, p. 81
25. D, p. 81
26. B, p. 82
27. D, p. 83
28. D, p. 85
29. B, p. 85
30. C, p. 86
31. E, pp. 85-87
32. B, p. 87

Circle the correct response

33. Slowly, p. 88
34. Are not, p. 88
35. Papilloma, p. 89
36. Sarcoma, p. 89
37. Anaplasia, p. 90
38. Oncologist, p. 90
39. Biopsy, p. 92
40. Staging, p. 92
41. Appetite, p. 92

Seven Warning Signs of Cancer, p. 90

42. Sores that do not heal
43. Unusual bleeding
44. A change in wart or mole
45. A lump or thickening in any tissue
46. Persistent hoarseness or cough
47. Chronic indigestion
48. A change in bowel or bladder function

True or false

49. T, p. 96
50. F (slowly), p. 96
51. F (white), p. 96
52. T, p. 96
53. F (regeneration), p. 96
54. T, p. 98
55. T, p. 98

Applying what you know

56. No. Trent most likely has a common cold.
57. Pinworm
58. Disinfection
59. A "gene pool" indicates the "risk" of inheriting a disease-causing gene specific to members of a certain ethnic group. The knowledge of a "gene pool" can alert you to early detection of disease.
60. Shane is considering a "high risk" profession because of the paramedic's frequent exposure to body fluids. Hepatitis B is transmitted by body fluids and therefore vaccination is recommended.

Crossword

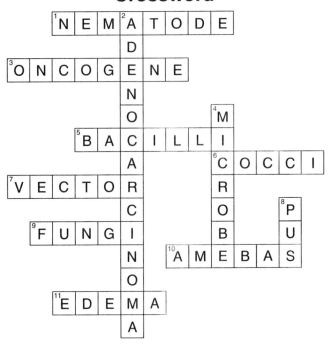

Major Groups of Pathogenic Protozoa

1. Amoebas
2. Flagellates
3. Ciliates
4. Sporozoa

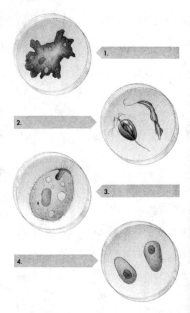

Examples of Pathogenic Animals

1. Nematodes
2. Platyhelminths
3. Arthropods

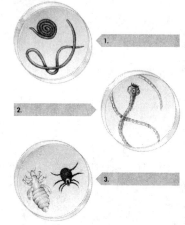

Major Groups of Pathogenic Fungi

1. Yeasts
2. Molds

CHAPTER 5
THE INTEGUMENTARY SYSTEM AND BODY MEMBRANES

Select the best answer

1. B, p. 105
2. D, p. 107
3. C, p. 107
4. A, p. 105
5. B, p. 105
6. D, p. 107
7. C, p. 107
8. C, p. 107

Matching

Group A
9. D, p. 107
10. A, p. 107
11. B, p. 107
12. C, p. 115
13. E, p. 107

Group B
14. A, p. 109
15. D, p. 109
16. E, p. 109
17. C, p. 110
18. B, p. 109

Select the best answer

19. A, p. 108
20. B, p. 110
21. B, p. 110
22. A, p. 110
23. A, p. 109
24. B, p. 110
25. B, p. 110
26. B, p. 110
27. B, p. 110
28. A, p. 108

Fill in the blanks

29. Protection, temperature regulation, and sense organ activity, p. 115
30. Melanin, p. 109
31. Lanugo, p. 111
32. Hair papillae, p. 112
33. Alopecia, p. 112
34. Arrector pili, p. 112
35. Light touch, p. 113
36. Eccrine, p. 114
37. Apocrine, p. 114
38. Sebum, p. 114

Circle the correct answer

39. Will not, p. 116
40. Will, p. 116
41. Will not, p. 117
42. 11, p. 116
43. Third, p. 117

Choose the correct response

44. B, p. 115
45. A, p. 115
46. D, p. 118
47. D, p. 119
48. A, p. 117
49. D, p. 120
50. C, p. 120
51. A, p. 123

Unscramble the words

52. Epidermis
53. Keratin
54. Hair
55. Lanugo
56. Dehydration
57. Third Degree

Applying what you know

58. 46%
59. Pleurisy
60. Sunbathing. Mrs. Collins cannot repair UV damage and thus is very prone to skin cancer.
61. Fingerprints

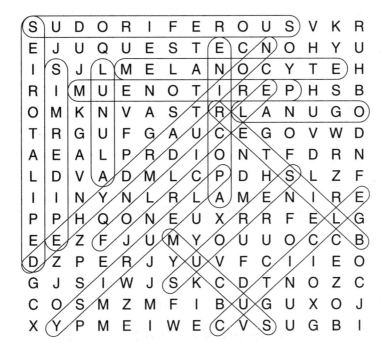

Crossword

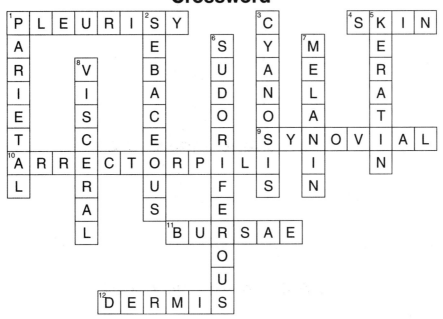

Longitudinal Section of the Skin

1. Pigment layer
2. Stratum corneum
3. Hair shaft
4. Openings of sweat ducts
5. Dermal papilla
6. Meissner's corpuscle
7. Epidermis
8. Dermis
9. Subcutaneous fatty tissue
10. Pacinian corpuscle
11. Sweat gland
12. Papilla of hair
13. Hair follicle
14. Sebaceous (oil) gland
15. Arrector pili muscle

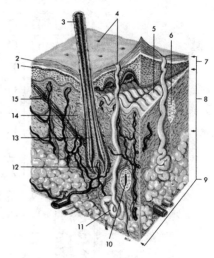

Rule of Nines

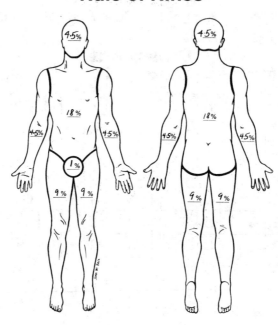

CHAPTER 6
THE SKELETAL SYSTEM

Fill in the blanks

1. 4, p. 131
2. Medullary cavity, p. 132
3. Articular cartilage, p. 132
4. Endosteum, p. 132
5. Hemopoiesis, p. 131
6. Red bone marrow, p. 131
7. Periosteum, p. 132
8. Long, short, flat, and irregular, p. 131

9. Calcium, p. 131
10. Move, p. 131

Matching

Group A
11. D, p. 132
12. B, p. 132
13. E, p. 132
14. A, p. 132
15. C, p. 134

Group B
16. D, p. 132
17. A, p. 134
18. E, p. 132
19. B, p. 134
20. C, p. 132

True or false

21. T, p. 134
22. Epiphyses, not diaphyses, p. 136
23. Osteoblasts, not osteoclasts, p. 134
24. T, p. 134
25. T, p. 140
26. Juvenile, not adult, p. 136
27. Diaphysis, not articulation, p. 136
28. T, p. 134
29. Ceases, not begins, p. 136
30. T, p. 136

Multiple choice

31. A, p. 136
32. D, p. 137
33. A, p. 143
34. D, p. 145
35. C, p. 146
36. C, p. 149
37. D, p. 146
38. D, p. 149
39. A, p. 149
40. B, p. 137
41. A, p. 143
42. B, p. 148
43. B, p. 145
44. B, p. 146
45. C, p. 149
46. A, p. 149
47. D, p. 137
48. C, p. 143
49. C, p. 142

Circle the one that does not belong

50. Coxal (all others refer to the spine)
51. Axial (all others refer to the appendicular skeleton)
52. Maxilla (all others refer to the cranial bones)
53. Ribs (all others refer to the shoulder girdle)
54. Vomer (all others refer to the bones of the middle ear)
55. Ulna (all others refer to the coxal bone)
56. Ethmoid (all others refer to the hand and wrist)
57. Nasal (all others refer to cranial bones)
58. Anvil (all others refer to the cervical vertebra)

Choose the right answer

59. A, p. 152
60. B, p. 152
61. B, p. 152
62. A, p. 152
63. B, p. 152

Matching

64. C, p. 137
65. G, pp. 145-146
66. J, L, M, and K, p. 149
67. N, pp. 149, 150
68. I, pp. 147, 148
69. A, pp. 137, 141
70. P, pp. 149, 151
71. D, B, pp. 137, 141
72. F, pp. 137-141
73. H, Q, pp. 139, 148
74. O, T, pp. 149-150
75. R, p. 137
76. S, E, pp. 137, 141

Choose the better answer

77. Diarthroses, p. 154
78. Synarthrotic, p. 154
79. Diarthrotic, p. 155
80. Ligaments, p. 155
81. Articular cartilage, p. 155
82. Least movable, p. 158
83. Largest, p. 157
84. 2, p. 156
85. Mobility, p. 156
86. Pivot, p. 156

Fill in the blanks

87. Arthroscopy, p. 159
88. Osteosarcoma, p. 158
89. Osteoporosis, p. 158

90. Osteomalacia, p. 159
91. Paget disease, p. 160
92. Osteomyelitis, p. 160
93. Simple fractures, p. 160
94. Comminuted fractures, p. 160
95. Osteoarthritis or degenerative joint disease (DJD), p. 160
96. Rheumatoid arthritis, gouty arthritis, and infectious arthritis, p. 163
97. Lyme disease, p.163

Unscramble the words

98. Vertebrae
99. Pubis
100. Scapula
101. Mandible
102. Phalanges
103. Pelvic girdle

Applying what you know

104. The bones are responsible for the majority of our blood cell formation. The disease condition of the bones might be inhibiting the production of blood cells for Mrs. Perine.
105. Epiphyseal cartilage is present only while a child is still growing. It becomes bone in adulthood. It is particularly vulnerable to fractures in childhood and preadolescence.
106. Osteoporosis
107. Slipped or herniated disk
108. WORD FIND

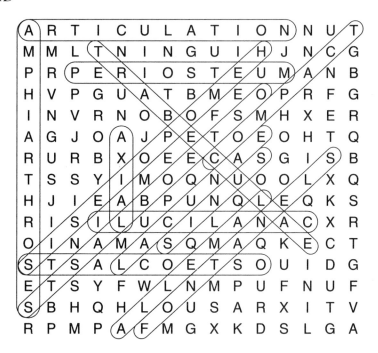

Crossword

Across/Down entries fill the grid:

- CHONDROCYTES
- LACUNAE
- THORAX
- DIARTHROSES
- HEMOPOIESIS
- SINUS

Down letters spelling:
- ACTIVICULATION
- STERNOCLAVICLAST
- OSTEOCLAVICLAST
- EPIPHYSIS
- PERIOSTEUM
- OSTEON
- OSTEOCYTE
- AXIAL

Long Bone

1. Articular cartilage
2. Spongy bone
3. Epiphyseal plate
4. Red marrow cavities
5. Compact bone
6. Medullary cavity
7. Yellow marrow
8. Periosteum

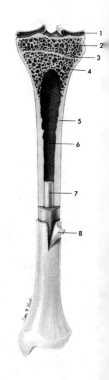

Anterior View of Skeleton

1. Orbit
2. Mandible
3. Sternum
4. Xiphoid process
5. Costal cartilage
6. Coxal
7. Ilium
8. Pubis
9. Ischium
10. Frontal
11. Nasal
12. Maxilla
13. Clavicle
14. Ribs
15. Humerus
16. Vertebral column
17. Ulna
18. Radius
19. Sacrum
20. Coccyx
21. Carpals
22. Metacarpals
23. Phalanges
24. Femur
25. Patella
26. Tibia
27. Fibula
28. Tarsals
29. Metatarsals
30. Phalanges

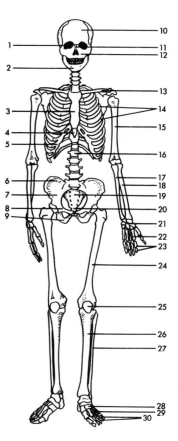

Posterior View of Skeleton

1. Parietal
2. Cervical vertebrae
3. Thoracic vertebrae
4. Lumbar vertebrae
5. Coccyx
6. Femur
7. Fibula
8. Tibia
9. Calcaneus
10. Occipital
11. Scapula
12. Coxal
13. Sacrum
14. Ischium

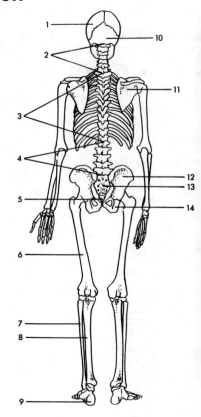

Skull—Right Side

1. Parietal bone
2. Squamous suture
3. Occipital bone
4. Lambdoidal suture
5. Temporal bone
6. External auditory canal
7. Mastoid process
8. Coronal suture
9. Frontal bone
10. Sphenoid bone
11. Ethmoid bone
12. Nasal bone
13. Zygomatic bone
14. Maxilla
15. Mandible

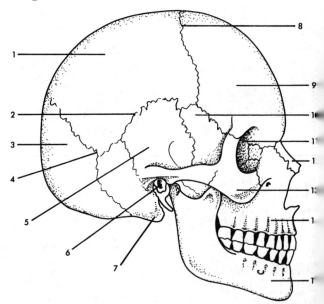

Skull—Front View

1. Sphenoid bone
2. Ethmoid bone
3. Lacrimal bone
4. Zygomatic bone
5. Vomer
6. Frontal bone
7. Parietal bone
8. Nasal bone
9. Inferior concha
10. Maxilla
11. Mandible

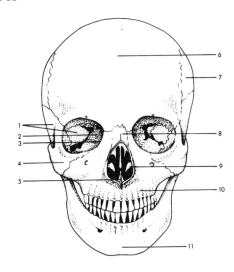

Diarthrosis Joint

1. Bone
2. Synovial membrane
3. Blood vessel
4. Nerve
5. Joint capsule
6. Periosteum
7. Bone
8. Articular cartilage
9. Bursa
10. Joint capsule

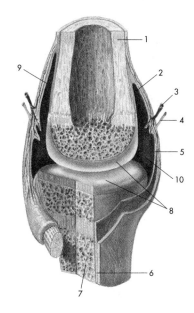

CHAPTER 7
THE MUSCULAR SYSTEM

Select the correct term

1. A, p. 169
2. B, p. 169
3. C, p. 169
4. C, p. 169
5. A, p. 169
6. B, p. 169
7. C, (may also be B), p. 169 and Chapter 2
8. A, p. 169
9. C, p. 169
10. C, p. 169

Matching

Group A

11. D, p. 169
12. B, p. 169
13. A, p. 169
14. E, p. 169
15. C, p. 170

Group B

16. E, p. 170
17. C, p. 171
18. B, p. 171
19. A, p. 171
20. D, p. 171

Fill in the blanks

21. Pulling, p. 171
22. Insertion, p. 171
23. Insertion, origin, p. 171
24. Prime mover, p. 171
25. Antagonist, p. 171
26. Synergist, p. 171
27. Tonic contraction, p. 173
28. Muscle tone, p. 173
29. Hypothermia, p. 173
30. ATP, p. 173

True or false

31. Neuromuscular junction, p. 174
32. T, p. 174
33. T, p. 173
34. Oxygen debt, p. 173
35. "All or none," p. 175
36. Lactic acid, p. 173
37. T, p. 175
38. T, p. 175
39. Skeletal muscles, p. 174
40. T, p. 174

Multiple choice

41. A, p. 175
42. B, p. 175
43. B, p. 175

44. C, p. 176
45. D, p. 176
46. A, p. 175
47. B, p. 175
48. C, p. 175
49. B, p. 176
50. D, p. 176

Matching

51. C, p. 188
52. F, p. 184; A and D, p. 188
53. F, p. 184 and B, p. 188
54. A, p. 188
55. C, p. 188
56. B, p. 188 and F, p. 181
57. A, p. 184, 188
58. A, p. 182 and D, p. 188
59. B, p. 184, 188
60. B, p. 182, 188
61. A, p. 182 and E, p. 180
62. B, p. 180
63. D, p. 180

Multiple choice

64. A, p. 186
65. D, p. 186
66. C, p. 186
67. A, p. 188
68. D, p. 188
69. C, p. 188

Circle the correct response

70. Myalgia, p. 189
71. Myoglobin, p. 190
72. Poliomyelitis, p. 190
73. Muscular dystrophy, p. 190
74. Myasthenia gravis, p. 190

Applying what you know

75. Bursitis
76. Deltoid area
77. Tendon

Crossword

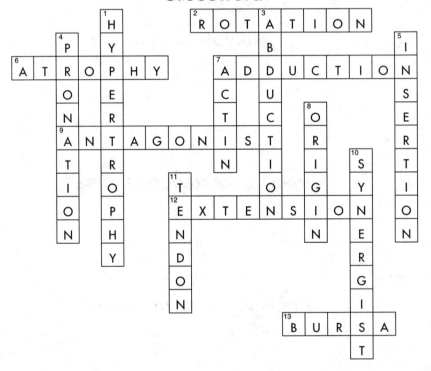

Muscles—Anterior View

1. Sternocleidomastoid
2. Trapezius
3. Pectoralis major
4. Rectus abdominis
5. External abdominal oblique
6. Iliopsoas
7. Quadriceps group
8. Tibialis anterior
9. Peroneus longus
10. Peroneus brevis
11. Soleus
12. Gastrocnemius
13. Sartorius
14. Adductor group
15. Brachialis
16. Biceps brachii
17. Deltoid
18. Facial muscles

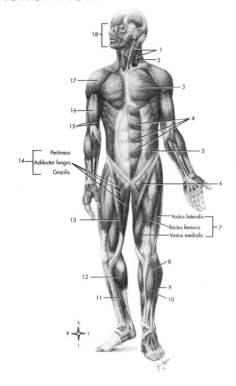

Muscles—Posterior View

1. Trapezius
2. External abdominal oblique
3. Gluteus maximus
4. Adductor magnus
5. Soleus
6. Peroneus brevis
7. Peroneus longus
8. Gastrocnemius
9. Hamstring group
10. Latissimus dorsi
11. Triceps brachii
12. Deltoid
13. Sternocleidomastoid

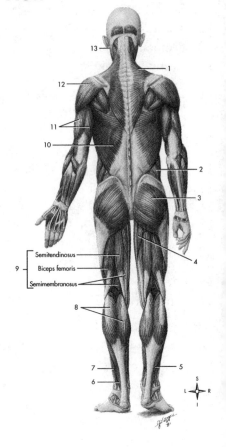

CHAPTER 8
THE NERVOUS SYSTEM

Matching

Group A
1. B, p. 199
2. C, p. 199
3. D, p. 199
4. A, p. 199

Group B
5. B, p. 199
6. D, p. 200
7. C, p. 199
8. A, p. 200
9. F, p. 203
10. E, p. 203

Select the best choice

11. A, p. 199
12. B, p. 199
13. B, p. 202

14. A, p. 199
15. A, p. 199
16. B, p. 200
17. B, p. 202
18. A, p. 199
19. B, p. 202
20. A, p. 200

Fill in the blanks

21. Two-neuron arc, p. 204
22. Sensory, interneurons, and motor neurons, p. 203
23. Receptors, p. 205
24. Synapse, p. 205
25. Reflex, p. 205
26. Withdrawal reflex, p. 206
27. Ganglion, p. 205
28. Interneurons, p. 206
29. "Knee jerk," p. 205
30. Gray matter, p. 206

Circle the correct word

31. Do not, p. 206
32. Increases, p. 206
33. Excess, p. 206
34. Postsynaptic, p. 208
35. Presynaptic, p. 208
36. Neurotransmitter, p. 209
37. Communicate, p. 208
38. Specifically, p. 209
39. Sleep, p. 209
40. Pain, p. 209

Multiple choice

41. E, p. 210
42. D, p. 210
43. A, p. 210
44. E, p. 212
45. E, p. 210-212
46. D, p. 212
47. B, p. 213
48. E, p. 215
49. B, p. 214
50. D, p. 214
51. D, p. 212
52. B, p. 213
53. A, p. 215
54. D, p. 215
55. C, p. 212

Select the best choice

56. H, p. 215
57. D, p. 216
58. E, p. 216
59. C, p. 217
60. J, p. 217
61. A, p. 217
62. B, p. 217
63. F, p. 217
64. I, p. 216
65. G, p. 216

True or false

66. 17 to 18 inches, p. 218
67. Bottom of the first lumbar vertebra, p. 218
68. Lumbar punctures, not CAT scan, p. 220
69. Spinal tracts, not dendrites, p. 218
70. T, p. 218
71. One general function, not several, p. 218
72. Anesthesia, not paralysis, p. 221

Circle the one that does not belong

73. Ventricles (all others refer to meninges)
74. CSF (all others refer to the arachnoid)
75. Pia mater (all others refer to the cerebrospinal fluid)
76. Choroid plexus (all others refer to the dura mater)
77. Brain tumor (all others refer to a lumbar puncture)

Cranial Nerves

78.

NERVE	CONDUCT IMPULSES	FUNCTION
I Olfactory		
II		Vision
III	From brain to eye muscles	
IV Trochlear		
V		Sensations of face, scalp, an teeth; chewing movements
VI	From brain to external eye muscles	
VII		Sense of taste; contraction muscles of facial expression
VIII Vestibulocochlear		
IX	From throat and taste buds of tongue to brain; also from brain to throat muscles and salivary glands	
X Vagus		
XI		Shoulder movements; turn ing movements of head
XII Hypoglossal		

Select the best choice

79. A, p. 225
80. B, p. 227
81. A, p. 226
82. B, p. 228
83. B, p. 226
84. A, p. 226
85. B, p. 226
86. B, p. 226

Matching

87. D, p. 229
88. E, p. 230
89. F, p. 230
90. B, p. 230
91. A, p. 229
92. C, p. 229

Multiple choice

93. C, p. 231
94. B, p. 231
95. B, p. 231
96. D, p. 231
97. A, p. 231
98. A, p. 231

Choose the correct response

99. B, p. 232
100. A, p. 232
101. A, p. 231
102. B, p. 231
103. A, p. 231
104. B, p. 231
105. A, p. 232
106. A, p. 232
107. B, p. 231
108. B, p. 232

Fill in the blanks

109. Acetylcholine, p. 232
110. Adrenergic fibers, p. 232
111. Cholinergic fibers, p. 232
112. Homeostasis, p. 232
113. Heart rate, p. 233
114. Decreased, p. 233
115. Neuroblastoma, p. 234

Unscramble the words

116. Neurons
117. Synapse
118. Autonomic
119. Smooth muscle
120. Sympathetic

Applying what you know

121. Right
122. Hydrocephalus
123. Sympathetic
124. Parasympathetic
125. Sympathetic; No, the digestive process is not active during sympathetic control. Bill may experience nausea, vomiting, or discomfort because of this factor. See p. 231.
126. WORD FIND

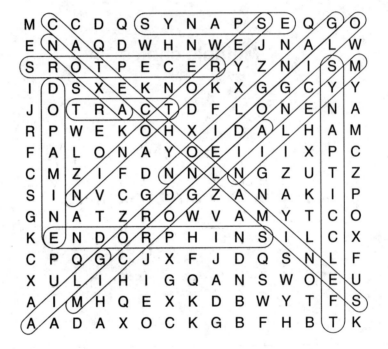

Crossword

```
              ¹A                              ⁴T R A C T  ⁵T
  ²R          S          ³R                              C
  E           T          E                   ⁶G          E              ⁷M
  C           R          F        ⁸D E N D R I T E S     Y              E
  E           O          L          A        G           L              D
  P           C          E          N        L           C              U
  T           Y          X    ⁹P O S T G A N G L I O N I C              L
  ⁹P O S T G A N G L I O N I C                O           H              L
  R           E          R                   N           ¹⁰N E U R O G L I A
  S           S          C        ¹⁰N E U R O G L I A    L
                                             ¹¹M E N I N G E S   ¹²S
                                             Y           N        Y
                                             E    ¹³N E U R O N    N
                                             L                     A
                                             I                     P
                         ¹⁴A X O N           ¹⁵P N                  S
                                                                   E
```

Neuron

1. Dendrites
2. Cell body
3. Nucleus
4. Axon
5. Schwann cell
6. Myelin
7. Mitochondrion

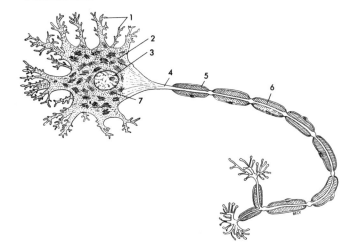

Cranial Nerves

1. Olfactory
2. Trigeminal nerve
3. Glossopharyngeal nerve
4. Hypoglossal nerve
5. Accessory nerve
6. Vagus nerve
7. Vestibulocochlear nerve
8. Facial nerve
9. Abducens nerve
10. Oculomotor nerve
11. Optic nerve
12. Trochlear nerve

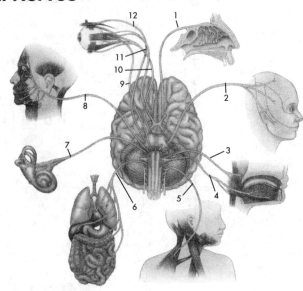

Patellar Reflex

1. Dorsal root ganglion
2. Sensory neuron
3. Stretch receptor
4. Patella
5. Patellar tendon
6. Quadriceps muscle
7. Motor neuron
8. Monosynaptic synapse
9. Gray matter
10. Interneuron

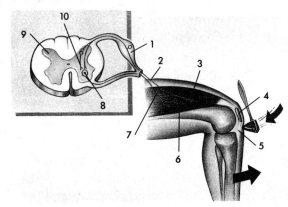

The Cerebrum

1. Occipital lobe
2. Temporal lobe
3. Lateral fissure
4. Frontal lobe
5. Central sulcus
6. Parietal lobe

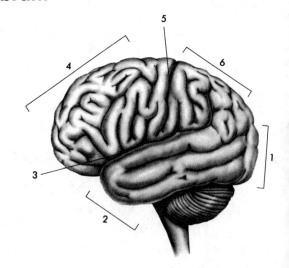

Sagittal Section of the Central Nervous System

1. Skull
2. Pineal gland
3. Cerebellum
4. Midbrain
5. Spinal cord
6. Medulla
7. Reticular formation
8. Pons
9. Pituitary gland
10. Hypothalamus
11. Cerebral cortex
12. Thalamus
13. Corpus callosum

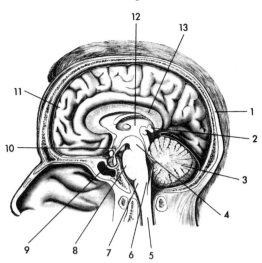

Neuron Pathways

1. Somatic motor neuron's axon
2. Cell body of somatic motor neuron
3. Cell body of preganglionic neuron
4. Collateral ganglion
5. Postganglionic neuron's axon
6. Preganglionic sympathetic neuron's axon

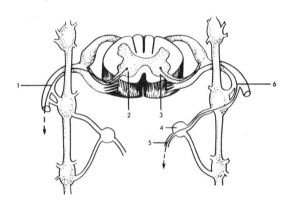

CHAPTER 9
SENSE ORGANS

Matching

1. D, p. 241
2. B, p. 242
3. C, p. 242
4. E, p. 242
5. A, p. 241

Multiple choice

6. C, p. 244
7. E, p. 244
8. B, p. 244
9. C, p. 244
10. E, p. 244
11. D, p. 244
12. A, p. 244
13. B, p. 244

14. C, p. 245
15. B, p. 246
16. D, p. 244
17. A, p. 246
18. D, p. 247

Select the best choice

19. C, p. 248
20. E, p. 248
21. F, p. 248
22. A, p. 248
23. J, p. 248
24. B, p. 250
25. H, p. 248
26. G, p. 250
27. I, p. 251
28. D, p. 250

Select the best choice

29. B, p. 252
30. C, p. 253
31. B, p. 252
32. A, p. 252
33. C, p. 254
34. A, p. 252
35. C, p. 253
36. B, p. 252
37. A, p. 252
38. C, p. 254

Fill in the blanks

39. Auricle and external auditory canal, p. 252
40. Eardrum, p. 252
41. Ossicles, p. 252
42. Oval window, p. 252
43. Otitis media, p. 253
44. Vestibule, p. 253
45. Mechanoreceptors, p. 253
46. Crista ampullaris, p. 253

Select the best choice

47. C, p. 255
48. A, p. 255
49. D, p. 253, 255
50. E, p. 255
51. B, p. 255
52. F, p. 256

Circle the correct word

53. Papillae, p. 256
54. Cranial, p. 257
55. Mucus, p. 257
56. Memory, p. 257
57. Chemoreceptors, p. 257

Applying what you know

58. External otitis
59. Cataracts
60. The eustachian tube connects the throat to the middle ear and provides a perfect pathway for the spread of infection
61. Olfactory
62. WORD FIND

Crossword

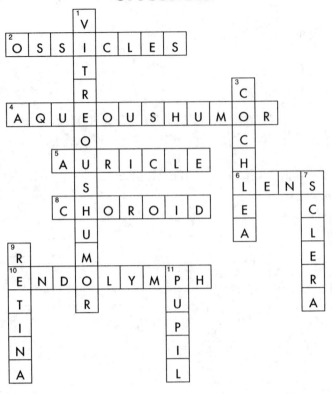

Eye

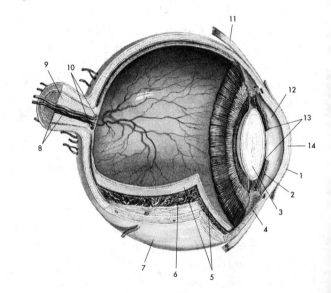

1. Conjunctiva
2. Iris
3. Lens
4. Ciliary muscle
5. Retina
6. Choroid layer
7. Sclera
8. Central retinal artery and vein
9. Optic nerve
10. Optic disc (blind spot)
11. Medial rectus muscle
12. Anterior cavity
13. Pupil
14. Cornea

Ear

1. Temporal bone
2. External auditory canal
3. Auricle (pinna)
4. Tympanic membrane (eardrum)
5. Malleus
6. Incus
7. Stapes
8. Auditory (eustachian) tube
9. Cochlea
10. Cochlear nerve
11. Semicircular canals

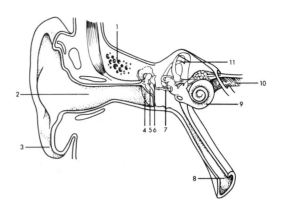

CHAPTER 10
ENDOCRINE SYSTEM

Matching

Group A
1. D, p. 264
2. C, p. 264
3. E, p. 264
4. A, p. 264
5. B, p. 264

Group B
6. E, p. 268
7. C, p. 270
8. A, p. 263
9. D, p. 263
10. B, p. 263

Fill in the blanks

11. Second messenger, p. 263
12. Recognize, p. 263
13. First messengers, p. 263
14. Target organs, p. 263
15. Cyclic AMP, p. 267
16. Target cells, p. 267
17. Steroid abuse, p. 269

Multiple choice

18. B, p. 271
19. E, p. 271
20. D, p. 271
21. D, p. 271
22. A, p. 271
23. C, p. 271

24. C, p. 272
25. B, p. 271
26. A, p. 271
27. A, p. 271
28. D, p. 272
29. B, pp. 273-274
30. A, p. 273
31. C, p. 274
32. C, p. 274

Select the best answer

33. A, p. 271
34. B, p. 271
35. B, p. 273
36. C, p. 274
37. A, p. 272
38. C, p. 274
39. A, p. 271
40. A, p. 271
41. A, pp. 271-272
42. C, p. 274

Circle the correct term

43. Below, p. 274
44. Calcitonin, p. 274
45. Iodine, p. 274
46. Do not, p. 274
47. Thyroid, p. 274
48. Decreases, p. 274
49. Hypothyroidism, p. 275
50. Cretinism, p. 276
51. PTH, p. 277
52. Increase, p. 277

Fill in the blanks

53. Adrenal cortex and adrenal medulla, p. 278
54. Corticoids, p. 279
55. Mineralocorticoids, p. 279
56. Glucocorticoids, p. 279
57. Sex hormones, p. 279
58. Gluconeogenesis, p. 279
59. Blood pressure, p. 279
60. Epinephrine and norepinephrine, p. 279
61. Stress, p. 280
62. General adaptation syndrome, p. 280

Select the best response

63. A, p. 282
64. A, p. 279
65. B, p. 280
66. A, p. 281
67. B, p. 280
68. A, p. 279
69. A, p. 281

Circle the term that does not belong

70. Beta cells (all others refer to glucagon)
71. Glucagon (all others refer to insulin)
72. Thymosin (all others refer to female sex glands)
73. Chorion (all others refer to male sex glands)
74. Aldosterone (all others refer to the thymus gland)
75. ACTH (all others refer to the placenta)
76. Semen (all others refer to the pineal gland)

Matching

Group A
77. E, p. 282
78. C, p. 282
79. B, p. 284
80. D, p. 284
81. A, p. 284

Group B
82. E, p. 284
83. A, p. 285
84. B, p. 285
85. C, p. 284
86. D, p. 284

Applying what you know

87. She was pregnant
88. Zona reticularis of the adrenal cortex

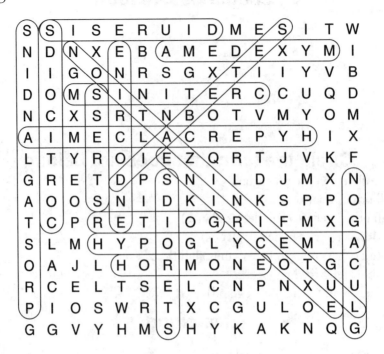

Crossword

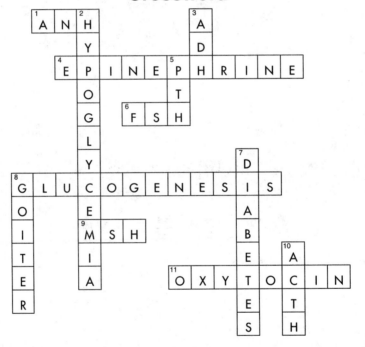

Endocrine Glands

1. Pineal
2. Pituitary
3. Parathyroids
4. Thymus
5. Adrenal
6. Pancreas
7. Ovaries
8. Testes
9. Thyroid

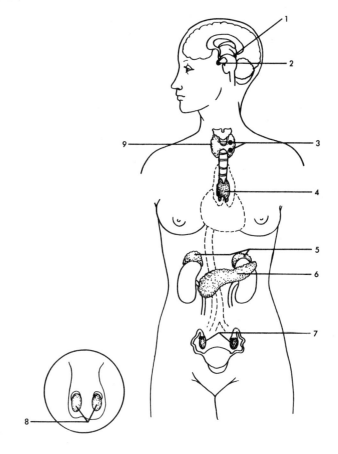

CHAPTER 11
BLOOD

Multiple choice

1. E, p. 293
2. D, p. 293
3. D, p. 293
4. B, p. 293
5. C, p. 293
6. A, p. 297
7. B, p. 296
8. D, p. 293
9. C, p. 296
10. D, p. 297
11. A, p. 298
12. B, p. 301
13. B, p. 303
14. B, p. 293
15. E, p. 295
16. B, p. 294-295
17. C, p. 294
18. D, p. 295

19. D, p. 296
20. D, p. 296
21. B, p. 301
22. D, p. 293
23. B, p. 300
24. C, p. 300
25. B, p. 300
26. A, p. 302
27. E, p. 303
28. B, p. 297
29. C, p. 298
30. A, p. 303
31. C, p. 301

Fill in the blank areas

32. p. 304

Blood Type	Antigen	Antibody
A	A	Anti-B
B	B	Anti-A
AB	A, B	None
O	None	Anti-A, Anti-B

Fill in the blanks

33. Antigen, p. 304
34. Antibody, p. 304
35. Agglutinate, p. 304
36. Erythroblastosis fetalis, p. 305-306
37. Rhesus monkey, p. 305
38. Type O, p. 305
39. Type AB, p. 305

Applying what you know

40. No. If Mrs. Payne were a negative Rh factor and her husband were a positive Rh factor, it would set up the strong possibility of erythroblastosis fetalis.
41. Both procedures assist the clotting process.
42. Anemia
43. Epstein-Barr virus (EBV), which causes infectious mononucleosis

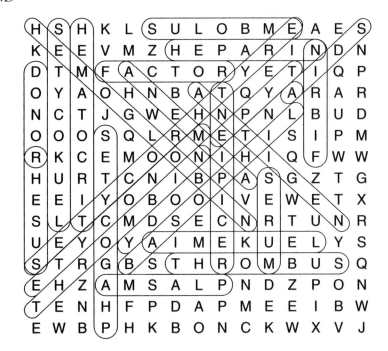

Crossword

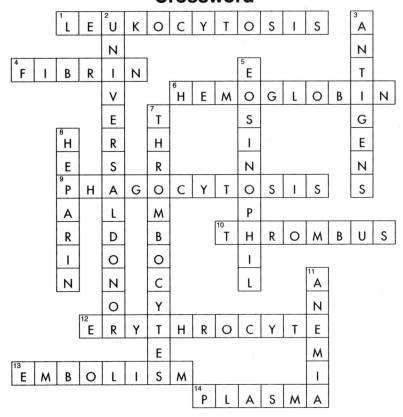

Human Blood Cells

1. Red blood cells
2. Platelets
3. Basophil
4. Neutrophil
5. Eosinophil
6. Lymphocyte
7. Monocyte

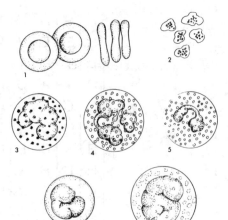

Blood Types

Recipient's blood		Reactions with donor's blood			
RBC antigens	Plasma antibodies	Donor type O	Donor type A	Donor type B	Donor type AB
None (Type O)	Anti-A Anti-B				
A (Type A)	Anti-B				
B (Type B)	Anti-A				
AB (Type AB)	(none)				

 Normal blood    Agglutinated blood

CHAPTER 12
THE HEART AND HEART DISEASE

Fill in the blanks

1. Circulatory system, p. 313
2. Apex, p. 313
3. Interatrial septum, p. 313
4. Atria, p. 313
5. Ventricles, p. 313
6. Myocardium, p. 313
7. Endocarditis, pp. 313-316
8. Bicuspid or mitral and tricuspid, p. 316
9. Visceral pericardium or epicardium, p. 316

10. Parietal pericardium, p. 316
11. Pericarditis, p. 316
12. Semilunar valves, p. 316
13. Mitral valve prolapse, p. 318
14. Rheumatic heart disease, p. 318

Select the best answer

15. F, p. 320
16. C, p. 320
17. D, p. 321
18. A, p. 318
19. B, p. 320
20. G, p. 321
21. E, p. 321
22. H, p. 321
23. J, p. 319
24. I, p. 321

Circle the correct response

25. B, p. 322
26. C, p. 321
27. A, p. 323
28. C, p. 325
29. A, p. 323
30. D, p. 323
31. C, p. 326
32. A, p. 326
33. B, p. 327
34. C, p. 327
35. A, p. 327
36. D, p. 326

Applying what you know

37. Coronary bypass surgery
38. Artificial pacemaker
39. The endocardial lining can become rough and abrasive to red blood cells passing over its surface. As a result, a fatal blood clot may be formed.
40.   3 Tricuspid valve
      6 Pulmonary arteries
      9 Bicuspid valve
      1 Vena cavae
      4 Right ventricle
     12 Aorta
      7 Pulmonary veins
      5 Pulmonary semilunar valve
     10 Left ventricle
      2 Right atrium
      8 Left atrium
     11 Aortic semilunar valve

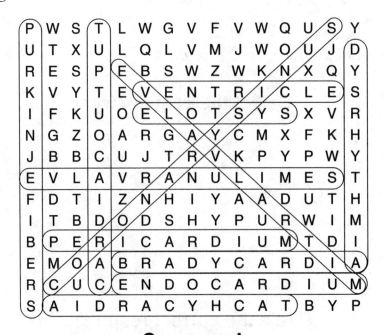

Crossword

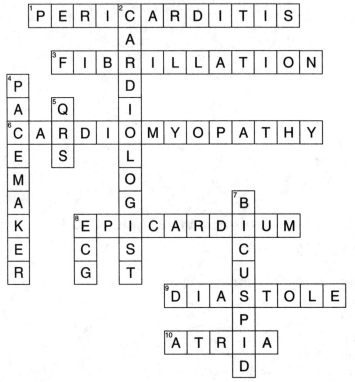

Heart

1. Aorta
2. Pulmonary arteries
3. Left pulmonary veins
4. Left atrium
5. Aortic semilunar valve
6. Bicuspid valve
7. Chordae tendineae
8. Left ventricle
9. Interventricular septum
10. Right ventricle
11. Tricuspid valve
12. Right atrium
13. Pulmonary semilunar valve
14. Superior vena cava

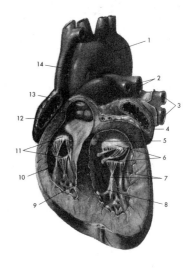

Conduction System of the Heart

1. Aorta
2. Pulmonary artery
3. Pulmonary veins
4. Mitral (bicuspid) valve
5. Left ventricle
6. Right and left branches of AV bundle
7. Inferior vena cava
8. Right ventricle
9. Tricuspid valve
10. Right atrium
11. Atrioventricular node (AV node)
12. Sinoatrial node (SA node or pacemaker)
13. Pulmonary veins
14. Superior vena cava

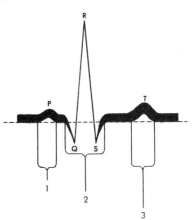

Normal ECG Deflections

1. Atrial depolarization
2. Ventricular depolarization
3. Ventricular repolarization

CHAPTER 13
CIRCULATION OF THE BLOOD

Matching

1. D, p. 333
2. B, p. 333
3. C, p. 333
4. G, p. 333
5. A, p. 333
6. E, p. 333
7. F, p. 333

Matching

8. I, p. 335
9. B, p. 335
10. D, p. 335
11. E, p. 335
12. A, p. 335
13. C, p. 339
14. F, p. 340
15. G, p. 341
16. J, p. 341
17. H, p. 339

Circle the correct choice

18. D, p. 341
19. C, p. 341
20. B, p. 341
21. B, p. 341
22. D, pp. 341-342
23. B, p. 345
24. B, p. 345
25. A, p. 345
26. D, p. 337

True or false

27. Highest/arteries; lowest/veins, p. 345
28. Blood pressure gradient, p. 345
29. Stop, p. 346
30. High blood pressure, p. 347
31. Decreases, p. 347
32. T, p. 347
33. T, p. 347
34. T, p. 347
35. Increases blood pressure/weaker heartbeat tends to decrease it, p. 347
36. Contract, p. 349
37. Relax, p. 349
38. T, p. 348

39. T, p. 348
40. Right, p.349
41. Artery, p. 349
42. T, p. 349
43. T, p. 349
44. Brachial, p. 349

Fill in the blanks

45. Septic shock, p. 350
46. Cardiogenic shock, p. 350
47. Anaphylaxis, p. 350; Anaphylactic shock, p. 350
48. Neurogenic shock, p. 350
49. Low blood volume, p. 350
50. Toxic shock syndrome, p. 350

Unscramble the words

51. Systemic
52. Venule
53. Artery
54. Pulse
55. Vessel

Applying what you know

56. Anaphylactic shock
57. Hypovolemic shock
58. (a) Varicose veins
    (b) Wear support stockings
59. Hemorrhage
60. WORD FIND

Crossword

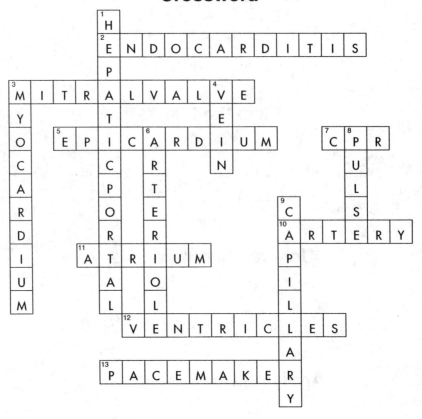

Fetal Circulation

1. Aortic arch
2. Ductus arteriosus
3. Pulmonary trunk
4. Abdominal aorta
5. Kidney
6. Common iliac artery
7. Internal iliac artery
8. Umbilical artery
9. Umbilical cord
10. Fetal umbilicus
11. Umbilical vein
12. Hepatic portal vein
13. Liver
14. Ductus venosus
15. Inferior vena cava
16. Foramen ovale
17. Ascending aorta
18. Superior vena cava

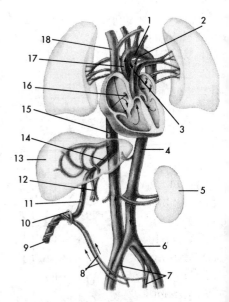

Hepatic Portal Circulation

1. Inferior vena cava
2. Stomach
3. Gastric vein
4. Spleen
5. Splenic vein
6. Gastroepiploic vein
7. Descending colon
8. Inferior mesenteric vein
9. Small intestine
10. Appendix
11. Ascending colon
12. Superior mesenteric vein
13. Pancreas
14. Duodenum
15. Hepatic (portal) vein
16. Liver
17. Hepatic veins

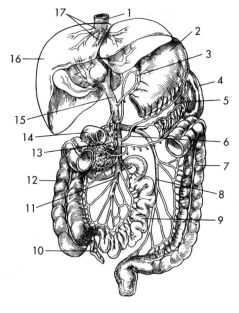

Principal Arteries of the Body

1. Occipital
2. Internal carotid
3. External carotid
4. Left common carotid
5. Left subclavian
6. Arch of aorta
7. Pulmonary
8. Left coronary
9. Aorta
10. Celiac
11. Splenic
12. Renal
13. Inferior mesenteric
14. Radial
15. Ulnar
16. Anterior tibial
17. Popliteal
18. Femoral
19. Deep femoral
20. External iliac
21. Internal iliac
22 Common iliac
23. Abdominal aorta
24. Superior mesenteric
25. Brachial
26. Axillary
27. Right coronary
28. Brachiocephalic
29. Right common carotid
30. Facial

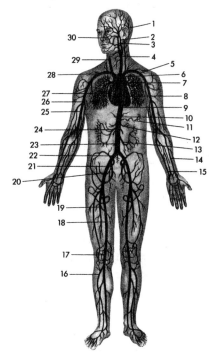

Principal Veins of the Body

1. Superior sagittal sinus
2. External jugular
3. Internal jugular
4. Left brachiocephalic
5. Left subclavian
6. Cephalic
7. Axillary
8. Great cardiac
9. Basilic
10. Long thoracic
11. Splenic
12. Inferior mesenteric
13. Common iliac
14. Internal iliac
15. Femoral
16. Popliteal
17. Peroneal
18. Anterior tibial
19. Posterior tibial
20. Great saphenous
21. Femoral
22. External iliac
23. Common iliac
24. Superior mesenteric
25. Median cubital
26. Hepatic portal
27. Hepatic
28. Inferior vena cava
29. Small cardiac
30. Pulmonary (right)
31. Superior vena cava
32. Right subclavian
33. Right brachiocephalic
34. Facial

CHAPTER 14
THE LYMPHATIC SYSTEM AND IMMUNITY
Fill in the blanks

1. Lymph, p. 355
2. Interstitial fluid, p. 355
3. Lymphatic capillaries, p. 355
4. Right lymphatic duct and thoracic duct, p. 355
5. Cisterna chyli, p. 357
6. Lymph nodes, p. 357
7. Afferent, p. 357

8. Efferent, p. 358
9. Lymphedema, p. 357
10. Lymphoma, pp. 358-359

Choose the correct response

11. B, pp. 359-360
12. C, p. 360
13. C, p. 360
14. A, p. 359
15. C, p. 360
16. A, p. 359
17. A, p. 359

Matching

18. C, p. 360
19. A, p. 361
20. E, p. 361
21. B, p. 361
22. D, p. 361

Choose the correct term

23. C, p. 366
24. A, p. 362
25. F, p. 362
26. B, p. 362
27. G, p. 362
28. D, p. 363
29. H, p. 366
30. E, p. 364

Multiple choice

31. D, p. 365
32. D, p. 366
33. C, pp. 366, 367
34. C, p. 366
35. C, p. 366
36. E, p. 366
37. E, p. 367
38. C, p. 367
39. E, pp. 367-368
40. E, p. 369
41. A, p. 368
42. B, p. 369

Circle the correct response

43. Hypersensitivity, p. 370
44. Allergens, p. 370
45. Anaphylactic shock, p. 370
46. Lupus, p. 370
47. Isoimmunity, p. 371
48. HLAs, p. 371

Select the correct response

49. B, p. 373
50. A, p. 372
51. A, p. 372
52. B, p. 373
53. A, p. 372

Unscramble the words

54. Complement
55. Immunity
56. Clones
57. Interferon
58. Memory cells

Applying what you know

59. Natural active immunity
60. AIDS
61. Baby Easton had no means of producing T cells, thus making him susceptible to several diseases. Isolation was a means of controlling his exposure to these diseases.
62. WORD FIND

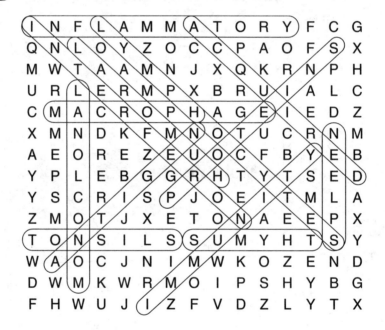

Crossword

```
1 2
S P L E E N
  L
3 M A C R O P H A G E S
  S
  M
4 A N T I B O D I E S
  C
5 M E M O R Y 6 C E L L S
  L         O
  L         M
  S         P      7 C
            L        L
            O        O       8 B
9 I N T E R F E R O N        C
            M      10 E F F E R E N T
11 A F F E R E N T 12 T      L
   I               N C       L
   D               T E
   S                 L
                     L
```

Principal Organs of the Lymphatic System

1. Cervical lymph nodes
2. Thymus
3. Thoracic duct
4. Spleen
5. Cisterna chyli
6. Popliteal lymph nodes
7. Inguinal lymph nodes
8. Lymph vessels
9. Axillary lymph nodes
10. Submandibular nodes

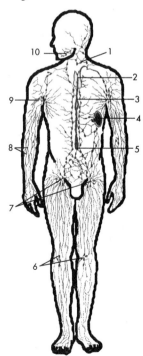

CHAPTER 15
THE RESPIRATORY SYSTEM

Matching

1. J, p. 379
2. G, p. 379
3. A, p. 379
4. I, p. 382
5. B, p. 382
6. F, p. 382
7. C, p. 379
8. H, p. 379-382
9. D, p. 379
10. E, p. 379

Fill in the blanks

11. Air distributor, p. 379
12. Gas exchanger, p. 379
13. Filters, p. 379
14. Warms, p. 379
15. Humidifies, p. 379
16. Nose, p. 379
17. Pharynx, p. 379
18. Larynx, p. 379
19. Trachea, p. 382
20. Bronchi, p. 382
21. Lungs, p. 382
22. Alveoli, p. 379
23. Diffusion, p. 379
24. Respiratory membrane, p. 379
25. Surface, p. 379

Circle the one that does not belong

26. Oropharynx (the others refer to the nose)
27. Conchae (the others refer to paranasal sinuses)
28. Epiglottis (the others refer to the pharynx)
29. Uvula (the others refer to the adenoids)
30. Larynx (the others refer to the eustachian tubes)
31. Tonsils (the others refer to the larynx)
32. Eustachian tube (the others refer to the tonsils)
33. Pharynx (the others refer to the larynx)

Choose the correct response

34. A, p. 385
35. B, p. 385
36. A, p. 383
37. A, p. 383
38. A, p. 382
39. B, p. 385
40. B, p. 385

41. C, p. 385
42. A, p. 385
43. B, p. 386
44. A, p. 388

Fill in the blanks

45. Trachea, p. 388
46. C-rings of cartilage, p. 388
47. Heimlich maneuver, p. 387
48. Primary bronchi, p. 388
49. Alveolar sacs, p. 389
50. Apex, p. 390
51. Pleura, p. 390
52. Pleurisy, p. 390
53. Pneumothorax, p. 392

True or false

54. Breathing, p. 393
55. Expiration, p. 393
56. Down, p. 395
57. Internal respiration, p. 395
58. T, p. 395-396
59. 1 pint, p. 395
60. T, p. 395
61. Vital capacity, p. 398
62. T, p. 398

Multiple choice

63. E, p. 393
64. C, p. 395
65. C, p. 395
66. B, p. 394
67. D, p. 398
68. D, p. 398
69. D, p. 398

Matching

70. E, p. 398
71. B, p. 401
72. G, p. 401
73. A, p. 401
74. F, p. 401
75. D, p. 401
76. C, p. 401

Fill in the blanks

77. Pneumonia, p. 402
78. Tuberculosis, p. 402
79. Emphysema, p. 403
80. Asthma, p. 403

Unscramble the words

81. Pleurisy
82. Bronchitis
83. Epistaxis
84. Adenoids
85. Inspiration

Applying what you know

86. During the day Mr. Gorski's cilia are paralyzed because of his heavy smoking. They use the time when Mr. Gorski is asleep to sweep accumulations of mucus and bacteria toward the pharynx. When Mr. Gorski awakes, these collections are waiting to be eliminated.

87. Swelling of the tonsils or adenoids caused by infection may make it difficult or impossible for air to travel from the nose into the throat. The individual may be forced to breathe through the mouth.

88. During expiration, the alveoli are unable to force out a normal amount of air. Residual volume is increased at the expense of the expiratory reserve volume. Pulmonary infections can cause inflammation and an accumulation of fluid in the air spaces of the lungs. The fluid reduces the amount of space available for air and thus decreases the vital capacity.

89. WORD FIND

Crossword

```
S P I R O M E T E R
        O
        N
        S          H               T
    B   I           E        E R V
P A R A N A S A L   S I N U S      A
    O   L           M              C
    N   A L V E O L I               H
    C   E            I              E
    H   C          C O N C H A E
    I   T          H
      L O
      A M
P L E U R I S Y
      Y
    A P N E A
      X
```

Sagittal View of Face and Neck

1. Sphenoid air sinus
2. Pharyngeal tonsil (adenoids)
3. Auditory tube
4. Soft palate
5. Uvula
6. Palatine tonsil
7. Lingual tonsil
8. Esophagus
9. Thyroid cartilage
10. Vocal cords
11. Epiglottis
12. Hyoid bone
13. Mandible
14. Tongue
15. Hard palate
16. Inferior concha
17. Middle concha
18. Nasal bone
19. Frontal air sinus
20. Superior concha

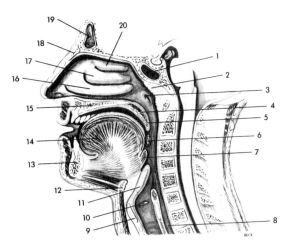

Respiratory Organs

1. Pharynx
2. Left primary bronchus
3. Bronchioles
4. Right primary bronchus
5. Trachea
6. Alveoli
7. Alveolar duct
8. Alveolar sac
9. Capillary

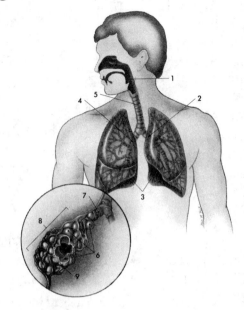

Pulmonary Ventilation Volumes

1. Total lung capacity
2. Inspiratory reserve volume
3. Tidal volume
4. Expiratory reserve volume
5. Residual volume

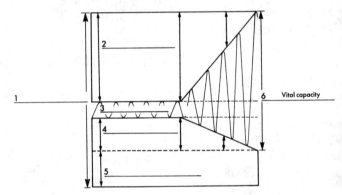

CHAPTER 16
THE DIGESTIVE SYSTEM

Fill in the blanks

1. Gastrointestinal tract or GI tract, p. 411
2. Mechanical, p. 411
3. Chemical, p. 411
4. Feces, p. 411
5. Digestion, absorption, and metabolism, p. 411
6. Visceral peritoneum, p. 411
7. Mouth, anus, p. 411
8. Lumen, p. 411
9. Mucosa, p. 411
10. Submucosa, p. 411
11. Peristalsis, p. 411
12. Serosa, p. 411
13. Mesentery, p. 411

Choose the correct answer

14. A, p. 413
15. B, p. 413
16. B, p. 413
17. A, p. 413
18. A, p. 413
19. A, p. 413
20. A, p. 413
21. A, p. 413
22. B, p. 413
23. B, p. 413
24. B, p. 413
25. B, p. 413

Multiple choice

26. E, p. 412
27. C, p. 414
28. E, p. 415
29. D, p. 416
30. B, p. 416
31. C, p. 415
32. D, p. 415
33. D, p. 415
34. D, p. 417
35. A, p. 417-418
36. C, p. 417
37. A, p. 417-418
38. A, P. 415
39. B, p. 415
40. C, p. 415

Fill in the blanks

41. Pharynx, p. 418
42. Esophagus, p. 418
43. Stomach, p. 418
44. Cardiac sphincter, p. 419
45. Chyme, p. 419
46. Fundus, p. 419
47. Body, p. 419
48. Pylorus, p. 419
49. Pyloric sphincter, p. 420
50. Small intestine, p. 420

Matching

51. D, p. 419
52. J, p. 420
53. G, p. 420
54. A, p. 418
55. H, p. 418

56. B, p. 419
57. C, p. 419
58. E, p. 421
59. I, p. 418
60. F, p. 420

Multiple choice

61. C, p. 421
62. B, p. 421
63. A, p. 423
64. A, p. 425
65. B, p. 423
66. E, p. 423
67. D, p. 425
68. D, p. 424
69. B, p. 424
70. C, p. 424

True or false

71. Vitamin K, p. 426
72. No villi are present in the large intestine, p. 427
73. Diarrhea, p. 429
74. Cecum, p. 427
75. Hepatic, p. 428
76. Sigmoid, p. 428
77. T, p. 430
78. T, p. 430
79. Parietal, p. 430
80. Mesentery, p. 431
81. Diverticulitis, p. 429
82. T, p. 429
83. T, p. 430, 434
84. Ascites, p. 432

Multiple choice

85. B, p. 432
86. D, p. 432
87. C, p. 432
88. C, p. 432
89. C, p. 433

90. Fill in the blank areas on the chart below.

CHEMICAL DIGESTION

DIGESTIVE JUICES AND ENZYMES	SUBSTANCE DIGESTED (OR HYDROLYZED)	RESULTING PRODUCT
SALIVA		
1.	1. Starch (polysaccharide)	1.
GASTRIC JUICE		
2.	2.	2. Partially digested proteins
PANCREATIC JUICE		
3.	3.	3. Peptides and amino acids
4.	4. Fats emulsified by bile	4.
5.	5. Starch	5.
INTESTINAL ENZYMES		
6.	6. Peptides	6.
7. Sucrase	7.	7.
8.	8. Lactose	8.
9.	9.	9. Glucose

Applying what you know

91. Ulcer
92. Pylorospasm
93. Basal metabolic rate or protein-bound iodine to determine thyroid function
94. WORD FIND

Crossword

```
        ¹J              ²M                      ³D
    ⁴P   A          ⁵A  B  S  O  R  P  T  I  O  N
     E   U              S                      A
     R   N          ⁶E  T                      R
     I   D           M  I              ⁷F       R
     S   I           E  ⁸C  H  Y  M  E          H
     T   C           S  I              C       E
    ⁹A  ¹⁰P  E  N  D  I  C  I  T  I  S  E      A
     L   L           S  I              S
     S   I          ¹¹B  O  L  U  S  ¹²S
     I   C           N              L
     S   A                          C
              ¹³R  ¹⁴U  G  A  E      R
                    V              R
                    U
                    L
                    A
```

Digestive Organs

1. Tongue
2. Sublingual gland
3. Larynx
4. Spleen
5. Splenic flexure
6. Stomach
7. Descending colon
8. Sigmoid colon
9. Rectum
10. Anal canal
11. Vermiform appendix
12. Region of ileocecal valve
13. Cecum
14. Ileum
15. Ascending colon
16. Transverse colon
17. Hepatic flexure
18. Liver
19. Diaphragm
20. Esophagus
21. Trachea
22. Pharynx
23. Submandibular gland

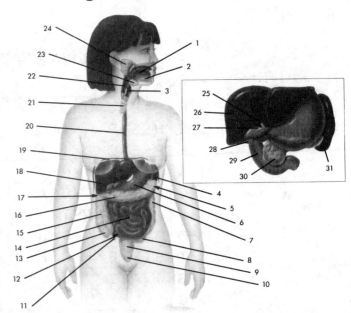

24. Parotid gland
25. Hepatic bile duct
26. Liver
27. Cystic duct
28. Gallbladder
29. Duodenum
30. Pancreas
31. Spleen

Tooth

1. Enamel
2. Pulp
3. Pulp cavity
4. Gingiva (gum)
5. Dentin
6. Periodontal membrane
7. Cementum
8. Root canal
9. Vein and artery
10. Nerve
11. Root
12. Neck
13. Crown

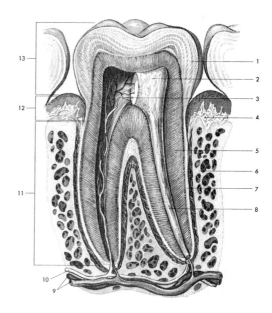

The Salivary Glands

1. Parotid duct
2. Parotid gland
3. Submandibular duct
4. Submandibular gland
5. Sublingual gland

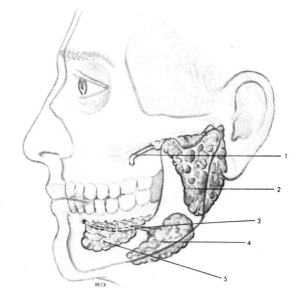

Stomach

1. Fundus
2. Body
3. Greater curvature
4. Rugae
5. Pylorus
6. Pyloric sphincter
7. Duodenum
8. Lesser curvature
9. Oblique muscle layer
10. Circular muscle layer
11. Longitudinal muscle
12. Cardiac sphincter
13. Esophagus

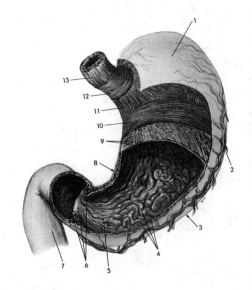

Gallbladder and Bile Ducts

1. Right and left hepatic ducts
2. Common hepatic duct
3. Common bile duct
4. Accessory duct
5. Pancreas
6. Pancreatic duct
7. Duodenum
8. Major duodenal papilla
9. Sphincter muscles
10. Minor duodenal papilla
11. Gallbladder
12. Cystic duct

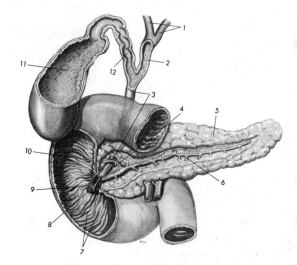

The Small Intestine

1. Mesentery
2. Plica
3. Mucosa
4. Submucosa
5. Circular muscle
6. Longitudinal muscle
7. Serosa
8. Epithelium of villus
9. Lacteal
10. Artery
11. Vein
12. Plica
13. Submucosa
14. Lymph nodules
15. Serosa
16. Circular muscle
17. Longitudinal muscle

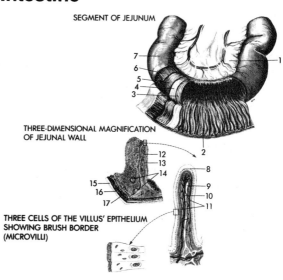

The Large Intestine

1. Splenic flexure
2. Descending colon
3. Sigmoid colon
4. Rectum
5. Vermiform appendix
6. Ileum
7. Cecum
8. Ileocecal valve
9. Ilium
10. Ascending colon
11. Hepatic flexure
12. Inferior vena cava
13. Aorta
14. Transverse colon

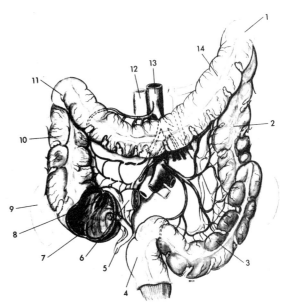

CHAPTER 17
NUTRITION AND METABOLISM

Fill in the blanks

1. Bile, p. 441
2. Prothrombin, p. 441
3. Fibrinogen, p. 441
4. Iron, p. 441
5. Hepatic portal vein, p. 441

Matching

6. B, p. 444
7. A, p. 441
8. C, p. 445
9. D, p. 446
10. E, p. 447
11. A, p. 441
12. E, p. 447
13. A, p. 441

Circle the word that does not belong

14. Bile (all others refer to carbohydrate metabolism)
15. Amino acids (all others refer to fat metabolism)
16. M (all others refer to vitamins)
17. Iron (all others refer to protein metabolism)
18. Insulin (all others tend to increase blood glucose)
19. Folic acid (all others are minerals)
20. Ascorbic acid (all others refer to the B-complex vitamins)

Multiple choice

21. C, p. 447
22. A, p. 447
23. C, p. 450
24. B, p. 450
25. B, p. 451
26. A, p. 451
27. C, p. 451
28. D, p. 451
29. D, p. 451

True or false

30. T, p. 452
31. Hypothermia, p. 452
32. T, p. 452
33. Heat stroke, p. 452
34. Malignant hyperthermia, p. 452

Choose the correct response

35. B, p. 444
36. C, p. 449
37. G, p. 449
38. F, p. 449
39. A, p. 449
40. H, p. 450
41. E, p. 449
42. D, p. 449

Unscramble the words

43. Liver
44. Catabolism
45. Amino
46. Pyruvic
47. Evaporation

Applying what you know

48. Weight loss and anorexia nervosa
49. (a) Iron
    (b) Meat, eggs, vegetables, and legumes
50. He was carbohydrate loading, or glycogen loading, which allows the muscles to sustain aerobic exercise for up to 50% longer than usual
51. WORD FIND

Crossword

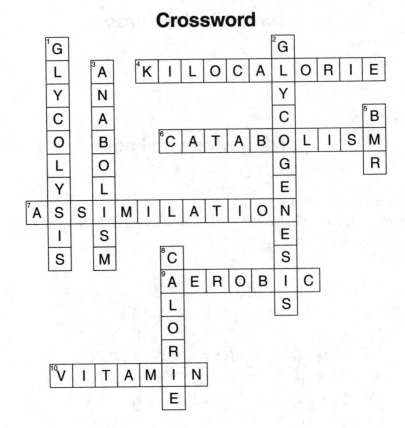

CHAPTER 18
URINARY SYSTEM

Multiple choice

1. E, p. 457
2. C, p. 460
3. E, p. 460
4. C, p. 460-463
5. E, p. 464
6. C, p. 464
7. B, p. 464
8. E, p. 464
9. C, p. 464
10. C, p. 465
11. B, p. 465 (review Chapter 10)
12. D, p. 465

Choose the correct term

13. G, p. 457
14. I, p. 463, Table 18-1
15. H, p. 463, Table 18-1
16. B, p. 457
17. K, p. 460
18. F, p. 457

19. J, p. 460
20. D, p. 457
21. L, p. 460
22. C, p. 457
23. E, p. 457
24. A, p. 457

Choose the correct term

25. C, p. 468
26. B, p. 467
27. C, p. 468
28. A, p. 466
29. B, p. 467
30. C, p. 468
31. C, p. 468
32. A, p. 466
33. C, p. 467 Figure 18-8
34. B, p. 467
35. A, p. 466
36. B, p. 468

Fill in the blanks

37. Urinalysis, p. 466
38. Mucous membrane, p. 466
39. Centrifuge, p. 466
40. Anuria, p. 466
41. Bladder infections or cystitis, p. 468
42. Semen, p. 468
43. Urinary meatus, p. 468

Fill in the blanks

44. Micturition, p. 468
45. Urination, p. 468
46. Voiding, p. 468
47. Internal urethral sphincter, p. 468
48. Exit, p. 468
49. Urethra, p. 468
50. Voluntary, p. 468
51. Emptying reflex, p. 469
52. Urethra, p. 469
53. Retention, p. 469
54. Suppression, p. 469
55. Automatic bladder, p. 469

Select the best choice

56. I, p. 470
57. C, p. 469
58. G, p. 469
59. F, p. 470
60. K, p. 470

61. A, p. 471
62. H, p. 474
63. J, p. 474
64. B, p. 469
65. D, p. 471
66. E, p. 471
67. L, p. 470

Applying what you know

68. Polyuria
69. Residual urine is often the cause of repeated cystitis
70. A high percentage of catheterized patients develop cystitis, often because of poor aseptic technique when inserting the catheter.
71. Hemorrhage causes a drop in blood pressure, which decreases urine output and can eventually lead to kidney failure.
72. WORD FIND

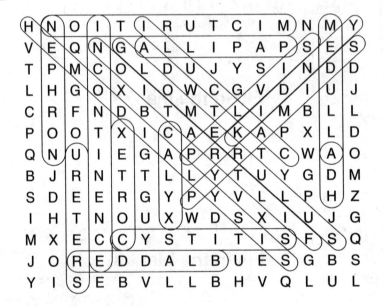

Crossword

```
        ¹M                      ²L   ³C Y S T I T I S      ⁴
         I            ⁵         I   A              N
         C            T         T   L              C
         T            R         H   Y              O
  ⁶G     U            I         O            ⁷A N U R I A
   L     R            G         T   X           T
   Y     I            O         R               I
  ⁸C A T H E T E R I Z A T I O N                N
   O     I                     P               E
   S     O            ⁹P        T               N
   U     N       ¹⁰O   O         O               C
   R          ¹¹G L O M E R U L U S             E
   I             I                 Y
   A             G                 U
                 U                 R
                 R                 I
                 I                 A
                 A
```

Urinary System

1. Spleen
2. Renal artery
3. Renal vein
4. Kidney (left)
5. Inferior vena cava
6. Abdominal aorta
7. Common iliac vein
8. Common iliac artery
9. Urinary bladder
10. Ureter
11. Kidney (right)
12. Tenth rib
13. Adrenal glands
14. Liver

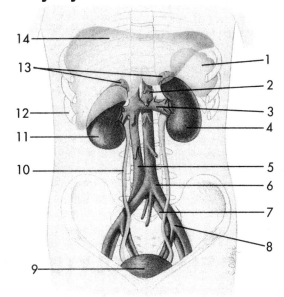

Kidney

1. Renal artery and vein
2. Pelvis
3. Ureter
4. Cortex
5. Pyramid
6. Medulla
7. Calyx
8. Papilla

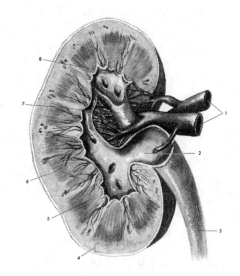

Nephron

1. Proximal convoluted tubule
2. Collecting tubule
3. Descending limb of Henle's loop
4. Ascending limb of Henle's loop
5. Segment of Henle's loop
6. Artery and vein
7. Distal convoluted tubule
8. Peritubular capillaries
9. Afferent arteriole
10. Juxtaglomerular apparatus
11. Efferent arteriole
12. Glomerulus
13. Bowman's capsule

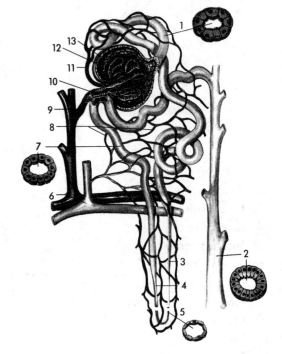

CHAPTER 19
FLUID AND ELECTROLYTE BALANCE
Circle the correct response

1. Inside, p. 481
2. Extracellular, p. 481
3. Extracellular, p. 481
4. Lower, p. 481
5. More, p. 481
6. Decline, p. 481

7. Less, p. 481
8. Decreases, p. 481
9. 55%, p. 481
10. Fluid balance, p. 481

Multiple choice

11. A, p. 484
12. D, p. 484
13. A, p. 484
14. C, p. 483
15. E, p. 483
16. D, p. 484
17. D, p. 484
18. C, p. 486
19. B, p. 486
20. D, p. 489
21. E, p. 487
22. B, p. 488
23. B, p. 488
24. B, p. 485

True or false

25. Catabolism, p. 483
26. T, p. 481
27. T, p. 484
28. Nonelectrolyte, p. 484
29. T, p. 485
30. Hypervolemia, p. 486 Figure 19-5
31. Tubular function, p. 489
32. 2400 ml, p. 483
33. T, p. 487
34. 100 mEq, p. 486

Fill in the blanks

35. Dehydration, p. 488
36. Decreases, p. 488
37. Decrease, p. 488
38. Overhydration, p. 488
39. Intravenous fluids, p. 488
40. Heart, p. 488

Applying what you know

41. Ms. Titus could not accurately measure water intake created by foods or catabolism, nor could she measure output created by lungs, skin, or the intestines.
42. A careful record of fluid intake and output should be maintained and the patient should be monitored for signs and symptoms of electrolyte and water imbalance.
43. Jack's body contained more water. Obese people have a lower water content than slender people.

Crossword

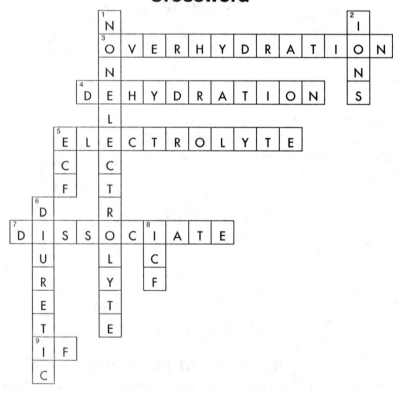

CHAPTER 20
ACID-BASE BALANCE

Choose the correct term

1. B, p. 495
2. A, p. 495
3. A, p. 496
4. B, p. 495
5. B, p. 495
6. B, p. 495
7. B, p. 496
8. A, p. 496
9. B, p. 496
10. B. p. 496

Multiple choice

11. E, p. 495
12. E, p. 495
13. A, p. 496
14. E, p. 498-499
15. C, p. 499
16. D, p. 499
17. C, p. 499
18. B, p. 499
19. D, p. 499
20. E, p. 500
21. E, p. 500

True or false

22. Buffer instead of heart, p. 495
23. Buffer pairs, p. 496
24. T, p. 496
25. T, p. 498
26. Alkalosis, p. 499
27. Reverse—arterial blood has a higher pH, p. 495
28. T, p. 499
29. Kidneys, p. 502
30. Lungs, p. 502

Matching

31. E, p. 501
32. G, p. 502
33. F, p. 501
34. A, p. 502
35. I, p. 501
36. B, p. 502
37. H, p. 502
38. C, p. 502
39. D, p. 502
40. J, p. 501

Applying what you know

41. Normal saline contains chloride ions that replace bicarbonate ions and thus relieve the bicarbonate excess that occurs during severe vomiting.
42. Most citrus fruits, although acid tasting, are fully oxidized with the help of buffers during metabolism and have little effect on acid-base balance. Cranberry juice is one of the few exceptions.
43. Milk of magnesia. It is base. Milk is slightly acidic. (See chart, p. 496.)
44. WORD FIND

Crossword

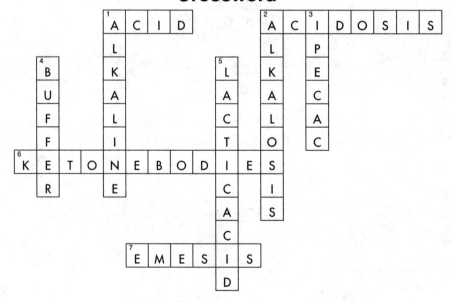

CHAPTER 21
THE REPRODUCTIVE SYSTEMS

Matching

Group A
1. D, p. 507
2. C, p. 507
3. E, p. 507
4. B, p. 508
5. A, p. 507

Group B
6. C, p. 508
7. A, p. 508
8. D, p. 507
9. B, p. 508
10. E, p. 508

Multiple choice

11. B, p. 509
12. C, p. 509
13. A, p. 511
14. D, p. 509
15. E, p. 509
16. D, p. 511
17. C, p. 512
18. C, p. 511
19. A, p. 511

Fill in the blanks

20. Testes, p. 507
21. Spermatozoa or sperm, p. 509
22. Ovum, p. 511
23. Testosterone, pp. 511-512
24. Interstitial cells, p. 512
25. Masculinizing, p. 512
26. Anabolic, p. 512

Choose the correct term

27. B, p. 513
28. H, p. 513
29. G, p. 513
30. A, p. 512
31. F, p. 513
32. C, p. 513
33. I, p. 513
34. E, p. 513
35. D, p. 513
36. J, p. 513

Fill in the blanks

37. Oligospermia, p. 515
38. 2 months, p. 515
39. Cryptorchidism, p. 515
40. Benign prostatic hypertrophy, p. 515
41. Phimosis, p. 516
42. Impotence, p. 516
43. Hydrocele, p. 516
44. Inguinal hernia, p. 516
45. Prostate, p. 515

Matching

46. D, p. 516
47. C, p. 517
48. B, p. 517
49. A, p. 517
50. E, p. 516

Choose the correct structure

51. A, p. 521
52. B, p. 521
53. A, p. 521
54. B, p. 519
55. A, p. 521
56. A, p. 521
57. A, p. 521
58. B, p. 516-517

Fill in the blanks

59. Gonads, p. 516
60. Oogenesis, p. 518
61. Meiosis, p. 518
62. One half (or 23), p. 518
63. Fertilization, p. 518
64. 46, p. 518
65. Estrogen, p. 518
66. Progesterone, p. 518
67. Secondary sexual characteristics, p. 519
68. Menstrual cycle, p. 519
69. Puberty, p. 519

Choose the correct structure

70. A, p. 520
71. B, p. 520
72. C, p. 521
73. B, p. 520
74. A, p. 519
75. B, p. 520
76. A, p. 520
77. A, p. 519
78. C, p. 521

Matching

True or false

Choose the correct hormone

Choose the correct response

Applying what you know

112. Yes. The testes are not only essential organs of reproduction, but are also responsible for the "masculinizing" hormone. Without this hormone, Mr. Belinki will have no desire to reproduce.

113. Sterile. The sperm count may be too low to reproduce but the remaining testicle will produce enough masculinizing hormone to prevent impotency.

114. The uterine tubes are not attached to the ovaries and infections can exit at this area and enter the abdominal cavity.

115. Yes. Yes. Without the hormones from the ovaries to initiate the menstrual cycle, Mrs. Harlan will no longer have a menstrual cycle and can be considered to be in menopause (cessation of menstrual cycle).

116. No. Mrs. Kelly still will have her ovaries, which are the source of her hormones. She will not experience menopause as a result of this procedure.

117. WORD FIND

Crossword

2. CLITORIS
3. AREOLA
5. SEMEN
6. GAMETES
7. VULVA
10. TESTOSTERONE

Male Reproductive Organs

1. Ductus deferens
2. Bladder
3. Prostate gland
4. Urethra
5. Glans penis
6. Testis
7. Epididymis
8. Bulbourethral gland
9. Anus
10. Seminal vesicle
11. Rectum

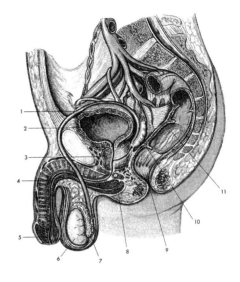

Tubules of Testis and Epididymis

1. Ductus (vas) deferens
2. Body of epididymis
3. Septum
4. Lobule
5. Tunica albuginea
6. Seminiferous tubules

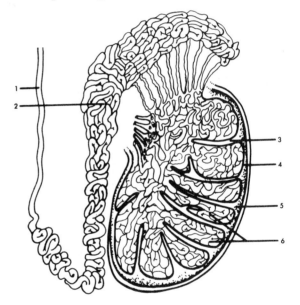

Vulva

1. Mons pubis
2. Clitoris
3. Orifice of urethra
4. Labia majora
5. Opening of greater vestibular gland
6. Anus
7. Vestibule
8. Orifice of vagina
9. Labia minora
10. Prepuce

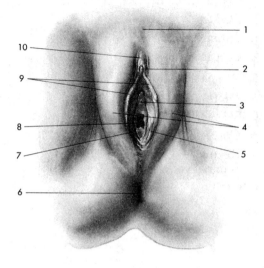

Breast

1. Clavicle
2. Pectoralis major muscle
3. Intercostal muscles
4. Nipple
5. Lactiferous duct
6. Alveoli
7. Suspensory ligaments of Cooper

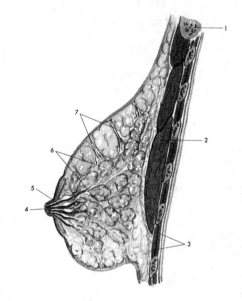

Female Pelvis

1. Fallopian tube (uterine)
2. Ovary
3. Uterus
4. Urinary bladder
5. Symphysis pubis
6. Urethra
7. Vagina
8. Cervix
9. Rectum

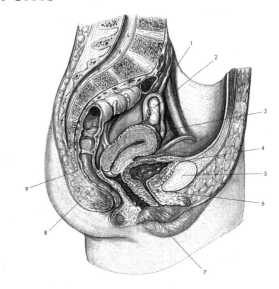

Uterus and Adjacent Structures

1. Fundus
2. Endometrium
3. Myometrium
4. Cervical canal
5. Vagina
6. Cervix
7. Body
8. Uterine (fallopian) tube
9. Ovary
10. Fimbriae

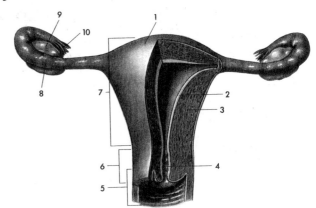

CHAPTER 22
GROWTH AND DEVELOPMENT

Fill in the blanks

1. Conception, p. 537
2. Birth, p. 537
3. Embryology, p. 537
4. Oviduct, p. 537
5. Zygote, p. 537
6. Morula, p. 537
7. Blastocyst, p. 537
8. Amniotic cavity, p. 539
9. Chorion, p. 541
10. Placenta, p. 541

Choose the correct term

11. G, p. 540
12. F, p. 542
13. C, p. 548
14. B, p. 542
15. A, p. 540
16. H, p. 544
17. E, p. 544
18. D, p. 542
19. I, p. 542
20. J, p. 548

True or false

21. T, p. 546
22. T, p. 546
23. Placenta previa, p. 547
24. Abruptio placentae, p. 547
25. Preeclampsia, p. 547
26. Stillbirth, p. 548
27. T, p. 548

Multiple choice

28. E, p. 549-550
29. E, p. 550
30. E, p. 551-552
31. A, p. 551
32. B, p. 551
33. C, p. 552
34. B, p. 552
35. D, p. 552
36. E, p. 552
37. D, p. 553
38. A, p. 553
39. C, p. 553
40. C, p. 553
41. C, p. 553
42. E, p. 553

Matching

43. F, p. 549
44. A, p. 550
45. C, p. 553
46. H, p. 552
47. D, p. 553
48. B, p. 550
49. E, p. 553
50. G, p. 553
51. I, p. 555

Fill in the blanks

52. Lipping, p. 555
53. Osteoarthritis, p. 555
54. Nephron, p. 555
55. Barrel chest, p. 555
56. Atherosclerosis, p. 555
57. Arteriosclerosis, p. 555
58. Hypertension, p. 555
59. Presbyopia, p. 555
60. Cataract, p. 556
61. Glaucoma, p. 556

Unscramble the words

62. Infancy
63. Postnatal
64. Organogenesis
65. Zygote
66. Childhood
67. Fertilization

Applying what you know

68. Normal
69. Only about 40% of the taste buds present at age 30 remain at age 75.
70. A significant loss of hair cells in the Organ of Corti causes a serious decline in ability to hear certain frequencies.
71. Each baby girl had her own placenta.
72. WORD FIND

Crossword

```
        ¹P              ²E
         A      ³H       M      ⁴B      ⁵N      ⁶P
         R       I       B       L       E       R
         T       S       R       A       O       E
         U       T       Y     ⁷S  E  N  E  S  C  E  N  C  E
         R       O       O       T       A       B
         I       G       L       O       T       Y              ⁸G
      ⁹A  T  H  E  R  O  S  C  L  E  R  O  S  I  S              L
         I       N       G       Y       P                      A
         O       E       Y               I                      U
         N       S                       ¹⁰C  A  T  A  R  A  C  T
                 I                       H                      O
                 S                    ¹¹M  O  R  U  L  A        M
                                        R                      A
                                        I
                                     ¹²Z  Y  G  O  T  E
                                        N
```

Fertilization and Implantation

1. Developing follicles
2. Corpus luteum
3. Ovary
4. Ovulation
5. Spermatozoa (fertilization)
6. First mitosis
7. Uterine (fallopian) tube
8. Divided zygote
9. Morula
10. Uterus
11. Blastocyst
12. Implantation

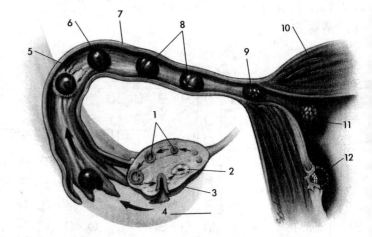

CHAPTER 23
GENETICS AND GENETIC DISEASES
Matching

1. E, p. 563
2. A, p. 563
3. B, p. 563
4. C, p. 563
5. D, p. 563

Fill in the blanks

6. Genes, p. 566
7. Dominant, p. 566
8. Recessive, p. 566
9. Carrier, p. 566
10. Codominance, p. 566
11. Sex, p. 567
12. Female, p. 567
13. Mutation, p. 569
14. Genetic mutation, p. 569

Matching

15. E, p. 570
16. D, p. 569
17. J, p. 569
18. F, p. 570
19. C, p. 570
20. G, p. 570
21. A, p. 570
22. H, p. 571
23. B, p. 570
24. I, p. 571

Multiple choice

25. D, p. 572
26. B, p. 574
27. C, p. 573
28. C, p. 575
29. D, p. 575
30. D, p. 576
31. B, p. 577

True or false

32. T, p. 575
33. Electrophoresis, p. 576
34. Gene augmentation, p. 575
35. T, p. 577
36. T, p. 573

Unscramble the words

37. Carrier
38. Trisomy
39. Gene
40. Pedigree
41. Chromosome
42. Inherited

Applying what you know

43. In a form of dominance called *codominance*, the effect will be equal, causing "light brown" to occur.

44. One in four, or 25%

45. Amniocentesis or chorionic villus sampling. The counselor will then produce a karyotype to determine anomalies.

46. PUNNETT SQUARE

    <u>Mr. Fortner PP</u>

    <u>Mrs. Fortner pp</u>

    A. 100% chance of brown eyes and 0% chance of blue eyes

    B. Yes

    C. 25%

    <u>Mrs. Rhoades Pp</u>

    <u>Mr. Rhoades Pp</u>

    A. Normal pigmentation 25%

    B. Carriers 50%

    C. Albinism 25%

47. WORD FIND

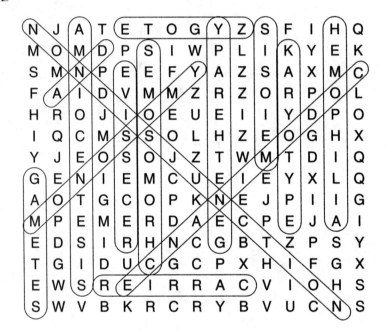

Crossword

```
                    D
          A U T O S O M E S
                    W
          A L B I N I S M
                    S           M           T
                    Y           U           R
          D O M I N A N T       T           I
                    D           A           S
          P E D I G R E E       G           O
          K               O       G E N O M E
          U               M           N       Y
                  G E N E T I C S
```